Distillery Operations

How to Run a Small Distillery

Payton Fireman, JD

Morgantown, West Virginia

ISBN: 978-0-9833376-4-5

Front and back cover photos courtesy of Gabe DeWitt.

Production services:
Populore Publishing Company,
Morgantown, West Virginia,
with cover design by Jenna Britton

What is it that is not poison? All things are poison and nothing is without poison. It is the dose only that makes a thing not a poison. Paracelsus (1493–1541).

We have to keep learning because it is the only way to remember anything. Bo McDaniel, 2008.

Knowledge is only as broad as experience. Giambattista Vico (1668–1744).

Contents

Introduction

This book describes the physical, regulatory and business aspects of operating a small distillery.

When I started my distillery in 1998, my goal was to bring authentic corn whiskey based moonshine to market in a legal and accountable manner. I became the first licensed distiller in West Virginia since the end of Prohibition. I have made my products for almost twenty years and during that time I have acquired a good deal of useful knowledge. This book serves to document what I have learned both for myself and for the benefit of others.

This work fits into the literature of distilling between two types of existing works. The first type are highly technical books written about large scale industrial operations. The second type are very basic texts designed for understanding fermentation and distillation on a kitchen-sink scale.

My physical plant and processes are large enough to require some specialized equipment, but they are conducted on an artisan scale rather than an industrial scale. The business model I have undertaken can be duplicated with just ordinary amounts of ingenuity and capital.

In reading other textbooks and manuals I found that while the published methods and data were valuable, they would be more useful if they were accessible in Excel workbook form. Accordingly, I have written up what are essentially my lab notes from operating my distillery as worksheets that perform the calculations needed to operate my facility. The workbook that embodies these calculations can be obtained from either of my web presences listed below.

The first section of Chapter 1 became more complex than I anticipated because of the equations I developed while writing it. You will probably find that the remainder of the chapter is easier to follow. Some readers may want to skip over section 1.1 ("Distillation") and return to it later.

Chapter 13 contains some history of how my distillery came to be, as well as my observations and experiences of running a distillery apart from just the technical side.

Also associated with this text is a video that was filmed over the course of an entire production cycle at my distillery. I have uploaded several clips from the video to my YouTube channel: https://www.youtube.com/user/MoonshineDistilling.

One other contribution I have made to making a distiller's life a little easier was in writing my alcohol blending software called ABS Software. Its function was to automate the application of the US government tables required to be used in alcohol blending operations.

The websites associated with my business and software are: http://www.mountainmoonshine.com/ and http://www.alcoholblending.com/.

I hope this book and its associated workbook and DVD provide a good survey of the processes necessary to produce quality beverage grade alcohol on an artisanal scale.

CHAPTER 1 Overview of the Process and Equipment

1.1 Distillation

Distillation is the process of separating two liquid compounds by using the difference in their boiling points to achieve the separation.

Alcohol is more volatile than water. This means that it evaporates more readily than water does. As we all know if a glass of wine or a bottle of beer is left open overnight it loses much of its original alcohol content because a higher proportion of the alcohol than the water has evaporated into the air.

Distillation uses heat to accelerate the process of separating alcohol from water. Pure alcohol vaporizes at 173.1° F (78.4° C). Pure water does not vaporize or become a gas (steam) until the temperature reaches 212° F (100° C).

When I first began distilling I thought my still would begin running when the temperature reached the boiling point of alcohol. It didn't. Starting with a fermented mash of between 12% and 18% alcohol by volume, my still would not begin running alcohol until it reached a temperature somewhere in the mid-190s F. At first I thought maybe my equipment was not working correctly. Eventually I learned that the boiling point of alcohol and water mixtures varies with the amount of alcohol contained in them and that when alcohol content increases, the boiling point goes down.

My experience has confirmed that when my fermentations are successful in producing a good deal of alcohol, the still will begin running alcohol at a lower temperature than with fermentations that have not proceeded as well.

% Alcohol at 60° F	15.00%
Proof of Liquid	30.00
Temp Still will begin running alcohol	194.96

TABLE 1—Refer to Boiling Temp & Liquid Proof Worksheet

In order to find the boiling point of any alcohol and water mixture we can use the worksheet in the *Distilling Manual Workbook*. Starting with a mash fermented to 15% alcohol by volume we find that equivalent proof is 30 proof and that the boiling point is 194.96° F (Table 1).

When applying the calculated value to an actual fermented mash one will find a small discrepancy between the temperature at which the still begins running and the boiling point of pure alcohol as calculated by the worksheet. The still will begin running a few degrees below the boiling temperature of alcohol. The reason is that the fermented mash contains lower boiling point compounds such as acetone that, in small quantities, are natural by-products of fermentation. Some of these by-products and their boiling points are listed in Table 2, *infra*. The compounds with a boiling point that are less than that of alcohol are known as the "heads," which contain compounds that are even more toxic than alcohol itself. People insist on tasting the first distillate that comes out of the still and it is really a dumb thing to do. It smells like nail polish remover and is extremely toxic.

The compounds listed *infra*, with a boiling point greater than alcohol, other than water, are known as "tails." Even though some of the tail compounds have boiling points substantially above the temperature of the still and some of them are even above the boiling point of water, some of their molecules do acquire the energy to escape from liquid form and contaminate the vapor driven off by the still. At the end of a run, they accumulate to the degree that they begin to affect the taste of the distillate and its appearance. The character of these compounds are oily and greasy; the taste sticks to your mouth and won't leave.

	°C	°F
Acetone	56.50	133.70
Methanol	64.70	148.46
Ethyl acetate	77.10	170.78
Ethyl Alcohol	78.40	173.12
Propyl Alcohol	97.2	206.96
Water	100.0	212.00
Butyl Alcohol	117.5	243.50
Amyl Alcohol	137.8	280.04
Furfural	161.0	321.80

TABLE 2—*Refer to* Boiling Points *Worksheet*

Of course, the still temperature rises during the course of the run, since more and more alcohol is leaving the still, and the alcohol remaining in the still becomes a smaller fraction of the base stock. As the temperature rises above 205° F or so the distillate will become hazy and eventually cloudy, and up around 209° F it will even acquire a greenish tinge even though the still is still flowing 80 proof alcohol (Table 2).

At the beginning of a distillation run, when the first heads are condensed out of the still, the initial flow is a mixture of water, low boiling point compounds and alcohol since, just like wine evaporating from a glass, a mixture of water and alcohol will evaporate, not just one or the other. After a while most of the really volatile chemicals will have been driven off and the temperature of the still will more accurately reflect the alcohol content in it.

The following table shows the relation between alcohol content and boiling point[1] (Table 3).

Vapor Liquid Equilibrium for Ethanol & Water Mixtures at 760 mmHg

Data Point	Liquid Molar % Alc = Xe	Liquid Proof	Vapor Molar % Alc = Ye	Vapor Proof	Temp (°C)	Temp (°F)	Liquid % by Vol @ 60° F
1	1.90%	11.79	17.00%	82.27	95.5	203.9	5.90%
2	7.21%	40.74	38.91%	139.11	88.4	191.12	20.37%
3	9.66%	52.45	43.75%	147.6	86.7	188.06	26.23%
4	12.38%	64.38	47.04%	152.82	85.3	185.54	32.19%
5	16.61%	80.87	50.89%	158.41	84.1	183.38	40.44%
6	23.37%	102.83	54.45%	163.15	82.7	180.86	51.42%
7	26.08%	110.39	55.80%	164.85	82.3	180.14	55.20%
8	32.73%	126.56	58.26%	167.81	81.5	178.7	63.28%
9	39.65%	140.48	61.22%	171.17	80.7	177.26	70.24%
10	50.79%	158.27	65.64%	175.79	79.8	175.64	79.14%
11	51.98%	159.9	65.99%	176.14	79.7	175.46	79.95%
12	57.32%	166.7	68.41%	178.47	79.3	174.74	83.35%
13	67.63%	177.74	73.85%	183.29	78.74	173.732	88.87%
14	74.72%	184.01	78.15%	186.72	78.41	173.138	92.01%
15	89.43%	194.37	89.43%	194.37	78.15	172.67	97.19%

TABLE 3—*Refer to* Regression for Book *Worksheet*

The reason that the chart tops out at 194.37 proof is that it is not possible to directly distill alcohol above that temperature. At that proof the mixture becomes an azeotrope which is a mixture of two or more liquids that when boiled give off vapors of exactly the same composition as the liquid and further separation is not possible. In order to create pure absolute alcohol one must perform an azeotropic distillation that uses a third chemical

---

1   The data underlying this chart was compiled by Harvey Wilson of Katmar Software by converting molar values to proof using AlcoDens and obtaining a correlation between proof and temperature from data obtained from the work of JS Carey and WK Lewis and published in *Ind. Eng. Chem.* 24 882-3 (1932). For a full explanation of the procedure see the Find Vape Temp 2 worksheet. Note: Data from other sources, and regressing the Carey and Lewis data, suggests that data point two should be 88.4° C rather than 89° C as reported in the Carey and Lewis data.

such as benzene or trichloroethylene to bond with the remaining water so pure alcohol can be drawn off separately.

Charting the data in the table shows the curves along which this process takes place and also provides two equations (Equations 1 and 2) that can be used to predict the boiling point or vaporization proof of any mixture of alcohol and water.

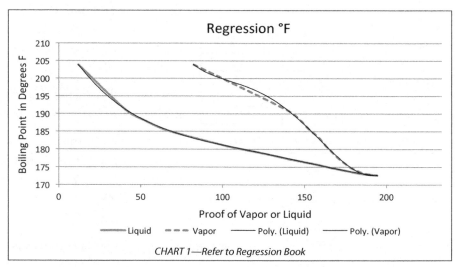

CHART 1—Refer to Regression Book

Equation 1 (solid line) $y = 7.609\text{E-}08x^4 - 4.051\text{E-}05x^3 + 7.928\text{E-}03x^2 - 7.716\text{E-}01x + 2.120\text{E+}02$

Equation 2 (dashed line) $y = 9.8565\text{E-}07x^4 - 5.2026\text{E-}04x^3 + 9.8636\text{E-}02x^2 - 8.2147\text{E+}00x + 4.5666\text{E+}02$

Note that the trend lines for both vapor and liquid temperature do not precisely follow the graphed lines. Using a fourth-order polynomial equation provided the best fit possible but there is still some discrepancy in the formula results and the underlying data. This imprecision will lead to slight variations of two to three proof in the results obtained in the portion of the trend line where it does not align with the graphed line. Unfortunately the largest discrepancy is located between 190° and 200° F which is precisely where my still begins running on a stripping run based on fermented mash. That uncertainty along with the fact that the still will begin running low boiling point compounds first will further complicate an accurate determination.

I have never tried this but one might be able to sweeten their mash with heads and tails left over from the prior run to increase the alcohol content and recover the good alcohol in the heads and tails along with the alcohol fermented by the batch. For some reason it has never occurred to me to do this mostly because I have to do a double run anyway and I'm saving my heads and tails for that but occasionally I have an excess of them and could use them in this way. Since I have to heat up the still anyway, why not have as much alcohol in it as is available.

Of course this is subject to the limitation that running heads and tails through a pot still that has little or no rectification occurring will not really result in a larger yield. One will just be boiling the same heads and tails back into the heads and tails tank. It will simply take more time and energy to get through a stripping run.

The table and chart also show the temperature of the vapor and its associated boiling point. These values are in accord with my experience when using my pot still that does not provide any significant rectification of the alcohol to a higher proof than its vaporization proof. Accordingly, in a pot still setup the proof of the condensate is a good indicator of the temperature of the still itself and of the alcohol content of the liquid in the still as well.

Taking our 15% alcohol by volume mash and finding its boiling point will allow us to use the vapor proof trend line and its associated equation to predict the proof of the condensate that a pot still will produce. It shows that a 15% mash content will begin running distillate (heads) at around 125 proof.

% Alcohol at 60° F	15.00%
Proof of Liquid	30.00
Calculated Boiling point ° F (Eq. 1)	194.96
Proof of Vapor	127.2
% Alcohol at 60° F	63.6%
Calculated Boiling Point ° F (Eq. 2)	194.96

TABLE 4—Refer to Regression ° F *Worksheet*

By adjusting the proof of the vapor to match the boiling temperature of the mash we see that the still should flow 127.2 proof alcohol from a 15% alcohol by volume fermented mash used as a base stock (Table 4).

The result of 127.2 proof is consistent with my experience in using my big pot still, within the margins of error we have defined.

In order to make this calculation predictive, so that we don't have to manually adjust the liquid proof by trial and error, we need to reverse the X and Y axes and create two additional trend lines and show the equations applied to plot them (Equations 3 and 4).

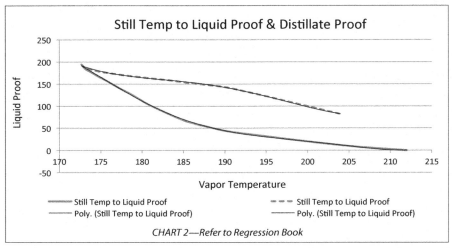

CHART 2—Refer to Regression Book

Equation 3 (solid line) $y = 1.2791047E\text{-}05x^5 - 1.2334044E\text{-}02x^4 + 4.7471645E\text{+}00x^3 - 9.1143333E\text{+}02x^2 + 8.7272704E\text{+}04x - 3.3331679E\text{+}06$

Equation 4 (dashed line) $y = 4.3304221E\text{-}04x^4 - 3.2886929E\text{-}01x^3 + 9.3502526E\text{+}01x^2 - 1.1798715E\text{+}04x + 5.5782638E\text{+}05$

These equations will have an equal and opposite discrepancy from the original ones but because the original fit of the trend line to the data is better for liquid than that of vapor the total outage will not be as great as the trend line for the vapor proof.

Proof of Vapor	127.2	Proof Still is Running
% Alcohol at 60° F	63.6%	
Calculated Boiling Point ° F (Eq. 2)	194.96	Temperature of Still
From Boiling point of Still Contents find Proof of Liquid in Still		
Proof of Liquid in Still (Equation 3)	30.19	
% Alcohol at 60° F	15.1%	
Difference in Proof of Still Contents	0.19	

TABLE 5—Refer to Regression for Book *Worksheet*

Applying Equations 2 and 3 in series to our initial distillate proof shows a 0.19 proof variation in the proof of the contents of the still (Table 5).

At the beginning of a run one can use the proof of the liquid in the still and the 60° F volume of the contents to calculate the number of Proof Gallons contained in the still. Proof Gallons consist of US fluid gallons (231 cubic inches) of 100 proof alcohol and are the US standard quantity of measuring alcohol for accounting and taxation (Table 6, next page).

It is important to note that one must use only the volume of alcohol and water in the still. If one is distilling just fluid, where the solids have been filtered out, then the total volume can be used. If one is using a mixture of corn and water that contains the corn solids in it, one cannot use the total volume because the solids take up volume as well. The easy way around this is to note the

Find Proof Gallons in Still from Volume and Proof of Still Contents	
Volume of Alcohol in Still (60° F Vol.)	390.00
Proof of Liquid In Still	30.19
Proof Gallons in Still	117.75

TABLE 6— Refer to Regression for Book *Worksheet*

amount of water originally contributed to the batch and this will serve adequately to estimate the Proof Gallon result of a fermentation. In my case, my still holds 500 gallons but I only use 390 gallons of water in my mash. The remainder of the volume is taken up by the 1,500 pounds of corn I use to ferment with.

Using the results of a stripping run that started out at about 15% alcohol by volume we see that I collected 109.1 Proof Gallons and that the still was still running 35.5 proof when I shut it off (Table 7).

Alcohol Collected	**Lbs.**	**Hours**	**Lbs. per Hr.**
Drum 1 net Lbs.	413.0	3.00	137.7
Drum 2 net Lbs.	421.0	2.75	153.1
Drum 3 net Lbs.	149.0	1.25	119.2
Total Lbs. Condensed	983.0	7.0	Total Hrs. Condensing Time
Hours of Condensing Time	7.0	140.4	Avg. Lbs. Per Hour
Total Wine Gallons	125.2	17.9	Avg. Wine Gallons Per Hour
Total Proof Gallons	109.10	15.6	Avg. Proof Gallons Per Hour
Proof Gal./Wine Gal. * 100 = Avg. Proof	87.14	125.0	Highest Proof During Run
% By Vol. @ 60° F	43.6	35.5	Ending, Lowest, Proof

TABLE 7—Refer to Strip Run 1 *Worksheet*

As to the remaining Proof Gallons in the still, when Equation 2 is applied to proofs outside the data set from which it is derived, it generates incorrect results. Accordingly, using temperature and proof data I had collected during stripping runs I developed a low proof equation (Equation 5) that is applicable to low proofs.

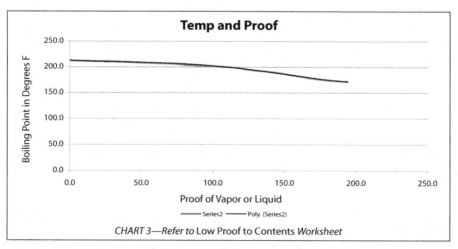

CHART 3—Refer to Low Proof to Contents *Worksheet*

Equation 5 $\quad y = 1.07289\text{E-}07x^4 - 4.12494\text{E-}05x^3 + 3.78490\text{E-}03x^2 - 1.79037\text{E-}01x + 2.12594\text{E+}02$

Applying the ending proof of the run through both equations shows (Table 8):

Interpolated Formula	Low Proof formula	Original Formula	
Proof of Distillate	35.00	35.00	Proof of Distillate
% Alcohol at 60° F	17.5%	17.5%	% Alcohol at 60° F
Boiling Point of Still Contents (Eq. 5)	209.36	269.15	Boiling Point of Still Contents (Eq. 2)
From Temp of Still Contents find Proof of Liquid in Still			
Proof of Liquid in Still (Equation 2)	1.93	29260.13	
% Alcohol at 60° F	0.96%	14630.1%	
From Proof of Liquid in Still Find Find Proof Gallons			
Volume of Alc/Water in Still (60° F Vol.)	390.00	390.00	
Volume of Alcohol Distilled (60° F Vol)	0.00	0.00	
Volume Remaining in the still	390.00	390.00	
Liquid Proof of Alcohol in Still	1.93	29260.13	
Proof Gallons in Still	7.52	114114.52	

TABLE 8—Refer to Low Proof to Contents *Worksheet*

The original Equation 2 is generating nonsensical results but the low proof equation (Equation 5) is fairly representative of the Proof Gallons remaining in the still at 7.52 Proof Gallons.

% Alcohol at 60° F	15.00%
Proof of Liquid	30.00
Temp Still will begin Running Alc. (Eq. 1)	194.96
Proof of Distillate (Eq. 4)	122.04
% Alcohol at 60° F	61.0%

TABLE 9—Refer to Boiling Temp & Liquid Proof *Worksheet*

One other permutation is possible and that is to use Equation 1 to obtain the boiling temperature of the still contents and then Equation 4 to calculate the initial proof the still will begin running alcohol (Table 9).

Applying Equation 4 has resulted in a 5 proof differential from that required by manually adjusting Equations 1 and 2, going from 127 proof down to 122. This is the least reliable method but still gives a general idea what the proof of the initial distillate will be.

Proof of Vapor	82.27	Proof Still is Running
% Alcohol at 60° F	41.1%	
Calculated Boiling Point ° F (Eq. 2)	203.90	Temperature of Still
Enter Proof of Liquid	11.79	Proof of Still Contents
% Alcohol at 60° F	5.90%	
Calculated Boiling point ° F (Eq. 1)	203.94	Temperature of Still

TABLE 10—Refer to Regression for Book *Worksheet*

As the stripping run progresses, the alcohol content of the still decreases and the temperature rises and using Equations 2 and 1, we can see why I am able to take off 82 proof alcohol at the end of a run, when the still temperature has reached 204° F even though the alcohol content of the still is very depleted at 11.79 proof or 5.9% by volume (Table 10).

Then using Equations 2 and 3 we find that it is possible to eliminate the need to manually adjust the liquid proof to match the boiling point, and one can find a fairly accurate value for the proof of the contents of the still (Table 11, next page).

My stripping runs only produce alcohol at an average proof of about 100 or so. This alcohol is not suitable for blending to bottling proof because it is full of heads and tails that need to be removed.

In order to increase the proof and clean up my single run alcohol I accumulate it over five fermentations of about 100 gallons collected during each run and then load the whole 500 gallons back into the still in order to re-distill it. This is known as a double run or finished spirits run.

When I do this, I find that the still begins running at about 185° F and that the alcohol begins running at about 162 proof. These values are confirmed by using Equations 1 and 4 assuming we are beginning with 100 proof alcohol as our base stock (Table 12).

From this we can conclude that my pot still does not concentrate or rectify alcohol above its boiling point.

Taking the temperatures and running them back through Equations 4 and 3 shows substantial agreement with our assumed values (Table 13).

However, running from the proof of the distillate back through Equations 2 and 3 results in some uncertainty in the boiling point and this is reflected in the proof of the still contents and ultimately results in a 10% discrepancy in Proof Gallons contained in the still (Table 14).

Numerous comparisons and checks are built into the worksheets that embody these calculations, with some caution exercised against relying too heavily on the numbers generated by them, it is possible to gain some insight into the relationships between temperature, distillate proof and the alcoholic content of the still itself.

One final application can be made of the spreadsheets, and that is to find the amount of rectification that occurs when I use my fractionator still with a column that separates the alcohol. In that case I do achieve a concentration of alcohol above the boiling point and this is reflected in the temperature separation in the fractionating column itself.

Loading my fractionating still with 100 proof alcohol, it will begin running alcohol at around 185 proof. The calculated boiling point of 173° F matches what I see at the top of the column and the still temperature also matches what I measure at 181° F. This slight 9° F separation increases the alcohol content from 165 proof when using my pot still up to 185 proof when using the fractionator (Table 15, next page).

From Proof of Distillate find Temp of Still Contents		
Proof of Distillate	82.27	Vapor Proof
% Alcohol at 60° F	41.1%	
Boiling Point of Still Contents (Eq. 2)	203.90	
From Boiling point of Still Contents find Proof of Liquid in Still		
Proof of Liquid in Still (Equation 3)	12.42	
% Alcohol at 60° F	6.21%	

TABLE 11—Refer to Still Proof to Contents *Worksheet*

% Alcohol at 60° F	50.00%
Proof of Liquid	100.00
Temp Still will begin Running Alc. (Eq. 1)	181.22
Proof of Distillate (Eq. 4)	162.02
% Alcohol at 60° F	81.0%

TABLE 12—Refer to Boiling Temp & Liquid Proof *Worksheet*

Temperature of Still Running Alcohol ° F	181.22
Proof of Distillate (Equation 4)	162.02
Proof of Liquid in Still (Equation 3)	100.00
Find Proof Gallons in Still from Volume and Proof of Still Contents	
Starting Fluid Vol. in Still (60° F Vol.)	500.00
Proof Gallons in Still	500.01

TABLE 13—Refer to Boiling Temp & Liquid Proof *Worksheet*

From Proof of Distillate find Temp of Still Contents	
Proof of Distillate	162.02
% Alcohol at 60° F	81.0%
Boiling Point of Still Contents (Eq. 2)	181.46
From Boiling point of Still Contents find Proof of Liquid in Still	
Proof of Liquid in Still (Equation 3)	97.85
% Alcohol at 60° F	48.92%
From Proof of Liquid in Still Find Proof Gallons	
Volume of Alc/Water in Still (60° F Vol.)	500.00
Liquid Proof of Alcohol in Still	97.85
Proof Gallons in Still	489.23

TABLE 14—Refer to Still Proof to Contents *Worksheet*

Proof of Vapor	185.0	Proof Still is Running
% Alcohol at 60° F	92.5%	
Calculated Boiling Point ° F (Eq. 2)	173.21	Temperature of Still
Enter Proof of Liquid	100.00	Proof of Still Contents
% Alcohol at 60° F	50.0%	
Calculated Boiling point ° F (Eq. 1)	181.22	Temperature of Still

TABLE 15— Refer to Regression for Book Worksheet

Returning to simple distillation, when the still contents vaporize, that vapor rises from the surface. The vapor stream is then channeled through a copper coil that is immersed in water. As the vapor travels through the coil the heat it contains is absorbed by the copper and that heat is transferred to the water. The result is to change the alcohol from a vapor back into a liquid. The water surrounding the condenser acquires the heat released by the alcohol as it cools and so the water must be refreshed from time to time so it does not become too hot itself. We cover this aspect of distillation more fully later in this work.

Still setup.

1.2 Brief Summary

Five basic operations define the cooking, fermentation and distilling process:

1. Creating a slurry (mash) containing a starch source (corn, potatoes, rye, etc.) and water that is heated and cooked so that the starch chains are loosened and bonded to water molecules (hydrolyzed).

2. Using enzymes in the form of partially sprouted grain (usually malted barley) or commercial liquid enzymes to induce the cooked starch to break up into smaller molecules of fermentable sugar.

3. Cooling the mixture to a temperature of less than around 95° F which will allow yeast to live and flourish in the sugar rich environment.

4. Allowing the yeast to metabolize, by fermentation, all the available fermentable sugars.

5. When all fermentable sugars are consumed, heating the mixture to vaporize its alcohol content and separate it as a concentrate of alcohol.

1.3 Extended Summary

Having covered distillation, at least initially, we can turn our attention to the cooking and fermentation processes that begin the breakdown of some form of starch (corn, potatoes, etc.) into fermentable sugars that can be metabolized by yeast to produce alcohol. This process is documented by my making moonshine DVD, portions of which are available on my YouTube channel: *moonshinedistilling*.

I use a one pot system for cooking my mash, fermenting it and then distilling it. In a more sophisticated setup one might have a separate cooker and a separate fermenter as well. It took several sets of coils to transfer all the heat I needed into the still. Even though I had coils in the bottom I still had to put coils on the underside because the bottom four inches of the still would not heat at all without heat being added from the very bottom.

1. In my operation I make corn whiskey so my starch source is corn meal which I buy in 50-lb. bags from the local feed store. How the corn is dried can affect the taste of the alcohol you obtain. Use gas dried corn meal, not oil fire dried, to eliminate off odors or taste. The meal should be ground not quite to flour. A finer grind increases the surface area for starch conversion to sugar but a flour can be too fine and clump up if not treated correctly when mixed with water. I have used cracked corn and ground some of my own corn and rye but the best results I've obtained are with corn meal.

Coils under the still.

2. Slurrying the corn in water of the proper character: Fill the tank first and bring the temperature up to around 100° to 120°. If the water is too cold the corn meal will want to clump up; contrawise if the water is too hot you will make giant corn dumplings that are impossible break up. The density of the slurry is generally around 90 gallons of water to 200 pounds of grain. This translates to about a 25-gallon-per-bushel mash. I will explain more about mash density a little later.

3. The slurrying process is assisted by adding a small dose of starch cutting enzyme. This reduces the tendency of the corn to clump up into balls. This enzyme can be in the form of malted barley or in my case I use a commercial liquid enzyme in lieu of a little malted barley to help keep the mixture thin enough to stir while it heats up.

4. Heating the mixture and cooking it in order to gelatinize the corn and prepare the starch chains for enzymatic breakdown into fermentable sugars: The mixture must be kept sufficiently agitated during this process in order for it to cook properly. My biggest mechanical problems have been with getting sufficiently powerful agitation equipment to do the job. The better your agitation equipment the more starch you can pack into each batch and consequently the more sugar you can produce, resulting in more alcohol per batch. Having a thin slurry is secondarily more inefficient because the extra water in a thin mash takes up tank space and must be heated to distillation temperature, which costs additional energy. However, more water does have the advantage of providing more of a buffer for metabolic waste products, including alcohol, to accumulate in. Too little water can retard alcohol production because the yeast poison themselves with their waste products before all the fermentable sugars have been consumed.

Interior of the still showing heating coils and mixer paddles.

5. When the temperature of the slurry in the tank rises above 175° one will add additional liquefying enzyme, and allow it to work at its designed temperature of between 175° to 203° F (85–95° C). We must also do our best to ensure that the mash has the correct pH for the enzyme to work effectively. This enzyme requires a 30- to 60-minute holding period within the enzyme operating temperature range and also within the proper pH range to work effectively. My two boilers will drive the temperature up about 1° F a minute so it will take 18 minutes to reach the high side of the enzyme operating temperature and a few more to reach the terminal cooking temperature.

6. Continuing to heat the mixture beyond the liquefying enzymes maximum temperature: Enzymes are relatively inexpensiveso we will thermally destroy the enzyme as we continue cooking the mixture up to around 206° F. We don't have to boil the mixture but we do want to kill as many microbes as possible to prevent them from eating the sugar we are so carefully preparing for our yeast. Another reason we do not boil the mixture is that the last 10 degrees from 202° to 212° are very hard to come by. You are lucky to get 1/2 a degree a minute rise out of the boilers and you end up turning the shop into a sauna bath with all the steam you are driving off the cooking pot even if you cover the pot. You have to let some steam out because this is not a pressure cooker at the moment. It will become one when we attach the still lid but not during the cooking process. Another reason you do not take the mash batch all the way up to boiling point is that for every degree you go up you have to use energy and time and for every degree you cool it takes energy and time. So it costs you double for every minute you spend heating. Finally, boiling is not necessary in order to achieve effective starch conversion to sugar. The enzymes do that at their designed temperature and pH most effectively.

Using a motorized winch to lift the lid.

7. Stop cooking when the temperature reaches 206° which is about 18 to 30 minutes after the first dose of liquefying enzyme. Allow the temperature to fall as you uncover the cooker, take off the insulation and carefully hook up the cooling hoses. Keep the mixture stirring during this time. The temperature will fall quickly at first and then slow down. When the temperature falls below 203° you can add a third dose of liquefying enzyme to replace the dose that was thermally destroyed when the mash was heated beyond the maximum operating temperature of the enzyme in order to reach the terminal cooking temperature.

8. During this second half of the liquefaction holding period we will cool the slurry by running cold water through the circulating pipes in the tank, stirring the mixture and blowing filtered compressed air up through it. By the time the temperature of the slurry has fallen below the operating range of the liquefying enzyme, 185° F, it will have been more than one hour in total that the enzyme has been working. It will continue to work, although less efficiently, at lower temperatures but by now the mash should be pretty thin but not very sweet.

9. Preparing the mash slurry for the addition of the sugar making (saccharifying) enzyme that will be used to effectively cut the long hydrolyzed starch chains into shorter low molecular weight sugars: So far we are dealing just with starch. If you taste the mash it tastes like corn mush. It is not sweet like corn on the cob. What we have accomplished is to dissolve the starch in the corn into long chains of starch by hydration. The starch has picked up water molecules and formed structures that can be broken down further into sugar. Now we have to cut the starch structure into sugar. If you measure the sugar content

of this mash with a refractometer you will see 15% sugar but the mash will not taste sweet yet. These are as yet unfermentable sugars because the starch chains are still too long to taste like sugar. In order to use a hydrometer to test the sugar content of this not sweet tasting mash you must first cool the mash to 59° or 60° which is the temperature most sugar measuring hydrometers are calibrated to. More on this later as you monitor the fermentation of the mash.

10. In order to cut starch chains into sugar you need a second type of enzyme. This time we will use a sugar making (saccharifying) enzyme. I use a product called Novozym 25001. It has a designed operating temperature of between 149° F and 131° F. As we cool the mixture we will add this enzyme at the high side of its operating temperature which is 149°. Then we will turn off the cold water circulating in the cooling pipes and consequently slow down the cooling rate. This will allow the enzyme to work within its designed operating temperature for between 30 to 120 minutes. During this time we will check the pH of the mixture and do our best to ensure that it is less than 6.0 and if necessary reduce the pH to 5.5 with sulphuric acid, phosphoric acid or just plain vinegar or lemon juice. (Don't use battery acid. It has other things in it that are bad, bad, bad for mash.) My experience is that this enzyme works quickly and that the change in sweetness is immediately noticeable. This enzyme will also continue to work at lower temperatures, just less efficiently.

11. Final cooling of the mixture to less than 95° F which is the maximum that yeast organisms can comfortably live in: I usually cool down to 86° F or 30° C because the yeast metabolism will drive the temperature of the batch back up as they begin their life cycle. Turn on the cooling circulating water and resume reducing the temperature of the batch. The cooling system, along with thermal radiation from the pot, can result in a temperature drop of between about 1° to 2° degrees per minute. So, to go from 131° to 86° degrees will take between 20 and 45 minutes depending on the circumstances. As with heating the mash, the last 10° are the most difficult to remove. The reason for this is that large temperature differences transfer heat more quickly than small ones do. As the cooling water becomes closer to the batch temperature it takes more time to achieve a reduction in temperature. Another consideration is that you want to allow your cooling water to acquire as much heat as possible while it is in the cooling coils. One will simply waste water by blasting it through the cooling coils while not picking up all the heat it can. Contrawise, running the water too slowly wastes time.

12. One more thing we can do to reduce the temperature is to add 50 gallons of cold water to the batch pot in order to fill it to the top. This water replaces water evaporated during the cooking process. Also remember that we added only 350 gallons of our 390 gallons of water to the batch at the start. This is because the cooking process and agitation by the mixer throws mash up against the side of the tank and it would spill over if we used all the water we intend to put into the batch. Another reason is that when we dump in the corn the water tends to splash and we want to keep all the corn and water in the tank. Now, we can slow down the mixer to a crawl so that the mash is still circulating against the cooling pipes and add cold water. This has the effect of simply restoring my water to corn ratio to that which I started with and it helps to cool the mixture too. The only downside of this is that this water, fresh from the tap, has 1 ppm of chlorine in it. Eventually this chlorine will evaporate but until then it will act as an anti-microbial agent which is good for keeping the bacteria count down but also inhibits the yeast we will be adding. If you have time, let your water stand in a container for a day and the chlorine will evaporate away just like it does in swimming pools.

13. Adding sufficient amounts of yeast to efficiently use the sugar as food for their metabolism: One of the metabolic waste products of yeast is the alcohol we (they) are making. The fermentation process lasts between two and seven days. During this time the mixture, known as mash, becomes enriched in alcohol.

14. Distillation: At the conclusion of the fermentation process the now pretty flat corn mash of about 10% alcohol and 90% water is heated to drive off the volatile alcohol and leave the water behind. The alcohol vapor is directed through a pipe covered in water. The water gets hot and the alcohol cools back down to a liquid.

1.4 Bushel Volume Compared to Weight

In making a mixture of corn and water to cook in a batch one has to decide how thick or thin to make the mixture. Distillers refer to the corn and water slurry used for fermentation as a mash, wort, wash, or beer and the thickness or thinness is determined by the amount of water per bushel of corn or other starch like wheat or rye that is used in the "mash bill" for each batch. Ordinarily distillers will use between 14 and 30 US gallons of water per bushel.

I purchase my corn already milled to meal and so measure the grain component of my batches by the weight of material. However, much of the technical literature regarding the production of alcohol uses yields based on the amount of alcohol produced per bushel of corn and also by tons of starch. In order to have a meaningful comparison of yields it is necessary for me to be able to convert to bushels and tons of starch.

Because a bushel is defined as a unit of volume rather than one of weight there is some uncertainty in measurement that is introduced as we attempt to compare our results with other producers in the industry.

Cubic Inches per Bushel	2,150.42
Cubic Inches per Gallon	231.00
Gallons per Bushel	9.31

TABLE 16—Refer to Mash Den 1 *Worksheet*

One US bushel is equal to 2,150.42 cubic inches of volume. The definition of a US liquid gallon is that it encompasses a volume of 231 cubic inches. Accordingly there are 9.31 US gallons per bushel.[2] This translates to 35.24 liters per bushel using 3.7854118 liters per gallon[3] (Table 16).

This volume-to-weight translation is complicated further by the fact that the moisture content of the corn used in a batch will affect the weight of the bushel volume used. The more moisture in the corn the heavier each bushel will be. For our purposes a bushel of corn at about 17% moisture weighs between 55 and 56 pounds. One reason this value is an estimate is that corn grain is irregular in shape and there is air space between the kernels which varies depending on how the kernels line up in any given mixture. Some technical data will use 55-pound bushels and some reports will use 56-pound bushels. As you read articles on alcohol yield per bushel you will need to keep this difference in mind.[4]

In the following worksheet (Table 17, next page) I measured the mass of 1 liter of corn meal and calculated the lbs. per bushel from it using the value, derived in the worksheet, of 35.2391 liters per bushel.

---

2   This is slightly in conflict with the definition of a bushel which defines it as eight corn/dry gallons but all of my other calculations are based on US liquid gallons so I am confident that my conversion to liters is accurate.

3   This does not account for the fact that a US gallon is defined as that volume at 60° F and a liter is defined as a volume of water at 3.98° C which is the maximum density of water. Water actually becomes less dense as its temperature is lowered from 3.98 ° C to 0° C, its freezing point, because of intermolecular forces that begin to operate to align the water molecules into the open arrangement whereby ice increases in volume by about 10% over the volume the water occupies in a liquid state.

4   Bushels of different substances have different densities and volumes. Some of the common ones are: corn: 56 lb. = 25.401 kg , malted barley: 34 lb. = 15.422 kg, wheat and soybeans: 60 lb. = 27.215 kg, oats USA: 32 lb. = 14.5149 kg, barley: 48 lb. = 21.772 kg.

The result shows that a one-bushel volume of corn meal is about 56.38 pounds per bushel which is a value very close to the standard value of between 55 and 56 lbs. per bushel.

This indicates a very small volume reduction due to milling. This was a surprising result to me. I was expecting more reduction in volume from whole corn to corn meal. I will have to mill some corn myself to verify this.

Corn Bushel of Corn Meal - Volume & Wt.			
Liter Vol.	1.00		
Liters to Gallons	0.26417205		
Gal. Vol. per Liter	0.26417205		
Cu In per Gal.	231.00		
Gal per Liter * Cu In. per Gal. = Cu In. per Liter.	61.0237	61.0237	Cubic Inches per Liter
Cu In. per Bushel	2,150.42	2150.42	Cu In. per Bu. (PF Value)
Liters per Bushel Result	35.2391	35.23907048	Liters per Bu.
Lbs. per Liter (Measured)	1.60		
Lbs. per Bu.	56.38		
Kg per Bushel	25.57		

TABLE 17—Refer to Mash Den 1 *Worksheet*

What we can also learn from this is that our 50-lb. bags of corn meal contains 88.7% of a bushel (50/56.38 = 0.887). This means that we can multiply the number of bags we put in the still by 88.7% to obtain the bushels employed (Table 17).

The actual amount of starch contained in each kernel of corn will also affect the alcohol yield which can be achieved. It is generally assumed that corn contains 73% starch. I do not assume such a high starch content and use 72% starch as my standard. We will address this further when we discuss adding components to a batch more fully.

The densest batch that I can ferment in my still contains 1,500 lbs. of corn meal per batch. I have traditionally assumed 17% moisture and 56 pounds per bushel. Accordingly 1,500/56 = 26.78 bushels per batch. If I used 55 pounds per bushel the calculations would result in 1500/55 = 27.27 bushels per batch which would effectively increase my yield per bushel by 2%.[5]

By making consistent judgments about how to translate weight into volume and keeping in mind the uncertainties associated with doing so we can usefully compare our results with those described in distilling literature that reports results based upon the number of bushels employed.

In order to determine what density of mash to ferment, distillers refer to the thickness or thinness of their mash by the ratio of the gallons of water per bushel of grain employed.

A blend of corn and water beginning with 30 gallons of water to 1 bushel of corn is a thin mash. A thin mash is easier to work with. You can mix in finer corn flour and it is easier to mix or clump up during the cooking process. After cooking, a thin mash is easier to pump from one place to another. A thin mash also provides more of a buffer for alcohol and other biological waste products to accumulate in during the fermentation process. However, using more water means that you have to have a container large enough to contain the additional water volume and supply the additional energy needed to heat the extra water during cooking and again during distillation.

A thick mash is one made with 15 gallons of water to 1 bushel of corn. It is twice as thick as a 30-gallon mash. This is quite thick and without a strong mixer unit and constant agitation it will result in a thick slurry that

---

5   These uncertainties are only the first of many we will encounter. As you read distilling literature from countries using the English Imperial system of measurement you will do well to remember that they may be describing their yields based on Imperial bushels which are much larger and consequently give higher alcohol yields per bushel.

is more like corn mush. A thick mash like this is very difficult to deal with unless you have the right tools. However, this thick mash will pack in a lot of starch and subsequently sugar for the yeast to metabolize and give you the most yield per batch processed. One way to reduce the consistency of a thick mash is to use high temperature liquefying enzymes that cut long starch chains quickly and prevent the mash from getting too thick to manage.

1.5 Size of Vessel

We need to calculate the size of the vessel we are dealing with.

The capacity of my still is 514.84 gallons. I estimate that the coils inside take up about 4 gallons of volume leaving 510 gallons of volume available for my batches. It is capable of fermenting 1,500 pounds of corn at a time. Because the corn takes up volume in the tank I use a total of 390 gallons of water to set my batches with. The remainder of the volume in my vessel is taken up by the 1,500 pounds of corn that I add. This combination of ingredients fills the still virtually to its maximum and assuming a 10-gallon margin so I don't overfill the tank means that the corn displaces about 104 gallons of water as it is added to the batch. The method of calculating the volume of a round vessel follows (Table 18):

Calculate Size of Round Vessel			
Diameter of Vessel in Inches	52.50		
Radius = Diameter/2	26.25		
Radius Squared	689.06		
Pi	3.14159		
Radius Sq * Pi = Area Sq In.	2,164.75		
Height of Vessel inches	56.00		
Sq in. * H = Cubic Inch Volume	121,226.21		
Cubic Inches per Cubic Foot	1,728.00		
Total Cubic In./Cubic in per cubic foot =Cubic Feet	70.15	1.98676	Cubic Meters
Cubic Inches per Gallon	231.00		
US Gallon Capacity of Vessel	524.79	1,986.76	Liters of Volume
Second Method			
Size of Vessel in Gal.	514.84	1,948.88	Liters of Volume
Liquid Gal. to Cubic Feet	0.13368		
Cubic Feet of Vessel	68.82	1.949	Cubic Meters

TABLE 18—Refer to Size of Vessel Worksheet

I confirmed this value by metering in 510 gallons of 60° F water into the vessel with a water meter that is probably accurate to 1% of the total flow.[6]

1.6 Mash Density

Mash density is measured by calculating how many gallons of water are used per unit of grain in a batch. Usually this is expressed in a ratio of gallons to bushels of grain and called a beer or wort. A 30-gallon beer has 30

---

6   If the meter is used at a reasonable rate of flow through it and with the water itself close to the standard temperature of 60° F.

gallons of water for each bushel of grain. This would be a thin beer with lots of water for the yeast to live in. It would be easy to get it cooked and hydrolyzed.

Because I use a powerful hydraulic mixer I am able to use a mash that is as low as 14.5 gallons per bushel but most distillers conduct their mashing operations at levels between 20 and 30 US gallons of water per bushel. The densest, thickest mash that my enzyme manufacturer, Novozym, recommends that their products be used with is a 20-gallon mash. The thinnest mash they recommend is a 24-gallon mash.

Using 500 kilograms or 1,102.312 lbs. of corn with 433 gallons of water as our example will make the results convenient to relate to the metric system and results in a 22-gallon mash (Table 19).

Gallon Mash Expressed as Gallons of Water Per Volume (Bushels) of Grain				Constants	
Pounds of Grain	1,102.312	500.000	Kg Grain	0.453592	Lbs. to Kg
Pounds per Bushel	56.00	25.401	Kg per Bu.	3.7854	Gal. to Liters
Lbs./Lbs. Per Bu = Bushels	19.68			0.028320	Cubic Feet to Cubic Meters
Gallons of Water	433.00	1,639.08	Liters	8.328230	Pounds Per Gal. @ 60° F
Pounds of Water	3,606.12	1,635.71	Kg Water	0.13368	Water Gal. to Cubic Feet
Water Gal./Bu. = Gal. per Bushel or Gallon Mash	22.00			1.24446	Bushels to Cu Feet
Total Lbs. of Batch	4,708.44	2,135.71	Total Kg		
Grain Wt. %	23.41%				
Water Wt. %	76.59%				
Ratio of Parts H$_2$O to grain	3.271				

TABLE 19—Refer to Mash Den 1 *Worksheet*

The worksheet provides the total weight of the batch and the percent by weight.

Now that we know the percent by weight we can use the weight of the grain and the percentage it constitutes of the batch and the worksheet will calculate the gallon beer value for us. This allows us to obtain the same results without having to use bushels except to cross-check the results (Table 20).

Mash Density by % of Grain			
Pounds of Grain To use	1,102.312	0.45359	Lbs. to Kg
Grain % of Mash	23.41%	500.00	Kilograms
Water %	76.59%		
1/ % = Ratio of % to Whole	4.2717		
Lbs. * Ratio = Total Batch Wt.	4,708.72	2,135.84	Total Kg
Batch Wt. - Grain Wt.= H$_2$O Lbs.	3,606.41	1,635.84	Kg Water
Pounds per Gal. of H$_2$O	8.328230		
Gallons of Water	433.03	1,635.84	Liters
Pounds per Bushel	56.00		
Grain wt./lbs. per Bu = Bushels	19.68		
Gal./Bu = Gal. per Bushel	22.00		

TABLE 20—Refer to Mash Density by % *Worksheet*

Sometimes it is easier to think in terms of gallons of water and percentage of weight as the primary inputs since water is the larger component, rather than of the weight of the grain. Rearranging the worksheet gives a method to set the percentage of water first and have the grain amount as a result (Table 21).

Mash Density by % Water and Gallons of Water			
Gallons of Water	433.03	1,635.82	Liters
Water % of Mash	76.59%	8.32823	Lbs. per Gal.
Grain %	23.41%		
Pounds of Water To use	3,606.37	1,635.82	Kilograms
1/ % = Ratio of % to Whole	1.3057		
Lbs. * Ratio = Total Batch Wt.	4,708.67	2,135.82	Total Kg
Batch Wt. - H$_2$O Lbs.=Grain Wt.	1,102.30	499.99	Kg Grain
Pounds per Bushel	56.00		
Grain wt./lbs. per Bu =Bushels	19.68		
Gal./Bu = Gal. per Bushel	22.00		

TABLE 21—Refer to Mash Density by % *Worksheet*

Another method we can use is to employ the parts of water and parts of grain (Table 22).

Mash Density by Parts Grain and Water Ratio			
Scale of Grain Lbs.	1,102.312	500.00	Grain Kg
Grain Parts	1.00		
Water Parts	3.271	1,635.50	Water Kg
Total Parts	4.27		
Lbs. of H$_2$O	3,605.66	1,635.50	Liters
Pounds per Gal. of H$_2$O	8.328230	2,135.50	Batch Kg
Gallons of H$_2$O	432.944		
Water %	76.59%		
Grain %	23.41%		
Total Batch Weight	4,707.97		
Pounds per Bushel	56.00		
Bushels	19.68		
Gal./Bu = Gal. per Bushel	22.0	Gallon Mash	

TABLE 22—Refer to Mash Density by % *Worksheet*

Lastly we can use water gallons as the basis for adding components by parts of water (Table 23, next page).

As you can see the conversion errors are starting to mount up in this sheet and the gallons of water per bushel is now only 21.99 rather than 22.00 even though we are using the same input numbers. The reasons for this are that the conversion constants are not perfect to begin with and are only good to the decimal places provided. When calculations are performed in a series of steps it is necessary to use rounding to significant digits and this rounding is an additional source of uncertainty in the calculations, in this case yielding slightly different results.

I have developed a thicker mash for my operation. If I am going to run a batch I want to have as much starch in it as I can successfully ferment. Table 24 shows a very thick batch I developed which is a 14.56-gallon mash. This type of batch is not for beginners. Start with a thin mash and work down to starch densities this high. I will describe how I persuade a batch this dense to ferment completely as we go along. This is the mash density as the batch is actually set to work. During the cooking phase the batch is even denser because I only use 350 gallons to cook with. Frankly, my batch is probably too dense. I'm probably wasting starch and should back off to an 18-gallon or 20-gallon beer. But corn is relatively cheap and I can't afford to take a week to find out that I'm making less alcohol with a thinner mash when for 30 dollars I can pack another 200 pounds of corn (Table 24).

This density of 14.56 bushels per gallon is way denser than what manufacturers recommend as a mash density.

One thing I would like to point out is that you can add more grain and water volume to your cooker than it could hold if the components were added separately. This seems like an odd result but let's look at the batch and see (Table 25).

Even though I calculated that a bushel of corn meal weighed 56 pounds I have included a reduction in milling factor that can be set by the user to meet their requirements. I have set this at 10% reduction in volume as an example. Even with a reduction in volume due to milling, the total quantity of 82.14 cubic feet has been added to our cooker.

Mash Density by Parts Water Ratio to Grain			
Scale of Water Gallons	433.03	8.32823	Lbs. per Gal. of H_2O
Water Parts	3.271		
Grain Parts	1.00		
Total Parts	4.27		
H_2O Pts./Grain Pts.= Grain Ratio	0.3057	0.45359	Lbs. Avdp to Kg
Water Weight	3,606.37	1,635.82	Water Kg
H_2O Wt. * Ratio = Grain Weight	1,102.529	500.10	Grain Kg
Total Batch Weight	4,708.90		
Water %	76.59%		
Grain %	23.41%		
Pounds per Bushel	56.00		
Bushels	19.69		
Gal./Bu = Gal. per Bushel	21.99	Gallon Mash	

TABLE 23—Refer to Mash Density by % *Worksheet*

My 1500 pound batch			
Pounds of Grain	1,500.00	680.388	Kg Grain
Pounds per Bushel	56.00	25.401	Kg per Bu.
Lbs./Lbs. Per Bu = Bushels	26.79		
Gallons of Water	390.00	1,476.31	Liters
Pounds of Water	3,248.01	1,473.27	Kg Water
Water Gal./Bu. = Gal. per Bushel or Gallon Mash	14.56		
Total Lbs. of Batch	4,748.01	2,153.66	Total Kg
Grain Wt. %	31.59%		
Water Wt. %	68.41%		
Ratio of Parts H_2O to grain	2.165		

TABLE 24—Refer to Mash Den 1 *Worksheet*

Volume of Batch			
Gallons of Water	390.00		
Water Gal. to Cubic Feet	0.13368		
Cubic Feet of Water	52.135	1.476	Cubic Meters
Bushels of Grain	26.79		
Bushels to Cu Feet	1.24446		
Cubic Feet of Grain	33.33	0.944	Cubic Meters
Total Cubic Feet in Batch	85.47	2.420	Cubic Meters
Milling Reduction in Vol.	10%		
Cubic Feet of Reduction	-3.33	-0.094	Cubic Meters
Actual Vol. of Grain Added	30.00	0.850	Cubic Meters
Total Cubic Feet in Batch	82.14	2.420	Cubic Meters

TABLE 25—Refer to Mash Den 1 *Worksheet*

Comparing that value to the volume in our cooker demonstrates that I am able to add 20% excess volume to the cooker beyond the capacity of the tank itself (Table 26, next page).

Excess Fill Calculations			
Size of Vessel in Gal.	510.00		
Water Gal. to Cubic Feet	0.13368		
Cubic Feet of vessel	68.18	1.931	Cubic Meters
Total Cubic Feet in Batch	82.14	2.326	Cubic Meters
Excess of Cubic Feet Added	13.96	0.395	Cubic Meters
Excess Cu. Ft./Vessel Cu. Ft.	20.5%	Excess Fill %	
Excess Gallons	104.42	395.27	Liters

TABLE 26—Refer to Mash Den 1 *Worksheet*

We can see from the above-referenced worksheet that this batch consists of 20.5% more volume than the vessel will hold, amounting to 104.42 gallons of excess volume.

By the application of Archimedes's principal a solid should displace an amount equal to its volume.

Yet, as we cook our corn it does not behave like an ordinary solid. The addition of corn to water does not increase the total volume of the combined components in direct proportion to each of their volumes. This is the same principle that you see when you add tablespoons of sugar to a glass of water without changing the volume of the solution appreciably.[7]

In the case of corn meal and water some of the corn starch dissolves into the water and in this configuration the molecules take up less volume.

It is also similar to the same effect we will see in our blending worksheets where the mixing of alcohol and water will also result in a reduction in volume.

During the cooking process more water is hydrated onto the starch chains and the volume decreases further.

However, in the case of corn meal the process of mixing the corn into the water's molecular interstices does not happen as quickly as with sugar.

The reduction in volume effect is not immediate; there is some lag time as the mixer does its job. While it is possible to add corn meal continuously it is not possible to dump it all in at once.

Because the process of cooking mash is messy and the mixer forces the mash up the sides of the vessel I only add 350 gallons to cook with and then add 40 gallons of yeast slurry and additional water to fill the tank when I actually set the batch to ferment. Since my grain is already milled I set the milling reduction in volume to zero. My overfill calculations show that my overfill is 17% in the cooking phase, but based on the same total volume of the vessel (Table 27, next page).

Some additional gallons, above the 40 I reserve, can be added because of evaporation that occurs during the cooking process. Additional water can be added during fermentation to increase the buffer because there is some evaporation during the fermentation process.

Again, good judgment must be used since the cooker is also the still and when the batch is sealed and heated to drive off the alcohol one does not want the expansion of the water due to heating it to choke the still for surface area for the alcohol to evaporate from as it is heated.

If the mash expands and fills up the tank and starts to climb up the column you will not be able to successfully distill it and will have to let some out before the still will work properly. I've had to do this.

To quantify this expansion both for cooking and distilling, we can look at the expansion of water itself (Table 28, next page).

---

7   In the blending regulations the conversion ratio for sugar weight to 1 gallon of volume is 13 pounds of sugar to 1 pound of volume.

Volume of Batch			
Gallons of Water	350.00		
Water Gal. to Cubic Feet	0.13368		
Cubic Feet of Water	46.788	1.476	Cubic Meters
Bushels of Grain	26.79		
Bushels to Cu Feet	1.24446		
Cubic Feet of Grain	33.33	0.944	Cubic Meters
Total Cubic Feet in Batch	80.12	2.269	Cubic Meters
Milling Reduction in Vol.	0%		
Cubic Feet of Reduction	0.00	0.000	Cubic Meters
Actual Vol. of Grain Added	33.33	0.944	Cubic Meters
Total Cubic Feet in Batch	80.12	2.420	Cubic Meters
Excess Fill Calculations			
Size of Vessel in Gal.	510.00		
Water Gal. to Cubic Feet	0.13368		
Cubic Feet of vessel	68.18	1.931	Cubic Meters
Total Cubic Feet in Batch	80.12	2.269	Cubic Meters
Excess of Cubic Feet Added	11.94	.338	Cubic Meters
Excess Cu. Ft./Vessel Cu. Ft.	17.5%	Excess Fill %	
Excess Gallons	89.35	338.24	Liters

TABLE 27—Refer to Mash Den 1 Worksheet

Volume Correction For Alcohol using Table 37b method.				
Sample Temp. of Alcohol or Water	60.00	0.0000	Thermometer Cor.	
Apparent Proof	0.00	0.0000	Hydrometer Cor.	
True Proof Result	0.00			
Present Gallons of Alcohol or Water	510.00		1,930.56	Present Liters
Present °F Temp of Alc. Or Water	60.00		15.56	°C
FYI 60° Gal.	510.00		1,930.56	60° F Liters
Gallon Change from Present Gallons	0.00		0.00	Liters Change
Temp at which it is Desired to know vol.	180.00		82.22	°C
Gallons at Desired Temperature	523.77		1,982.69	Liters at Temp
Gallon Change from Present Gallons	13.77		52.13	Liters Change

TABLE 28—Refer to Vol Cor Alc T37b Worksheet

The water expansion from 60° to 180° F is 13.77 gallons. This is more than 1/4 of the 40 gallons of freeboard we are keeping in reserve.

Now at the end of the fermentation process we are not dealing with water. We are dealing with a 10% alcohol and water mixture which is equal to 20 proof. However the expansion coefficient has not increased substantially (from 13.77 gallons in Table 28 to 15.30 gallons in Table 29, next page).

Still, this is enough to choke the still when the batch is heated for the stripping run at the end of the fermentation.

Volume Correction For Alcohol using Table 37b method.				
Sample Temp. of Alcohol or Water	60.00	0.0000		Thermometer Cor.
Apparent Proof	20.00	0.0000		Hydrometer Cor.
True Proof Result	20.00			
Present Gallons of Alcohol or Water	510.00		1,930.56	Present Liters
Present ° F Temp of Alc. Or Water	60.00		15.56	° C
FYI 60° Gal.	510.00		1,930.56	60° F Liters
Gallon Change from Present Gallons	0.00		0.00	Liters Change
Temp at which it is Desired to know vol.	180.00		82.22	° C
Gallons at Desired Temperature	525.30		1,988.48	Liters at Temp
Gallon Change from Present Gallons	15.30		57.92	Liters Change

TABLE 29—Refer to Vol Cor Alc T37b *Worksheet*

1.7 Water Considerations

I would like to address some of the considerations relating to the water you will use in your batch.

For my batch I need 390 gallons of good water to start. My public water utility, the Morgantown Utility Board (MUB) provides verifiably excellent water for my operations. It meets the highest quality standards for public drinking water as set by the EPA. Even after being supplied good water to start with there are several things we want to be aware of.[8]

The following discussion is framed in terms of municipal water supply and why municipal water has certain characteristics that affect the water delivered rather than specifically how the water relates to the distilling process. It is written this way because it is important to learn all the upstream and downstream aspects of the distilling business. Each part and component of your products will have a unique journey to your distillery and the more you know about its history and composition the better. There is no component where this is more true than water.

Just to refresh our recollections, acids have a pH lower than 7 and bases have a pH higher than 7.

Bases have surplus electrons available to transfer to other molecules and acids are deficient in electrons and would like to acquire them. This is why you can mix an acid and a base together and obtain a neutral substance.

The starting pH of the water is significant because the acidity or alkalinity of the water I use is an important factor in determining how effective the enzymes I use to cut up starch chains into fermentable sugars will be. It also affects how well and how long the yeast will be able to survive in the mash environment as they ferment alcohol. The Morgantown Utility Board delivers water at an average pH of 7.11 which is just slightly more basic than neutral water, which would have a pH of 7.0.

The city water, at a pH of around 7.11, contains a small surplus of electrons, consequently it has less tendency to want to acquire electrons from electron rich metals like iron, copper and aluminum, all of which are used as water-carrying pipes. If both the metal in the pipes and the water each have an overall negative charge they repel each other and stay out of each other's way. Sending along surplus electrons in the water to begin with results in less corrosion of the system overall.

---

8   MUB Water Quality Report. Mub Report 2009 1.1

The surplus electrons in the water also serve to buffer the water against any acidic substances that might be encountered along the way and to keep the dissolved oxygen in the water from wanting to bond with metal pipes in the system. This is very important because most oxidation of pipes and the decay of sacrificial anodes is facilitated by oxygen bonding and the city water supply does have a significant amount of air and therefore of oxygen in it.[9] The reason that boiled water tastes different is because the process of boiling drives out the air from it. Oxygen and nitrogen, both being gasses at room temperature, are driven off by the heat applied and when the water cools it is depleted in atmospheric gasses.

Dissolved oxygen in water can also affect the specific gravity of the water since it will make it less dense. After any agitation or blending operation, the solution will be enhanced in atmosphere. Most of the small micro bubbles will rise to the surface and escape within a half hour or so. Allowing alcohol, water or any other mixture that has been agitated or blended to stand several hours or overnight will allow more of the dissolved atmosphere to leave. Eventually the solution will reach equilibrium with the atmospheric pressure. This equilibrium is governed by Henry's Law.[10]

However, boiled water will not reacquire dissolved atmosphere to the same extent as municipal water has when delivered even if left to stand for some time. Boiled water will only reacquire oxygen to the extent that Henry's Law describes and no excess oxygen will permeate it.

Restating the pH considerations we note that having a pH higher than 7.0 in the water system is better for the pipes than having acidic water with a pH less than 7.0. Acidic water has a deficit of electrons and an overall positive charge. Free oxygen in acidic water will seek to acquire electrons from the metals which make up the pipes in the water system.

The easiest way to prevent this from happening is to add calcium carbonate, $CaCo_3$ (limestone), to the water to bring the pH up above 7.0. This limestone goes into the water as a dissolved solid and adds to the total dissolved solids in the water and it also adds free electrons as the limestone goes into solution. These free electrons change the overall charge of the water and give up these electrons to oxygen or any other acidic, electron acquiring substance in the system.

Water Hardness: Water hardness is a function of the amount of dissolved calcium salts, magnesium salts, iron and aluminum in the water. These salts occur in a variety of forms but are usually calcium and magnesium bicarbonates (referred to as "temporary hardness") and sulphates and chlorides (referred to as "permanent hardness"). Although the most obvious effect of hard water is to prevent soap from lathering, most people cannot tolerate drinking water that exceeds 300 ppm of calcium carbonate, or 1,500 ppm of chloride, or 500 ppm of sulphate. Hard water is treated by either a zeolite process (home water softeners) or a lime-soda ash process (large operations).

Soft water is generally defined so that the total dissolved solids are less than 50 ppm. If the total dissolved solids in the water rises above 500 ppm with 300 ppm of that total being calcium carbonate, then the water crosses the threshold into very hard water.

---

9   Sacrificial anodes on ships' hulls and other metals exposed to salt or fresh water operate by the same principle and prevent oxygen from oxidizing (rusting) the metal to be protected. It is not the water or the salt that is primarily the problem. The salt does allow electrons to move more easily and creates an electrolyte but this just makes the process easier; it does not cause it as much as the oxygen does. It is the oxygen that does the bonding to create rust. A sacrificial anode of zinc has surplus electrons. The zinc bonds with dissolved oxygen in the water and is carried away as zinc oxide. Otherwise the oxygen would bond to the metal to be protected and stay in place but weaken the structure. Rusted objects become heavier, not lighter as Lavossier so ably demonstrated in the 18th century. Here we are trying to do the opposite, to simply carry the dissolved oxygen with the water and neutralize it with free electrons already in the water.

10   See Henry's Law Worksheets in the *Distilling Manual* workbook.

As to my city water supply, the range of total dissolved solids in the Morgantown system is between 159 and 200 ppm. Of that total between 83 and 125 ppm are calcium carbonate, $CaCo3$. The city actually adds some calcium carbonate (limestone, as stated above) to its water before it leaves the treatment plant. We put up with slightly hard water because it protects the pipes in our houses and the water system generally. In addition to protecting the pipes in the system, calcium carbonate is needed by yeast for their successful metabolism. So we don't want to do anything to remove this constituent of the water. In fact we might even want to add some calcium carbonate up to about 500 ppm. The Bourbon makers in Kentucky pride themselves on being located "on the limestone slab" which is a geologic formation whose aquifers provide very hard water, i.e., 300 to 500 ppm calcium carbonate, but with a very low iron content. Scotch producers in Scotland have varying water sources but generally tend towards hard water with enough dissolved calcium carbonate to aid in yeast metabolism; each distillery is also enamored with the unique quality of their particular water source.

Iron: The one thing that everyone agrees on is that no distiller wants to have iron in their water. Even a little bit is detrimental to the taste.

The iron content of MUB's water averages 0.01655 ppm. That is 16% of 1 ppm. One part per million is about one drop per ten gallons. This is acceptable. However it is still more than one half of the limit at which water quality is regulated. Anything over 0.3 ppm (30% of a ppm) begins to show up as a taste and defines the limit of acceptability from a drinking water taste standpoint although there is nothing poisonous about water with a high iron content until concentrations reach 500 ppm. But it does not take much iron in water to give it an off-taste and this is bad for whiskey production.

You might say, "how can that be, if you have 125 ppm of calcium carbonate and that is good, how can 16.5% of a ppm be so bad; after all, iron is not lead or some toxin, it's just a little rust." Well evidently, even a small amount of iron must taste bad so we need to have as little as possible in our mash. Fortunately, an activated carbon filter will absorb a good deal of iron.

Chlorine: The only other component of the city water supply that is necessary for our health but not wanted in our mash is chlorine. Chlorine is an antibacterial and keeps the water clean to drink, preserves the water and prevents microbes from growing in it. Water systems monitor coliform bacteria as a representative and dangerous bacteria and use chlorine to keep that level at zero to ensure safe drinking water.

In order to achieve this, the system runs with about 4 ppm of chlorine in it in summer when it is warm and conducive to bacterial growth and about 2 ppm in winter when the water is cold and growing conditions are poor because it is too cold for bacteria to grow.

This chlorine does not help a distiller. What we are trying to do is grow as many yeast cells as possible and chlorine is poisonous to them as well as to bacteria. So we want to remove as much chlorine as possible. Chlorine will evaporate, so if you just fill your batch a day before you use it you can eliminate some chlorine that way. However, you will increase the bacteria count in the water by letting it stand overnight. Sunlight also breaks down chlorine, a fact known to anyone who maintains a backyard swimming pool. So, if we could put our water out in the sunshine some chlorine would be eliminated this way. A final way to eliminate chlorine is to heat the water. This drives off the chlorine as a vapor. About 150° should do it, then let it cool overnight and you will have "chlorine-free" water. However, it costs energy to do this and it is not efficient. Also, the heat generated in cooking operations has the effect of driving off the chlorine so that the yeast have a hospitable environment free of this antimicrobial agent.

For batches that I blend to bottling proof I do treat my water by running it through a reverse osmosis system and we will describe that system *infra*.

For fermentations there are a few other things we want to do to the water like adding some nutrients for the yeast to use in their metabolism, and adjusting the pH so our enzymes will work efficiently. We will cover these topics later.

The pressure delivered to my shop is around 100 psi in the street but we use a water regulator to reduce the pressure to around 65 psi in the shop. At this pressure of 65 psi a 3/4"-inside-diameter hose will deliver about 8.5 gallons per minute so it will take around 41 minutes to transfer the first 350 gallons. We will add the final 40 or so gallons after the cooking process is over. Rather than stand around I set a timer and do other things till 5 minutes before the fill will be complete; check the tank but you don't have to stand there and watch it fill.

The water temperature coming into my shop varies by season. In the winter it can be as low as 42° F. In the summer it can rise to 72°. This reflects the ground temperature around the shop and the temperature of the pipes extending out for miles around. If you are using large amounts of water one may find it desirable to perform a volume correction to determine how much water at the standard volume of 60° F one needs.

With respect to other qualities of water one should be aware of, it is useful to note what contaminants a municipal water board monitors and addresses before that water is delivered to customers. Any distiller wanting to use "their special water" should be aware of what a responsibility that is and be prepared to monitor their water for contaminants to the same degree as a municipal water authority.

1.8 Water Standards

My distillery enjoys the benefits of being served by the Morgantown Utility Board as my water supplier. It operates a first class water treatment plant and distribution system. In order to ensure that tap water is safe to drink, the EPA promulgates regulations which limit the amount of certain contaminants in the water provided by all public water systems.

Table 30 presents the testing for inorganic chemicals by my water board during a recent year (2007–2008). For reference, one part per million (ppm), indicates that one pound of a substance is present in one million pounds of water. Roughly equivalent and on a smaller scale, one part per million is approximately one drop per 10 gallons of water, and one part per billion (ppb) is approximately one drop per ten thousand gallons of water. *MCL* indicates the maximum contaminant level allowed and it is the highest level of a contaminant that is allowed in drinking water. Values listed as *ND* (nondetectable) were too small to be detected.

Additional parameters are annualized. Some do not have MCLs associated with them (Table 31, next page).

Parameter	Units	MCL	Range of results
Nitrate	ppm	10	0.35 – 0.43
Antimony	ppb	6	ND
Arsenic	ppb	10	ND
Barium	ppm	2	0.044 – 0.047
Beryllium	ppb	4	ND
Cadmium	ppb	5	ND
Chromium	ppb	100	ND
Cyanide	ppb	200	ND
Fluoride	ppm	4	0.75 – 1.04
Mercury	ppb	2	ND
Nickel	ppb	100	ND
Selenium	ppb	50	ND – 0.0013
Thallium	ppb	2	ND

TABLE 30: Inorganic Contaminants Tested and Results

In addition the water board tests its source water for additional parameters (Table 32, next page).

Parameter	Units	MCL	Annual Average
Iron	ppm	0.3	0.023
Manganese	ppm	0.05	0.0015
PH	units	6.5 – 8.5	7.88
Alkalinity	ppm	-	59.7
Hardness	ppm	-	146.4

TABLE 31: Contaminants Tested on Annualized Basis

Source Water Assessment - Average Results		
Parameter	**Units**	**Source Water**
Silver (Ag)	ppm	0.002
Aluminum (Al)	ppm	0.256
Arsenic (Ag)	ppm	ND
Barium (Ba)	ppm	0.041
Cadmium (Cd)	ppm	ND
Copper (Cu)	ppm	0.037
Iron (Fe)	ppm	0.159
Manganese (Mn)	ppm	0.079
Sodium (Na)	ppm	31.95
Lead (Pb)	ppm	0.0001
Selenium (Se)	ppm	0.0006
Zinc (Zn)	ppm	0.0078
Fluoride (F)	ppm	0.145
Sulfate	ppm	137.0
Total Phosphorus (as P)	ppm	0.015
Nitrate Nitrogen (NO3-N)	ppm	0.42
Total Recoverable Phenolics	ppm	ND
Hardness (as Calcium Carbonate)	ppm	148
Total Dissolved Solids	ppm	296
Hexavalent Chromium (CrVI)	ppm	ND
Chloride	ppm	10.4
Alkalinity (Total)	ppm	47.6
Mercury (Hg)	ppm	ND
Turbidity	NTU	3.11

TABLE 32: Additional Parameters Tested

Parameter	Units	MRDL	Annual Average
Chlorine	ppm	4	1.57

TABLE 33: Chlorine Testing Results

Turbidity: Turbidity is generally thought of as the cloudiness of water. It is one way to measure the removal or inactivation of certain targeted microorganisms. At high levels it can impair the disinfection process.

Because chlorine is added to water, its contaminant level is set as the maximum that can be applied to drinking water as a maximum residual disinfectant level (Table 33).

The utility board performs a lead and copper analysis every three years on water samples throughout its water distribution system. The results showed that all but one of the 30 samples obtained and analyzed that year were below the detection limit for copper. Similarly, the same 30 samples showed that only one sample was above the detection limit for lead. The detectable copper sample was 0.114 mg/l, and the detectable lead sample was 0.012 mg/l.

Tests for coliform bacteria are used as an indicator of overall bacterial levels in the system. Its presence may indicate that other potentially harmful bacteria may be present. Of the 720 samples taken during the annual sampling period, all showed 0% presence of coliform bacteria.

Cryptosporidium, a protozoan, is also measured as an important bacteriologic contaminant. The board samples monthly for cryptosporidium, and found no occurrences of this contaminant for this entire 12-month sampling period.

Total organic carbon is naturally present in the environment. For this sampling period the average was 1.8 milligrams per liter.

Radiological Compound Testing: Certain naturally occurring minerals are radioactive and emit alpha particle radiation. The board tests its water for alpha activity and radium 226 and radium 228, and both were below detectable limits.

Regulated Volatile Organic Contaminants: Organic chemical contaminants, including synthetic and volatile organic chemicals, may be by-products of industrial processes and petroleum production. They may also come from gas stations, urban storm water runoff and septic tanks.

Of the 21 regulated VOCs required to be tested, all were non-detectable for the year surveyed.

Regulated Synthetic Organic Contaminants (pesticides, PCBs, herbicides, etc.): Regulated synthetic organic chemicals are tested twice every three years. The board's latest analysis, performed during a recent year, showed that all chemicals analyzed for were non-detectable.

Given the thoroughness with which my water board tests the water in their system, I have considerable confidence in my water supply and would never think of using any other source for both my batch cooking and bottling operations. I do run my blending water through a small commercial reverse osmosis system for the benefits it provides. There is a noticeable change in the taste of the water after it is treated, making a better final product.

1.9 Batch Mixing Temperature

This is a Goldilocks problem. The preferred method is to mix the corn and water or "mash in" with very hot water of around 190° or above. The reason to take this approach is to kill as many bacteria that are on and in the corn as soon as possible.

Large distilleries use steam jet cookers, also known as flash cookers, as the industrial solution to this problem.

For the rest of us with a batch of corn and water to cook, the drawback of mashing in hot is that above about 120° F the corn is shocked by the water temperature and will not mix in easily.

The result is that the corn meal will form corn balls where the outside is sticky and the inside is dry; the corn gelatinizes around uncooked centers and one ends up with a batch of uncooked dumplings of corn that are difficult to break up particularly if you are standing over a piping hot batch trying to beat them to pieces with a hoe or some other appropriate instrument. To mash in hot requires heavy duty mixing equipment to ensure complete agitation of the mash and a real knowledge of how to use and apply enzymes.

In order to help me mash in I have built a hydraulic mixer to agitate my batch as I add my corn.

My mixer consists of a hydraulic pressure pump that is attached to a high torque, low RPM motor like the ones used in small hydraulic earth movers (e.g., "bobcats"). It is regulated by a simple two-way valve like the kind on any log splitter. Its speed is regulated by a pressure bypass valve that can be adjusted to bleed some of the volume directly back to the tank instead of through the motor unit.

If the water is too cool, below 60° F, one also, rather oddly, runs into the same corn ball problem. Some corn will clump and float on the top and the balls will be difficult or impossible to break up. The rest will just sink to the

Mixer power pack with bypass and reverse.

Hydraulic mixer mounting.

bottom of the tank and not dissolve or "mash in" with the water. Also, by mixing cool water and corn together bacteria will begin to grow in the mixture while the temperature rises. This will remove some food for the yeast to eat and also provide a background bacterial culture that the yeast will have to compete against if the bacteria are not killed off during the cooking process.

Yeast and bacteria have very different multiplication rates. Bacteria can duplicate themselves in periods as quickly as 20 to 30 minutes per generation. Yeast is a larger and more complex organism. It is a eukaryotic cell, really more like an animal, because it stores its energy as glycerol rather than as starch. In a favorable environment yeast cells can bud off from a mother cell every 40 to 60 minutes. This differential in reproduction times can allow even a small number of starting bacteria to out-multiply the yeast and this can have many detrimental effects in addition to consuming the food we want the yeast to eat.

Bacteria produce metabolic waste products such as lactic acid. Some of these waste products have boiling points lower than that of water and therefore these waste products will be concentrated in the distillate you will be collecting as alcohol. Bacterial waste products also affect the pH of the mash and can make it so low that the yeast can no longer live in it.

The short story is that if you let the bacteria get a head start on a batch they can take over the batch and ruin it with their metabolic wastes and reduce your yield because of the sugar they eat.

But we are getting ahead of ourselves. During cooking there is no yeast to contend with, only the bacteria that are multiplying.

The goal is to use water that is as hot as possible consistent with getting all the corn dissolved in the water and not scalding yourself.

In my practice I start mixing in the corn and water when the temperature in the tank reaches about 100° F.

With both boilers running, the water temperature in the tank rises about 1° F per minute and it takes 20 minutes to add all the corn meal.

If everything goes smoothly the water temperature will be around 120° when I finish adding corn and this is still a comfortable temperature to be working over a batch.

If it takes longer, then you still have some margin of error before the batch would get so hot it is difficult to work above, say around 160° F or so.

After adding the corn one wants the temperature to rise as quickly as possible to prevent bacterial growth and to reach as high a temperature as economically feasible in order to kill any bacteria that do manage to grow.

Some large distilleries can develop system-wide infections that require treatment with antibiotics.

1.10 Historical Use of Grain in Whiskey Production

Historically, the starch source used in America for spirit production was rye grain grown on small family farmsteads as the second crop of the season or on land that was not fertile enough to support corn production. Corn was the primary staple crop and it was so highly valued as a food source for the farming family that no one would have considered using it to make whiskey. Corn was grown upon the best soil and during the best part of the growing season. The surplus starch in the family diet was therefore the rye. It was sown and raised for two potential purposes. First, in the event the corn crop was not sufficient to feed the family, rye could be consumed as a means to get the family through the winter and into the next growing season, and, secondarily, any surplus rye grain was used as a starch source for whiskey production. The whiskey thus produced was sold as a means of obtaining hard currency in order to purchase manufactured goods needed on the farm. Rye suited both of these purposes well. It was edible and it could be grown both earlier and later in the year than corn and upon soils that would not support corn cultivation. Rye whiskey was the dominant whiskey in American culture up and till the advent of Prohibition.

In order to use any type of starch, like rye, corn or potatoes as a starting material for fermentation, it must be cooked. The purpose of cooking is to reverse what the seed did in the first place which was to take sugar and convert it into a compact starch source. As such it is not available to the seed itself or to our yeast for fermentation until it is turned back into sugar.

In order to unlock the starch and make it available either for the seed to sprout or for yeast to eat, water must be allowed to combine with the starch molecules. The process of binding water molecules to starch is known as *hydrolysis*. In this process the tightly coiled starch molecules begin to unwind and lengthen into long starch chains. When this is accomplished the long starch chains must be cut into shorter, simpler, molecules of sugar. This second process is mediated by an enzyme. This art of starch conversion to sugar was common knowledge in the culture of 18th and 19th century America. Late in the cooking process malted barley[11] was added at about 15% of the total grain employed and it was applied at the correct temperature and pH in order to supply the enzymes necessary to break down starch into sugars that yeast could metabolize. Certain strains of barley grain have been specifically selected by mankind, over hundreds of years, to contain an excess of the enzymes necessary to accomplish this conversion from starch to sugar. These enzymes exist in every plant seed and are used by all plants to access the energy stored in the seed's starch so that the plant can begin to grow and to sustain it until it can begin photosynthesizing its own food.

In order to use barley grain to make sugar it is not simply added to the mixture as a whole grain; it must first be allowed to germinate into sprouts. During the process of germination the enzymes in the seed become active and begin breaking down the seed's own starch into sugar. In this process the seed's enzymes are consumed. If the process is not halted and the sprouts are allowed to get too large they will consume all the enzymes each contains and consequently reduce the ability to convert a larger batch of starch into sugar. However, if the process is only allowed to proceed partway the enzymes in the sprouting seeds are still plentiful. To preserve the enzymes and make the product portable the germination process is stopped by carefully drying the partially germinated seeds and then grinding them into a coarse meal. The result is an active material that will work on a larger batch of starch. At this point the product is known as malted barley, "malt" being the Old English word for grinding or crushing.

If malted barley was not available, then sprouted, dried and ground corn seeds (corn malt) or even sprouted rye (rye malt) could be used to assist in this process. The enzymes available in corn and rye are much less than those available using a specifically selected barley strain but they can suffice if enough sprouted material is used and the pH is low enough.

It is interesting to note that while the pioneer farmers in America were very sophisticated in their chemical treatment of starch to create sugars they did not understand why fermentation occurred. They were not aware of yeast as an organism. It was not until the 1850s when Louis Pasteur identified and isolated yeast organisms that their role as the agent of fermentation was identified. Until that time vats were just left to sit open and wild yeast simply floated in and colonized the vat of sugar rich material.

---

11   http://en.wikipedia.org/wiki/Malt, accessed September 15, 2015.

During Prohibition the black-market commercialization of alcohol production did away with the necessity for starch conversion to sugar in favor of the shortcut of using refined sugar as a starting medium for yeast to ferment into alcohol. The enormous profits possible during that era made it economical to simply purchase sugar, even if it was more expensive to do it that way.

This trend continued into the 1950s as a result of generous sugar subsidies which suppressed the price of refined sugar. It was, almost, as cheap to use sugar as to use starch and because the moonshiner was avoiding the excise tax on alcohol production he could afford to use sugar and not bother with converting starch to sugar. Using sugar also eliminated the need for any cooking process at all and saved energy costs.

As a result of these changes in our culture, the art of converting starch into fermentable sugars fell into disuse. Most moonshine was really *sugar liquor* in which corn played no part. Or if corn was used it was wasted because it had not been converted to sugar. It did nothing to increase the alcohol yield and simply took up space in the vat.

Generally the farmers made corn whiskey, and the moonshiner business operations made sugar liquor and simply told the customer nothing or that it was corn whiskey.

Because corn contains more starch than rye (corn 72% starch, rye 59%), distilleries prefer to use corn as their starting material. The reason is that the increased starch content of corn allows for the more efficient use of cookers, chillers, fermenters and stills in a commercial operation because you can process more starch per run.

There are other natural sugar sources that can undergo fermentation directly. Common ones are grapes, apples, pears, peaches and any other fruit or berry that contains sugar. Raisins are used to make "raisin jack." Corn syrup can also be considered as a starting material for a small distillation operation.

Another sugar source readily available is molasses which runs between 68% and 79% sugar as advertised and sold. Rum distillers use molasses as their fermentation medium. They simply dilute it with water to about 25% Brix and add yeast. Yeast will not ferment undiluted molasses. They must have water as well in order to conduct their metabolism. The detrimental effect of having too much sugar to start with is generally noticed at sugar concentrations above 25% Brix.

This is because the alcohol produced by yeast is poisonous to them. It is their waste product. If too little water is used as a buffer the alcohol concentrations will build up to a point where the yeast are poisoned by their own waste product before all the fermentable sugars are consumed.

Different yeast strains of *Saccharomyces cerevisiae* have different tolerance for alcohol ranging from 10% to 15% alcohol at the end of fermentation which equates to between 20 and 30 proof.

The object is to have sufficient water to go with the sugar so that the yeast are able to ferment all the sugars before reaching the level of toxicity which will kill them. With this in mind it is useful to add additional water to the batch during fermentations to increase the buffer available to the yeast for biological waste products, and alcohol, to accumulate in. While this will initially decrease the measured volume percentage of alcohol in the batch when it is tested, it can also increase the total alcohol produced since the yeast will live longer.

Another reason you do not want to add too much sugar to your batch is that the metabolic pathways for alcohol production change when yeast are stressed in any number of ways like having the wrong pH, nutrients in the mash, types of sugar available, or other organisms contaminating the mash and alcohol concentration. Yeast under a high alcohol content stress tend to produce alcohol which is off-tasting because of undesirable congeners like ethyl acetate and other molecules that are not desirable because they contribute disagreeable flavors and odors to the final product. These congeners are hard to separate in distillation with a pot still and reduce ethanol yield. They can be separated more efficiently by a refluxing still but still reduce ethanol yield.

1.11 Barley Malt

Before we get back to cooking and batch setting I want to take a minute and discuss using barley malt[12] to achieve both liquefaction, alpha enzyme reactions, and saccharification, beta or glucamalyase enzyme reactions.

When barley malt is used to liquefy and saccharify be aware that it is loaded with and covered in bacteria. When you add malt to your batch it contaminates your mash with many types of bacteria but particularly with *lactobacillus*. *Lactobacillus* is responsible for the souring of milk.

5.4	favors malt alpha amylase (higher pH)
5.1	favors malt beta amylase (lower pH)

When you use malt based enzymes you want to make sure that you are using them in the correct pH range.

Malted barley operates only in a narrow temperature range from between 148° F to around 152° F. Above this temperature the enzymes in malted barley are destroyed by the heat and will not reactivate when the temperature falls back into the optimal range.

Malt has the *maltase* enzyme. This enzyme creates *maltose* which is directly fermentable by yeast.

In terms of the diastatic power or sugar making enzyme in the malt itself, barley malt has far more enzymatic activity than corn does. Barley malt naturally and by selection has 10 to 20 times the amount of enzyme needed to break down the starch in its own seed. So 10 % malt will provide enough enzyme to break down all the starch in a mash batch. Corn only has enough enzyme to break down the starch in its own seed. Trying to use malted corn to make sugar can be accomplished but takes far more sprouted corn to accomplish.

A final nod in favor of commercial liquid enzymes is the fact that the liquid enzymes will continue to work at fermentation temperatures below 100° F. This means that the liquid enzymes will continue to create sugar throughout the fermentation process while the malted barley will not.

Malt is also very expensive. It is hundreds of pounds of another type of grain you have to keep in the shop and it loses some of its effectiveness as it ages.

---

12   Barley http://en.wikipedia.org/wiki/Barley. Malt http://en.wikipedia.org/wiki/Malt. Both accessed September 15, 2015.

CHAPTER 2 Cooking and Biology

2.1 Cooking

Now that the corn meal has been added to our water and initially mixed in we can discuss the various chemical reactions we will induce in the mixture.

The first thing we will do is to continue to apply heat. Thermal motion assists in breaking up the corn starch molecules. We will continue to heat our mixture up to a terminal temperature of around 206°. This will help us kill any bacteria that are in the batch to start with.

As the temperature goes up and the starch molecules begin to cook, they dissolve in and then combine with water.

The result is that the starch molecules unwind and lengthen into long chains. As they are mixed in the pot, these long chains get in each other's way and cause resistance to further agitation. This is not the clumping problem we addressed when we initially added in the corn. It is a much more serious problem if not managed properly.

We want to overcome this resistance quickly for two reasons. The faster you raise the temperature the less time bacteria can live in the mixture and if the corn sticks to the bottom of the vessel then it will cook onto the bottom as a goo and never be available to the yeast for food. This also prevents heat from being transferred from the boilers to the mash mixture because the hot water pipes deliver their heat to the bottom of the vessel. However, if one is using an open flame to cook with, then the corn can oxidize, caramelize and burn black on the bottom of the pot and this will affect the taste of the whole batch of alcohol produced.

The first way we overcome the resistance of the starch is to continue agitating the mixture. From start to finish the mixer must be turning fast enough to keep the mash swirling in the vessel.

The second way we overcome resistance and manage the mash density is to apply a liquefying enzyme to the mash while we are cooking it. We are going to apply this enzyme even though it is outside the operating temperature range and pH range for its effective use. The reason we are doing this is that the enzyme will have some effect even though it is not an optimal effect.

Broadly, the enzymes we employ are known as *diastase*. Diastase consists of a group of enzymes (http://en.wikipedia .org/wiki/Enzyme) which catalyze (http://en.wikipedia.org/wiki/Catalysis) the breakdown of starch into maltose (http://en.wikipedia.org/wiki/Maltose). Today, diastase means any Alpha α-, Beta β-, or Gamma γ- glucoamylase / γ-amylase (http://en.wikipedia.org/wiki/Amylase), all of which hydrolyze (*hydrolases*, http://en.wikipedia.org /wiki/Hydrolase), combine with water and can break down carbohydrates (http://en.wikipedia.org/wiki /Carbohydrates).

The type of enzyme we will use initially for liquefying the batch is an alpha amylase.[13] It is essentially the same enzyme that is contained in human saliva that initially breaks down starches when we chew food. That is part of the reason that starchy foods like potatoes and corn dissolve in our mouths as we chew them. It is possible to make mash with human saliva. African tribes spit into pots of starch and water and the enzyme breaks down the starch to sugar. Wild yeast that are in the air all around us waft along and are deposited in the open pots and eat the sugar. After some time the pot has an alcoholic content.

---

13   http://en.wikipedia.org/wiki/Amylase, accessed September 15, 2015.

In my case the alpha-amylase I use is a product called Termamyl SC produced by the Novozymes company.[14] This product is a bacterial alpha amylase enzyme. It is expressed by a bacillus. This means that Novozymes has colonies of bacteria that produce this enzyme as a metabolic product of their life cycle.

In one form of this process the company develops a plasmid or sequence of genetic code that will produce the enzyme structure that they desire. Then they identify a type of bacteria that will tolerate the presence of this plasmid or DNA sequence or self-replicating organelle in its genetic code or in its body. The bacillus must also be able to tolerate the chemical or compound that the plasmid, genetic code, organelle, will produce.

A colony of these genetically altered bacteria are allowed to grow and multiply. As they do they also produce the desired enzyme. At some point the production of the enzyme will become toxic to the colony and no more will be produced and the bacteria will die. At this point the manufacturer either extracts the desired enzyme from the mixture or, if the concentration is high enough, simply filters out the bacteria and sells the resulting mixture as the enzyme concoction.

Some commercial enzymes are expressed by fungi and are known as fungal enzymes. Yeast is also a fungus. In some cases the fungus is grown on wheat fiber. For now let us continue with the cooking process.

As the batch continues to heat up we will obtain some benefit from the liquefying enzyme we add even though it is not within the optimum range of the enzyme. It will noticeably affect the fluidity of the mash as it cooks. Still we will have to go around the side of the tank with a paddle and break up the layer of corn that accumulates there. But we want to be careful not to spend too much energy doing this because we don't want to wear ourselves out fighting the corn. We just want to manage the process and keep it within bounds. The mash will get thick and we just have to trust that as the temperature gets closer to the optimum for the enzyme to work that it will work and the mash will thin out. In the meantime as the temperature rises so does the density of the batch.

We can now prepare to apply our main dose of liquefying alpha enzyme. The specifications for my enzyme, which broadly represent application parameters for all commercial enzymes, are that they operate in a very broad range of pH from 5 to 6 but most effectively in relationship to the slurry

Termamyl SC			
pH 5.0	**pH 5.3**	**pH 5.6**	**pH >6**
80° C 176° F	85° C 185° F	90° C 194° F	95° C 203° F

TABLE 34—Enzyme Specifications

temperature and the pH of the solution. The specifications of this enzyme are listed in Table 34.

The stability and the performance of any alpha liquefying enzyme are influenced by pH, temperature and calcium concentration. It is apparent that the lower the pH the lower the temperature needed to get it to operate and the higher the pH we start with the higher the temperature we need to get the enzyme to operate effectively. This makes sense because the lower the pH the more free ions are available to engage in chemical reactions.

The pH of our water starts at about 7.1. The 1,500 pounds of corn that we add will naturally acidify water in our cooking tank so the pH of the slurry will drop to about 6.0 on its own. You should check your own values for how much the pH drops for the type of corn or other starch you are adding to your batch because it is an important consideration in how much alpha enzyme to use and how effective it will be.

---

14   According to the literature from Novozymes, Termamyl SC is a liquid enzyme preparation containing a heat-stable alpha-amylase expressed in and produced by a genetically modified strain of a bacillus microorganism. The systematic name for the enzyme is 1,4-alpha-D-glucan glucanohydrolase (EC 3.2.1.1).

The reason I am cautious about lowering the pH of the mash too much in order to achieve an optimum pH for the enzyme to work is that it is hard to increase it back up to an appropriate starting fermentation pH and we only have a limited volume in the tank so adding a lot of water is not an option. If I lower the pH of my mash to obtain optimum enzyme efficiency I also reduce the pH buffer that will help the mash ferment. Too much acidity will kill yeast, and also kill other bacteria, but it is the yeast we are concerned with and they are less tolerant of low pH than the bacteria are.

Acidity increases during fermentation because many of the metabolic by-products of yeast metabolism are acids. By the end of the fermentation the mash will be very sour with a pH of 3.8 or 3.5. This concentration of acid will kill off the yeast regardless of whether any fermentable sugars are left in the solution or not.

We need as much pH buffer as possible so the yeast will ferment all the sugars before the solution becomes toxic to them by virtue of the acidity. We want the alcohol concentration to kill the yeast, not the acidity of the solution.

When I lower the pH in cooking I have to replace the buffer and increase the pH during fermentation. I will do this by adding baking soda or some other gentle alkali at the end of the cooking process. You can also extend the total life span of a batch by raising the pH near the end of the batch.

Another reason I don't adjust the pH too much is that it is very difficult to reliably determine the pH of a hot solution. Test strips and digital pH meters are designed to sample at temperatures around 60 to 80 degrees F. My mash is 185 degrees when I'm cooking it and I don't have time to cool the mash down and take a reliable pH. If you overshoot the pH change and end up too acidic at the start of fermentation you will have to use a lot of baking soda to bring the pH back up just to start the batch in the range of 5.4 or so.

A word about backset stillage. If you use backset stillage to lower the pH of your mash do not allow it to ever fall below 160 degrees because bacteria will grow in it. Backset stillage is used in the sour mash process. It has a low pH and nutrients. But it also carries metabolic waste products and bacteria from a prior batch. It is a mixed bag of acid, nutrients and sewage from the last batch. You can never allow it to cool down from the time it leaves the still to when it is put into the next batch or else you are just adding a load of bacteria into your next batch.

The balance you are trying to achieve is to have a low enough pH for the enzymes to work in their effective range. Low pH also inhibits bacterial growth to some extent so this helps keep down the bacteria count. One also needs a pH high enough so that yeast can still thrive while bacteria do not.

The final ingredient is a sufficient buffer of volume so that the yeast can completely metabolize all of the sugar in the mixture and die from alcohol poisoning before the low pH kills them.

Adding additional water to the batch during fermentation is a way to increase the buffer of volume for the reaction to take place. It dilutes the toxins in the batch so the yeast can continue to live.

All of this is contingent on there actually being fermentable sugars left in the batch. When the batch has no more sugar to ferment you are done. The only thing that can happen to a batch with no more sugar is for the bacteria to begin eating the alcohol and reducing your yield.

If you do have to add water to the batch don't add chlorinated water to the batch to thin it out. The chlorine will kill some of the yeast. Also, in my experience, while activated carbon filters work to remove chlorine, they last only a short time, making them expensive and not worth the trouble. If you are going to add buffer to the batch I suggest you set aside 50 gallons of water in an open barrel and let the chlorine evaporate for a couple of days until it is needed as a buffer. Check the chlorine level before you add it in. You can use swimming pool chlorine strips to measure the amount in the water. Because the water has a pH of 7 or so it will act to raise the pH as well as provide more volume. If you want to add some baking soda then it will also increase the pH as well.

You might ask where is the spare volume in the tank for this to occur? During fermentation the volume of the tank will go down slightly. Evaporation and the metabolic process of carbon dioxide production will reduce the water volume. The result is that near the end of the fermentation process there is some room in the tank for buffer volume to be added.

2.2 Determining the Temperature of the Tank

There is a temperature differential between the top and bottom of the tank during cooking. Even though the heat is being delivered to the bottom of the tank the heat tends to concentrate in the top of the tank. My tank is 56 inches tall and during cooking there is generally about a 10° F difference in temperature between the top and the bottom of the tank and mash in it. It is my experience that this temperature gradient exists no matter how vigorously you stir your mash. So if the top of the mash has reached 185° and is ready for enzyme application the bottom of the tank is only 175° and not in the optimum temperature range. We work around this by adding our second dose of alpha enzyme when the top of the tank reaches the minimum application temperature of 175° and then continuing to cook the mixture until the top of the tank has reached 206° F. At this temperature the bottom of the tank has reached 196° which is 3/4 through the range of the enzyme's application temperature range.

The final consideration in applying this alpha amylase is the concentration of calcium carbonate. My alpha enzyme requires 5 ppm of Ca^{++}.

The second enzyme, the beta or saccharifying enzyme we will use requires 35 ppm calcium (chalk). Manufacturers recommend the addition of lime $Ca(OH)_2$ to bring the water solution up to this level of calcium.

I don't have this problem because my city water has 159 to 220 ppm of calcium carbonate already in it. If you did need to use lime to bring up calcium carbonate levels, a starting dosage of 0.5 kilograms, roughly one pound, of lime per ton of raw material (corn), is suggested. It may then be adjusted according to experience.

In terms of adding the enzyme to the batch it is advisable to dilute the enzyme with cold water before addition, e.g., 1 liter of enzyme with 10 liters of water. I don't do this, because I have such a small batch. I may dump the enzyme in a bucket of water and then add that in.

As a practical matter Novozymes sells me enzyme in 25 kilogram containers. I must keep it refrigerated in order to maintain its effectiveness. I use about 5 kilograms or 12 pounds a year so each batch I get would last me 5 years if I could get it to last that long. It doesn't stay effective for that long even if I keep it refrigerated so I just use as much as I want.

Table 35 lists the specifications of my current enzyme. You can follow this outline to construct a dosage calculator for your particular enzyme.

	Pounds	Kilos
Weight of Corn in Batch	1,500.00	680.39
Starch % of Corn to be Converted	72%	72%
Actual Starch Lbs. of Batch	1,080.00	489.89
% of metric ton of Starch used in Batch	49%	49%
	Kilos	**Pounds**
Alpha Enzyme Dose based on Metric Ton of Starch	1,000.00	2,204.62
	Grams	**Weight Oz.**
Lowest Recommended Dose Per Metric Ton of Starch	150.00	5.29
Highest Recommended Dose per metric ton of Starch	450.00	15.88
	Grams	**Weight Oz.**
Lowest Dose For Batch Size	73.48	2.59
Highest Dose For Batch Size	220.45	7.78
	Grams	**Weight Oz.**
My dose	1,077.14	38.00
Multiple of Lowest Dose	14.66	14.66
Multiple of Highest Dose	4.89	4.89
	Fluid Oz.	**Liters**
Measured as	32.00	0.95

TABLE 35—Refer to Alpha Enzymes *Worksheet*
Note: The dosage for this enzyme is given in grams rather than in liters even though it is a liquid enzyme.

As you can see the amounts required are tiny compared to the volumes I am required to purchase the enzymes in. As my batch has become more starch dense I have increased the amount of enzymes I use to keep it from overwhelming my mixing equipment as it cooks. I am now using roughly five times the highest dose but this still amounts to only one quart of enzyme per batch.

I apply a split dose using 16 ounces of volume (which really weighs 19 ounces or 539 grams) as early as possible, even as the corn is being mixed in. This helps keep the mash from getting too thick as it cooks. I then add an additional 16 ounces of volume (539 grams) once the top of the tank reaches about 175° to 180° and the mash is entering the optimum temperature.

Because the highest temperatures in the cooking cycle are around 206° F and as such are above the maximum operating temperature of the enzyme (203°) much of it will be thermally destroyed by the high temperature. Therefore it will not continue to work during the time when the mash will cool back down into the operating temperature range of the enzyme.

To compensate for the thermal loss of enzyme effectiveness I have sometimes added a third dose of liquefying enzyme consisting of 8 or 16 ounces after the boiler has been turned off and the temperature has begun to fall back into the temperature range that the enzyme will tolerate.

We will continue cooking the mixture up to around 206° F. We don't have to boil the mixture but we do want to kill as many microbes as possible to prevent them from eating the sugar we are so carefully preparing for our yeast. Another reason we do not boil the mixture is that the last 10 degrees from 202° to 212° are very hard to come by. At these high temperatures I am lucky to get a 0.5° F/minute rise out of the boilers and you end up turning the shop into a sauna bath with all the steam you are driving off the cooking pot even if you cover the pot. You have to let some steam out because this is not a pressure cooker, it is an open vat.

Another reason you do not take the mash batch all the way up to boiling point is that for every degree you go up you have to use energy and time and for every degree you cool it takes energy and time. So it costs you double for every minute you spend heating. Finally, boiling is not necessary in order to achieve effective liquefaction. The enzymes do this at their designed temperature and pH most effectively.

I stop cooking when the temperature reaches 206° F. Then, I turn off the boilers and circulating pumps, uncover the cooker, and remove the insulation blanket. The temperature will begin to fall by radiation and evaporation.

Then I hook up the hoses which will transform the internal heating coils into cooling coils. I keep the mixer motor running to continue stirring the mash during this time. The temperature will fall quickly at first and then slow down.

When the temperature at the top of the tank falls below 203° you can add a third dose of liquefying enzyme to replace the dose that may have been thermally destroyed when you heated the mash beyond the maximum operating temperature of the enzyme in order to reach the terminal cooking temperature.

During this second half of the liquefaction holding period we will cool the slurry by running cold water through the circulating pipes in the tank, stirring the mixture and blowing filtered compressed air up through it. By the time the temperature of the slurry both at the top and bottom of the tank has fallen below the optimum operating range of the liquefying enzyme, 175° F, it will have been more than one hour in total that the enzyme has been working within its designed operating range and at all temperatures throughout its range. Given the slight uncertainty and general bias towards less acid, higher pH mash that we employ the higher temperature range we have achieved will give the enzyme the best chance to operate. Therefore, in this scenario you should try to maximize the time you spend at the higher end of the temperature range in order to give the enzyme a chance to align with the pH in the tank and really do its work. It will continue to work, although less efficiently, at lower temperatures.

To effect this, one can wait ten minutes or so before actually beginning to run the cooling water through the internal pipes and just let radiation and evaporation control the cooling process. Usually the time it takes to hook up the hoses and be ready to apply cooling water is about that long.

By now the mash will be of a completely different character. It will be thinner than corn mush but not yet a gruel. As you begin to cool down the mash take a minute to check the sides of the tank with a paddle. Make sure that no layer of corn has cooked onto the side of the tank or at the bottom. Use the paddle to break up any clumps you find until you can touch bottom all the way around the tank. This is dangerous work if you do it with the mixer motor turning but if you shut it off then all the solids quickly go to the bottom of the tank and you don't get a real sense of how well cooked the mixture is or if any layer has adhered to the bottom. You can slow the mixer down somewhat. But be prepared to let go at any minute if the paddle gets into the mixer blades.

If you taste the mash during the cooking process it first tastes like corn mush. It is thick and substantial and bland. Now it tastes like corn soup, thin and watery but not quite so bland. Up to this point it has very little sweetness. What we have accomplished is gelatinize the starch in our corn by dissolving it in water.[15] This process is known as *hydration*. We will, in total, chemically bond with the starch about 6.5% of the water we use in this process. In our case 6.5% of 350 gallons is 22.75 gallons of water. This represents billions of chemical bonds as the water has joined up with the two major starch molecules in corn: 1. amylose[16] and 2. amylopectin.[17]

So, what is in this nice, thin mash? When we applied our Alpha Amylase (α-Amylase) liquefying enzyme, it operated to cut the long starch chains into shorter segments. It also assisted in bonding water molecules to both long and short starch chains. After liquefaction the chains are not long like spaghetti. They are short and consequently don't get into each other's way as much. This results in an overall thinning of the mash. The result of this cutting has been to create new molecular structures that are designated broadly as *dextrin(s)*.[18]

If you measure the sugar content of the mash with a refractometer at this time it will read about 15% sugar on the scale but the mash will not taste sweet yet. These dextrins are as yet unfermentable sugars and our yeast cannot consume them. They are too big or complex for yeast to metabolize.

Also, the molecular weight of these sugars is still too high to taste very sweet to us because the molecular configuration is still too complex. It is difficult to check the maltose and dextrin content of this mash by a hydrometer because in order to use a hydrometer you must first cool the mash to 59° or 60° which is the temperature most sugar measuring hydrometers are calibrated to.

Now that we have achieved all we can with the liquefying enzyme we will prepare to apply the second type of enzyme that is required in order to make fermentable sugars—sugars we can taste.

15   http://en.wikipedia.org/wiki/Starch_gelatinization, accessed September 15, 2015.

16   http://en.wikipedia.org/wiki/Amylose, accessed September 15, 2015.

17   http://en.wikipedia.org/wiki/Amylopectin, accessed September 15, 2015.

18   http://en.wikipedia.org/wiki/Dextrin, accessed September 15, 2015.

2.3 Saccharifying Section ———————————————————

In order to cut the residual starch chains and dextrins into lower molecular weight molecules of fermentable sugar one needs to use a sugar making (*saccharifying*) enzyme. These enzymes are broadly classed as *beta-amylase*.[19] Beta-amylase is found in malted barley as we have discussed above and will also cut dextrin molecules into smaller, lower molecular weight sugars.

One configuration of a beta enzyme is known as glucoamylase (Gluc-Amylase or γ-Amylase).

I use several versions of this enzyme in my shop as my sugar making (saccharifying) enzyme. The particular one we will be discussing is Novozym 25001. The brand name is not particularly important since the manufacturers change their product lines so often that I rarely am able to purchase the same enzyme twice, or the same yeast for that matter.[20]

The enzyme I use has features that are broadly representative of the commercial enzymes available including the dosages and operating parameters within which commercial liquid enzymes are most effective in converting dextrins into fermentable sugars.

The benefits of using commercial enzymes are the reduced risk of infection due to high operating temperatures up to 158° F, (70° C) as compared to barley malt which is stable only over the range of about 148° to 153° F.

Higher temperature tolerance before thermal degradation is also beneficial because heat assists the reactions to proceed. This extra heat I can use compensates somewhat for the higher pH of the mash batches I prepare.

Even the high side of the optimum pH is lower than my batch's pH naturally. Because this enzyme is more than 50% efficient from pH from 3.5 to 5.5, I must make some effort to get my batch to pH of 5.5 where the enzyme is 50% effective and then use a double dose to achieve full starch conversion. We will return to this pH problem in a moment.

As we continue cooling the batch, remember that the bottom of the tank never got as hot as the top. It always lagged 10° F. As the tank cools it will be the bottom of the tank that first falls into the operating temperature range of the enzyme, i.e., 158° F. At this time the top of the tank will be about 10° hotter. You could add the first dose of enzyme at this point but much of the enzyme would be thermally destroyed by the excessive heat.

To compensate for this problem, I allow the temperature at the top to fall to anywhere between 163° F and 160° before adding the enzyme. This cuts down on the thermal degradation of the initial dose but does catch the bottom of the tank within the enzyme's temperature range. This gives the bottom of the tank the most time to operate within the designed temperature range of the enzyme.

When the top of the tank reaches the high side of the temperature operating range, 158°, we then add the second dose of saccharifying enzyme to the mixture. We will then turn off the cooling water circulating in the pipes to slow down the cooling rate of the mash and allow the enzyme a longer time to operate within its designed optimum temperature range. This holding period should be between 30 and 120 minutes. As the temperature at the top of the tank falls closer to the optimum temperature of 149°, we can add a third dose of enzyme to speed things along. By this time the bottom of the tank will already be below the optimum temperature but the top and middle will still be inside the enzyme's prime operating range.

———————————————————

19   β-Amylase https://en.wikipedia.org/wiki/B-amylase, accessed September 15, 2015.

20   For information about the enzymes I am using you can contact Novozymes Switzerland AG Neumatt 4243 Dittingen Switzerland. See www.novozymes.com info@novozymes.com.

As the temperature falls, we keep the mixer spinning and we will check the pH of the mixture and do our best to ensure that it is less than 6.0 and if necessary reduce the pH to 5.5 with lemon juice, vinegar, sulphuric acid, or phosphoric acid. (Don't use battery acid as a substitute for real sulphuric acid. It has other chemicals in it that are designed for batteries and it is bad, bad, bad for mash, poisonous actually.) When properly applied, my experience is that this enzyme works quickly and that the change in sweetness is immediately noticeable. This enzyme will also continue to work at lower temperatures, even throughout the fermentation because the minimum temperature is 86° F or 30° C, just less efficiently.

As to the pH concerns, as the yeast begin to ferment the pH will begin to fall because of their activity. This long lived enzyme will continue to operate as the pH falls farther into its optimum operating range of 4.1 to 4.5 during the fermentation process.

As to temperature it will continue to work all the way down to 86° F which is below most fermentation temperatures. Another benefit of this very long lived enzyme is that as it works throughout the fermentation process, it will incrementally create sugar to feed the yeast during fermentation rather than poisoning the yeast with sugar in the initial mixture. This is a concern with high gravity, thick mash, fermentations. We don't want too much sugar. Too much food can be toxic to yeast as well.

How long a holding period should you observe? Well, you can't stop radiation from the tank and you can only wait so long. My practice is to pause the cooling water for 30 minutes when the top of the tank reaches 155°; during this pause the tank top temperature will fall to 145°. I then turn on the cooling water in the pipes and continue cooling directly down to fermentation temperature because of the time it takes overall to do so. It will take another hour to go from 145° to 86°. We are trying to accomplish this process in one day and it takes a full day any way you cut it. Also, I find that that enzyme works very quickly and we also have the luxury of using a large dose for reasons I have explained above.

2.4 pH Concerns

The only problem with this saccharifying enzyme is that the optimum pH is lower than I run my batches. I don't like sour batches and I want my mash as alkaline as possible when they start to ferment. A higher pH provides more pH buffer for the batch. If I lower the mash pH to the optimum then I have to add acid to do so. That means I have to add baking soda or another alkali before fermentation starts to get the pH back up to the optimum for fermentation so it does not fall too low too fast and stall the fermentation before all the sugar is metabolized. I don't want to be buffering and buffeting the mash back and forth like that, shocking it so to speak, so I will not reduce the pH to the optimum of this enzyme (Chart 4).

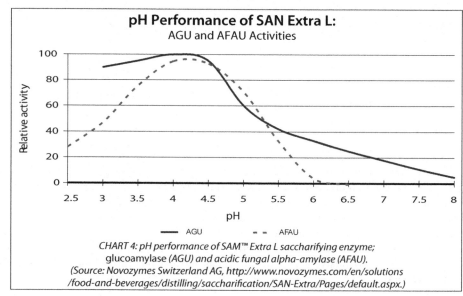

CHART 4: pH performance of SAM™ Extra L saccharifying enzyme; glucoamylase (AGU) and acidic fungal alpha-amylase (AFAU). (Source: Novozymes Switzerland AG, http://www.novozymes.com/en/solutions /food-and-beverages/distilling/saccharification/SAN-Extra/Pages/default.aspx.)

The specific operating parameters of this enzyme are as follows: Temperature: Optimum temperature is 149° F (65° C) but the range is huge: Range 86° F–158° F (30° C–70° C).

For this enzyme the optimum pH is 4.1 with a range of 3.5–5.5.

You can note that the broad pH peak of efficiency of this enzyme delivers 80% efficiency between pH 3.8 and 4.8. So any pH under 5.0 is good enough to work with and means I will not have to artificially decrease the pH any further just to obtain "optimum conditions." Throughout the entire range from 3.5 to 5.0 the efficiency is above 50% so you can start adding it in at 5.5 and then reduce the pH to 4.8 if you want to.[21]

In terms of origin, my glucoamaylase or saccharifying enzyme is a fungal enzymes expressed by the fungus *Aspergillus Niger*.[22] The Aspergillus fungus is grown on wheat fiber. Remember our first enzyme was expressed out of a bacillus. Now this second enzyme is being expressed by a fungus.

Glucoamalyase enzyme dose conversions for Novozym 25001.		
	Kilos	**Pounds**
Weight of Corn in Batch	680.40	1,500.00
Starch % of Corn to be Converted	72%	72%
Actual Starch Content of Batch	489.89	1,080.00
% of a metric ton of Starch used in Batch	49%	49%
	Kilos	**Pounds**
Glucoamalyase dose based on Metric Ton of Starch	1,000.00	2,204.62
	Liters	**Fluid Ounces**
Lowest Recommended Dose Per Metric Ton of Starch	0.50	16.91
Highest Recommended Dose per Metric Ton of Starch	0.80	27.05
For current batch	**Liters**	**Fluid Ounces**
Lowest Dose For Batch Size	0.24	8.28
Highest Dose For Batch Size	0.39	13.25
	Liters	**Fluid Ounces**
My dose	0.95	32.00
Multiple of Lowest Dose	3.86	3.86
Multiple of Highest Dose	2.41	2.41

TABLE 36—Refer to Gluc Enzymes *Worksheet*

Calculating the dose required for this enzyme to work properly: The dosage for this enzyme (Novozym 25001) is given in liters rather than in grams and just like the alpha amylase is applied based on the weight of the starch used and not the whole grain weight. Using my batch as a reference we find the following quantities are required (Table 36).

It is advisable to dilute the enzyme 10 to 1 with water before you apply it. My dose is again an overdose. Even though I am only using one quart the dose is 3.86 times the lowest dose and 2.4 times as much or 141% more than the highest rec-ommended dose to convert 49% of a metric ton of starch.

- Metric Ton: 2,204.62 lbs. or 1,000 kg
- Long Ton: 2,240 lbs. or 1,116.05 kg
- Short Ton: 2,000 lbs. or 907.18 kg

You have to be careful about what type of tons the manufac-turer is talking about when performing your calculations. In this case the manufacturer is using metric tons.

---

21   To illustrate this point we will compare my enzyme with another Novozymes product, AMG 300L with different speci-fications: Optimum Temperature 140° F (60° C). Range 86° F–149° F (30–65° C). It has an optimum pH of 4.5 with a pH range of 4.0–5.5. These specifications are better for my process on two counts. The lower optimum temperature is easier to work with and the higher optimum pH provides more enzymatic activity for my relatively high pH batch. This is actually a better enzyme for small scale distilling operations. So why don't I use this enzyme? Well it was superseded by Novozym 25001 and not available when I last purchased enzymes. The reason it was replaced is that Novozym 25001 has 400 activity units and is stronger in activity to AMG 300L which has 300 activity units. These activity units are expressed by the denominations AGU and AFAU.

22   Aspergillus Niger http://en.wikipedia.org/wiki/Aspergillus_niger, accessed September 15, 2015.

Getting the type of ton wrong is not as serious as getting the starch percentage of content of the batch wrong. This application data is expressed in metric tons of starch so our numbers must conform to that specification to obtain meaningful results.

One uncertainty in this application data is that we are basing our starch content on the starting dry starch weight of the corn. The reason I say this is that by the time this enzyme is employed, the starch has been hydrolyzed by cooking and application of the alpha amylase enzyme. While the starch chains are shorter, the total molecular weight of "starch" has gone up because of the chemical bonds that have been created with water molecules. This would result in about a 6.5 % increase in the total weight of the starch employed in the batch. But that is a question for another day. For now I am going to stick to the initial starch weight for conducting these calculations.

As noted above the measurement of starch to be converted, as opposed to measuring grain employed, has unintended and confusing consequences when you talk about alcohol yields from fermentation. Sometimes authors and manufacturers are relating their yields to tons of starch employed and others relate their data in terms of tons of grain employed. Using starch based figures will increase the alcohol yield produced per ton because it takes more whole grain to make up that ton of starch. If your grain is only 50% starch—rye, for example, is 59%—then it will take (almost) two tons to make up one ton of starch. You will definitely get more alcohol out of corn than with rye.

If you are using whole grain as your input quantity, and we are, because we use whole ground corn, then you must calculate your alcohol yields based on "whole grain employed." Conversely you must be prepared to convert your whole grain numbers into starch content numbers to usefully digest other producers' data that is expressed in that amount. If you compare your whole ground grain yields to starch only data you will be very disappointed at your results but unfairly so.

The total dose of this enzyme that I use is again only one quart. I add it to the batch in three partial doses as noted above. This has the effect of giving each stage of the application process more than 100% of the minimum dose to do its job.

The enzymes you purchase will come to you in 25-kilogram containers which are larger than 5-gallon jugs. The dose is only one quart per batch even at our dose rate so each can contains about twenty doses or runs of cooking per can.

For both liquefaction and saccharifying enzymes the storage requirements are to keep them between 0–10° C (32–50° F) in sealed packaging in a dry environment. I keep mine in a small refrigerator. However, even under these optimal conditions the enzymes gradually lose effectiveness over time. As the enzymes age you will need to use higher dosages. I try to use up my enzymes every two years with three years being the maximum. I generally double my dose in the third year. Each container costs about $10.00 per kilogram for 25 kilograms which is $250 every two or three years.

I suggest that you not taste either the liquefying or saccharification enzymes. They are not poisonous but it is an unforgettable and unpleasant taste; they smell bad enough and they taste like they smell. I had to siphon some one time and it was an experience I will never forget.

So why did we do all these calculations just to prove that we can just throw in a quart of each type of enzyme and forget about it? Well, first you can't just throw it in. Second, you have to understand where the uncertainties are. The data is always ratty, the instructions incomplete at best and usually contradictory to boot. You never get the whole story and you are forced to guess all the time. Knowing where and why you can cut corners and what the reasons and uncertainties are in your calculations will keep you from getting into trouble most of the time.

2.5 Sugar Production and Use in Fermentation ———————————

As we continue to cool the batch we can measure the sugar produced by our efforts by four methods. The first thing we can do is to taste the mash and it will now be almost too sweet. It tastes like sweetened corn cereal. You can eat a bowl of it and it would make a great sugar-filled breakfast.

The second test we can use is the iodine test. This is a qualitative rather than quantitative test. Even a small amount of starch will register a strong positive reaction. Only when starch becomes very scarce does iodine not react in a mild way. It is not a reliable measure of starch conversion. It is an absolute test. I have never been able to get the iodine test to not register some evidence of starch remaining in the batch after the saccharifying process.

The third method is to use a refractometer calibrated to 0% sugar with some distilled water. I routinely achieve 24% to 26% sugar as measured by a refractometer at the standard temperature of 20° C/68° F. This temperature is also the standard temperature for the Brix scale on the hydrometer you will use to cross-check the sugar production.

The fourth method is to use a triple scale mash and wine hydrometer. Using a mash and wine hydrometer at its designed operating temperature of 20° C (68° F). I usually achieve 22.5 % sugar on the Brix scale at the beginning of the fermentation.

The difference between refractometer readings and hydrometer readings is related to the types of measurements each instrument makes. The refractometer measures the bending of light through a prism and the hydrometer measures the density of the fluid. As we have seen during the cooking and liquefaction processes the refractometer measures sugars that do not taste sweet and so may not be fermentable sugars.

As to the hydrometers, wine, beer and mash hydrometers generally read in the following scales.

The Brix scale (symbol ° Bx) is a measure of sugar density. It is the weight to weight correlation between sugar and water. It can also be described as a measurement of the dissolved sugar -to-water mass ratio of a liquid. It is measured with a saccharimeter that measures the specific gravity of a liquid or more easily with a refractometer. A 25° Bx solution is 25% (w/w), with 25 grams of sugar per 100 grams of solution. Or, to put it another way, there are 25 grams of sugar and 75 grams of water in the 100 grams of solution. Brix hydrometers are calibrated to 68° F = 20° C.[23] Some hydrometers use the Balling scale for this weight to weight measurement. The Balling scale measures the concentration of a dissolved solid (mostly sucrose), as the weight percentage of sucrose at 17.5 °C. Therefore to accurately use the Balling scale on your triple scale hydrometer it must be set in a solution which is 63.5° F.

The second scale on the hydrometer is the Alcohol by Volume scale. This is not applicable to our present purpose which is to measure the amount of sugar produced, but it will be used later in the process to measure the alcohol produced during fermentation. Alcohol by Volume (abbreviated as ABV, abv, or alc/vol) is a standard measure of how much alcohol (ethanol) is contained in a given volume of an alcoholic beverage (expressed as a volume percent). It is defined as the number of milliliters of pure ethanol present in 100 milliliters of solution at 20° C. The number of milliliters of pure ethanol is the mass of the ethanol divided by its density at 20° C, which is 0.78924 g/mL.[24]

The third scale on the hydrometer is the specific gravity scale. This measures the density of the material with respect to the density of water at a specified calibration temperature. Water at that temperature is defined as

---

23   http://en.wikipedia.org/wiki/Brix, accessed September 15, 2015.

24   https://en.wikipedia.org/wiki/Alcohol_by_volume, accessed September 15, 2015.

having a specific gravity of 1.0 Any liquid less dense than that value has a density, relative to that of water, of a value less than 1.0. Pure alcohol has a specific gravity of 0.79365 (at 15.556° C) which means that it is 79.365% as dense as water is, when the water is 60° F or 15.556° C.

When estimating the potential alcohol that can be produced, one takes the measured specific gravity of the batch as the Original Gravity (OG), which is a measure of the specific gravity of an unfermented beverage. (OG is the "sugar before fermentation" measurement.) Final gravity (FG), sometimes called Terminal Gravity, is a measure of the specific gravity of the fermented beverage. (FG is the "sugar after fermentation" measurement.) Typically, FG is measured only once fermentation is completely finished and all of the fermentable sugars have been turned into ethanol.

The difference between OG and FG is a measure of the amount of sugar consumed in the fermentation, and therefore it can be used as a rough, indirect measurement of the alcohol content of the beverage. The following formula gives the approximate percent alcohol by volume (ABV) as a function of the original and final gravities:

$$ABV = \frac{OG - FG}{0.00738} \text{, for example: } \frac{1.050 - 1.010}{0.00738} = 5.42\% AVB$$

Sugar Production Per Batch 1	Corn	Sugar	
Water Weight per US Gallon	8.3282	8.3282	Water Weight per US Gallon
Gallons of Water	350.00	350.00	Gallons of Water
Water Weight Lbs.	2,914.88	2,914.88	Water Weight Lbs.
Corn Weight Lbs.	1,500.00	1,092.04	Weight of Sugar Added
Total Batch Weight Lbs.	4,414.88	4,006.92	Total Batch Weight Lbs.
Kilogram Converter	0.45359	27.25%	Sugar % by Weight
Kilograms	2,002.56	495.34	Kilograms of Sugar
Grams of Solution	2,002,556.11	4,006.92	Total Batch Weight Lbs.
% Sugar in Solution	23.0%	0.45359	Kilogram Converter
Grams of Sugar	460,587.91	1,817.50	Total Batch Kg.
Kilograms of Sugar	460.59	1,817,499.49	Grams of Solution
Pounds Converter	2.2046	13.50	Lbs. of Sugar Per Gal. Vol. increase.
Pounds Lbs. Avdp	1,015.42	80.89	Lbs. / Sugar Per Gal. Vol. = Gal.
# of 50 Lb. bags of sugar	20.31	430.89	Total Gallons in Tank
Cost to make Sugar from Corn	Costs	19%	"Gal. of Sugar" as % of Total Gal.
Corn 50 lb. Bag	$8.50	79.11	Gal. Available in Tank
Number of 50 Lb. Bags	30.00		
Corn Acquisition Cost	$255.00	34.75	Kg. of Sugar Dif
Enzyme Cost	$20.00	76.62	Lbs. of Sugar Dif:
Energy Cost	$150.00	79.11	Tank Gal till Full
Time Cost	$100.00		
Total Corn Sugar Cost	$525.00		
Refined Sugar Costs			
Refined Sugar 50 lb. Bag	$20.00	50.00	Lbs. per Bag of Sugar
Bags Needed	20.31	21.84	Bags Needed
Total Lbs.	1,015.42	$20.00	Cost per Bag
Total Sugar Cost	$406.17	$436.82	Total Sugar Cost
Sugar Cost Savings to Corn	$118.83	$88.18	Cost Difference

TABLE 37—Refer to Sugar Production *Worksheet*

In order to effectively use these scales you must cool the mash down to the calibrated temperature of the scale in order to obtain an accurate reading or employ a conversion factor or table to adjust for the number of degrees your test sample differs from the standard temperature upon which the scale is calibrated.

So what have we made with our 22.5% hydrometer-tested and 25% refractometer-tested sugar solution? We have finally made fermentable sugar. The primary fermentable sugars are maltose, fructose, and sucrose.[25]

The quantity we have made is rounded to 23% just for convenience in calculation (Table 37, previous page). From this figure we can determine how much sugar we have made and whether it is cost effective to do so. We do this by relating the Brix scale of sugar weight to the total weight of our batch. Note that we are only using 350 gallons of water because we have reserved 40 gallons of water to keep the mixer from throwing mash out of the batch during the cooking process and we will use these gallons later to pitch in our hydrated yeast, cool the batch before beginning fermentation, and provide additional water buffer for the fermentation. The final Brix at the time of setting the batch will be about 1° of Brix less than that measured at the end of cooking and sugar making but will add buffer for the yeast to live in.

While the total acquisition cost for refined sugar is higher, one can see that when other factors are considered it is actually cheaper to use refined sugar as your fermentation medium.

Dry Molasses 50 lb. Bag Cost	$15.40
% of Sugar of Dry Molasses	75%
Bags Needed to = 50 lb. Sugar	1.25
Cost per 50 lb. of 100% sugar	$19.25
Refined Sugar 50 lb. Bag	$20.00
Savings per Bag using Molasses	$0.75

TABLE 38—Refer to Sugar Production *Worksheet*

In terms of cheap sugar, using dry molasses or wet molasses can be even cheaper (Table 38). Assuming that dry molasses has 75% of the sugar content of white refined sugar we realize a savings per bag of $ .75.

Dry molasses has different types of sugars than refined, white, sugar but can also have a sugar making enzyme applied to it to perhaps cut some of the larger sugars down to size.

The cost savings for wet molasses can be even more than for dry molasses.

So, why are we choosing a more expensive method to make our alcohol? The reason is that we are making corn whiskey or rye whiskey and we must use corn as more than 51% of our mash bill to qualify as such.

Two final points about this sugar production: First we are only measuring the initial production of sugar in the saccharification process. The long lived saccharification enzyme we have used will continue to break down any remaining starch to sugar during the fermentation process. We really have no way of measuring how much but the cost difference will change for the better as the enzyme continues to make sugar throughout the fermentation process.

Second, I do see higher readings on the hydrometer, up to 25%; even though these readings are "hot" readings I don't see much change when I cool them down to calibration temperature and re-test them at that point. They still show up as 25%. These readings are taken before I dilute the mash with cooling water before setting it. Obviously, adding 40 gallons of cooling water and the relatively cool propagated yeast gallons, about 10 or so, dilutes the batch and reduces the Brix reading one obtains by testing it.

As a final check on the sugar production we can determine how much obscuring is occurring by seeing how much refractable "sugar" remains in the mash at the very end of fermentation when we are ready to run off the alcohol as a stripping run.

---

25   http://en.wikipedia.org/wiki/Glucose; http://en.wikipedia.org/wiki/Maltose; http://en.wikipedia.org/wiki/Fructose; http://en.wikipedia.org/wiki/Sucrose. All accessed September 15, 2015.

My hydrometer measurements of fermenting batches using the Brix scale show that the readings fall from 22.5% to less than 0% sugar during the fermentation process. By this measurement I am fermenting almost 25% sugar. This process runs to 0% sugar in 96 hours and then to -1% in a total of 120 to 168 hours. From a specific gravity standpoint I am fermenting all the sugar in the batch.

Comparing my hydrometer readings to my refractometer readings, generally I am still seeing 8% unfermentable sugars at the end of the run by the refractometer method. The lowest readings I get are about 6% sugar no matter how long I wait.

Clearly the refractometer has the ability to measure unfermentable sugars. Recall that after we added the liquefying enzyme that the sugar content registered 15 or so even though you could not taste any sugar in the batch. So what the refractometer is showing us may not be fermentable sugars. The sugars listed above are really fermentable, and different strains of yeast find different sugars more digestible than others. If your batch is composed of sugars that your yeast does not recognize as food then you will not make any alcohol. Also, other longer oligosaccharides show up on the refractometer as being in the sugar content even though they cannot be used unless they are later converted during the fermentation process by leftover glucoamylase enzymes still active in the batch.

Near the end of the run, you reach a point where bacteria endemic in the batch are using the alcohol for food faster than the yeast are making it with any leftover sugar. At the temperatures we ferment at, yeast have a short lifespan measured in days. They begin to die and the concentration of yeast drops. Even if there is sugar left in the mixture there are less and less yeast to ferment it and more and more bacteria to consume alcohol and the remaining sugar. You are making less alcohol from the sugar than the bacteria are eating. Lactobacillus in particular has a taste for alcohol and will metabolize it to vinegar or acetic acid. Also, because alcohol is more volatile than water, you will lose alcohol by evaporation throughout the fermentation. At some point, that only you can decide, the batch must be distilled because you are losing alcohol faster than the batch is making it.

I should try an experiment to try to restart the batch with fresh yeast and see if I can reduce the last remaining sugars in the batch by refractometer to zero within 144 hours. As we will see in the data compiled from four runs, the batches can continues to ferment for up to 168 hours or seven full days to a point where you will obtain negative readings on the hydrometer.

This brings up the last three means of determining when the batch has completed the fermentation process.

1. The batch will stop making carbon dioxide. The massive amounts of carbon dioxide produced by the mash when it is actively fermenting have an antibacterial effect because only anaerobic bacteria can survive in that environment. When the batch stops making sufficient quantities of carbon dioxide to give fizz to the batch then aerobic bacteria can begin colonizing the batch.

2. The temperature differential between the top and bottom of the tank will decrease. The reduction in metabolic activity is reflected in a decrease in heat. When the top of the batch falls to 65° in a cooler shop environment, then the batch is done. If you ferment in hot weather you will not see this effect very dramatically because the ambient temperature will determine what temperature the batch can fall to. For example if the shop temperature is 50° the temperature the batch can fall to is about 50°. But if the temperature of the shop, ground air is about 70° F as in the summer then the ground temperature will obscure the reduction in metabolic activity occurring in the batch and you will think your batch is still fermenting when in fact it is just sitting there losing alcohol to bacteria and evaporation.

3. The pH of the batch will fall throughout the fermentation. This also serves to inhibit bacterial growth but will eventually become poisonous to yeast as well.

Sometimes a batch will become too acidic before all the sugar is consumed. The acid will first deactivate the yeast and subsequently kill them if the pH gets too low before all fermentable sugars are consumed. You can unstick this batch by raising the pH with baking soda and see if you can get it going again. Raising it up above pH 4.0 should do it; adding more, un-chlorinated water will also help buffer the batch.

Generally fermentations will end around 3.6–3.8. However, pH is a usually a secondary quality of determining the end of the batch because the slowdown in metabolic activity is so apparent. The only time this is important is when you have a batch that is stuck for some reason and you want to know if it is even possible to re-start it. You can't restart a batch that is already at a pH of 3.5.

At a later point this data will provide us with the means of taking another approach, this time chemical, to what the alcohol production will be for this batch.

CHAPTER 3 Yeast Properties and Concentrations

3.1 Yeast

Almost all distillers use one strain or another of the yeast *Saccharomyces cerevisiae*. Because yeast are such small organisms, about 7 microns across, people think that they are like bacteria. In fact yeast are more closely related to animals than plants or bacteria.

The first and most basic of these characteristics that distinguishes yeast from bacteria is that yeast are eukaryotic, in that they have their genetic material in a nucleus; they also have other organelles inside their cell walls. This is in contrast to bacteria which use the cell wall itself to perform metabolic functions and to carry the genetic material for reproduction.

Yeast have a mitochondria organelle, which is the basic virus-based structure that all animals and most plants use to process chemical energy. Because of this, yeast use the same ATP (adenosine triphosphate) energy pathway for metabolism that all animals do.

That chemical pathway for this metabolic process is charted by the Embden–Meyerhof sequence of reactions. At right is a simplified version of this process that follows the metabolism of glucose to carbon dioxide and alcohol.

During this chemical process the individual reactions liberate a substantial amount of energy that shows up as heat. We will look at just how much a little later on.

While plant cells do contain a nucleus and use the ATP pathway for generating their energy requirements, they use photosynthesis to create carbohydrates. Lacking this trait, both animals and yeast are more akin to each other than to plants.

When I learned these things about the yeast I used in my fermentations, it made me appreciate them more. Previously I had a lower estimation of yeast because yeast are classified in the kingdom of fungi and that term is not one that people generally associate with animal-like characteristics. One characteristic that distinguishes all fungus species is that their cell walls contain chitin, which is the same molecule that forms the exoskeletons of insects, arthropods and bird's beaks.

Yeast are heterotrophs in that they must use organic carbon to grow and reproduce, unlike plants that can use carbon dioxide from the atmosphere, or other inorganic carbon dioxide, and the process of carbon fixation, usually through photosynthesis, to create organic molecules that all animals require to live and grow.

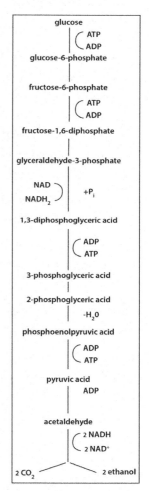

Figure 1: The Embden–Meyerhof Pathway.

Saccharomyces cerevisiae reproduce by budding rather than by division (mitosis). In budding the new organism develops from an outgrowth due to cell division at one site. It is more like birthing than division. Each time a yeast reproduces this way it leaves a budding scar and one can tell how many times a yeast has multiplied by the number of budding scars on its cell wall. Usually a yeast can bud three or four times during its life span. In favorable conditions yeast can reproduce every couple of hours. This is a fairly slow rate of reproduction compared to bacteria, which can reproduce every 30 minutes or so under favorable conditions.

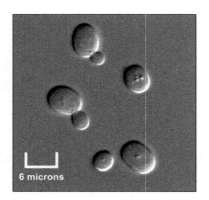

Budding yeast.

Yeast have the ability to use both respiration and fermentation as their method of metabolism. In fermentation yeast convert carbohydrates, in our case, fermentable sugars such as glucose, AKA dextrose, fructose, sucrose and maltose into alcohol and carbon dioxide. Saccharomyces cerevisiae cannot metabolize pentose sugars such as robose and other low molecular weight carbohydrates like dextrins.

Simple sugars are called monosaccharides and include glucose (also known as dextrose), fructose and galactose. The table or granulated sugar most customarily used as food is sucrose, a disaccharide. (In the body, sucrose hydrolyzes into fructose and glucose.) Other disaccharides include maltose and lactose.

Of course alcohol (ethanol) being a waste product of yeast metabolism is not digestible by yeast. But alcohol is digestible by bacteria, as well as by people. When I conduct fermentations using yeast I am essentially creating a pond of sugar that is, over the course of the fermentation, turned into a septic tank of yeast waste products so dense that the yeast are killed by their own waste product, alcohol, hopefully just as they metabolize the last of the sugar available to them. That is why one wants their mash to contain enough water as a buffer for the yeast to live in. With too little water and too dense a mash one can end up with a batch that is so high in alcohol content that the yeast die despite the fact that there is still sugar available for use as food.

Yeast are primarily anaerobic organisms, in that they do not require oxygen in order to metabolize and ferment sugar into alcohol. This process gives off carbon dioxide which is why yeast are used to make leavened bread.

However, yeast can also live and thrive under atmospheric conditions. Yeast are thus facultative anaerobe's in that they can make ATP by aerobic respiration if oxygen is present, but they can also make ATP even if oxygen is absent by using the anaerobic respiration process of fermentation.

While one of the by-products of yeast metabolism under either aerobic or anaerobic conditions is carbon dioxide, the production of alcohol as a by-product is much greater under anaerobic conditions.

Because aerobic metabolism generates greater amounts of ATP than anaerobic metabolic processes do, yeast will reproduce faster under aerobic conditions. This is why some distillers aerate their yeast propagation tanks. However, the air should be filtered, otherwise one is adding bacteria and wild yeast strains to the propagation tank.

Accordingly, when one is trying to grow yeast for later use in fermentation you want to encourage them to metabolize by respiration (aerobically) and when it is desirable to produce alcohol you want to encourage them to metabolize by fermentation which is an anaerobic pathway.

Fortunately at the concentrations of yeast that we inoculate and ferment batches, yeast will create their own anaerobic environment by virtue of the massive amounts of carbon dioxide they produce in the mash medium. However, because yeast like to reproduce and oxygen assists this process the yeast will tend to gather at the top of the mash where there is interface with the atmosphere but the vast majority of yeast are not exposed to oxygen and accordingly, they will be forced to use the anaerobic metabolic pathways and therefore produce greater amounts of alcohol as their primary waste product.

The yeast I am using at the moment is called Superstart.[26] It is an active dry yeast that is widely used in beverage alcohol fermentations. The qualities of this yeast are representative of many modern yeast strains that are commercially available. The products and strains of yeast change very often as improved versions are regularly introduced into the market. Superstart yeast has the following qualities that are broadly representative of commercial yeast strains. It has a high tolerance to temperature, pH, and osmotic stress. It is long-lived and resilient and produces a low level of fermentation by-products and is suitable for many types of beverage alcohol.

It ferments well at temperatures up to 93° F (34° C) and in a pH range of 3.5 to 6.0. In terms of temperature tolerance, it can be added to my mash at temperatures of 90° to 105° F (30° to 40° C).

One cannot allow fermentations to get too hot because you will make other metabolic products that are not desirable and eventually kill the yeast if the temperature gets above 105° F. Other strains of less temperature tolerant yeast may not be able to live at temperatures above 95° F.

I try to keep my fermentations proceeding in the mid-80s, a little cooler than the maximum. This is made easier for me because I usually cook and ferment during the fall and winter when the temperature in the shop is cooler. Late season weather means that less pollen, wild yeast and other live bacteria are floating around to get in the batch and spoil it so cold weather assists in keeping the bacteria count down. I know of some distilleries that shut down their fermentation operations in August because their batches become too hot for their cooling equipment to keep up with them.

At the other end of the scale, one cannot let a batch get too cold. In really cold weather where my shop temperature can be in the high 40s I insulate my batch with a top and with insulation consisting of 3/8-inch thick sheets of Styrofoam insulation wrapped around the tank to maintain a temperature in the mid to high 80s.

Active dry yeasts are sold in a highly concentrated form. Superstart yeast has 18–20 billion CFU which are Cell Forming Units per gram. Baker's yeast has only about 6 billion CFU per gram.

In terms of application rate, my Superstart yeast calls for using 1 to 2 pounds per 1,000 US gallons of mash, or 10 to 25 grams per hectoliter. The yeast is sold to me in 20 kilogram vacuum-sealed foil bags which are about 42 lbs. If I use 1 lb. for 500 gallons that is the high end of the dose recommended. At that rate I could ferment 42 runs per shipment. Other ways to calculate the dose for this yeast are: 2 lbs. per 40 bushels or 2 lbs. per 2,240 lbs. grain (a long ton not a metric ton) or 1 oz./70 lbs. grain used.

In order to get my yeast ready to go to work I rehydrate half of the yeast I will use in the batch and pitch the remainder in as dry yeast. The reason I do this is to check on the viability of the yeast I am using and also to try to propagate them so that I have more yeast going to work right away. To rehydrate yeast I add them gently to warm water of around 75–90° F. This adjusts the yeast to a water environment as gently as possible in order to prevent the breaking of their cell walls. Using cold water is hard on the yeast which, in its dried state, has a non-elastic cell wall. If cold water is used the yeast tend to burst.

To do this properly you need to set aside your city water, i.e. chlorinated water, in plastic buckets, a full day or at least 12 hours before you will use it so that most of the chlorine will evaporate out of it and won't act to poison the yeast.

Be gentle in stirring the yeast in but don't allow it to clump too long on the bottom into a gooey mass. I add enough sugar to get the Brix up to about 4 or 5%, so you can just taste it in the water. When the yeast begin to

---

26 My yeast is produced by Ethanol Technology: http://www.ethanoltech.com/index.html. This yeast strain is produced by Lallemand, Inc.

ferment the sugar they will create carbon dioxide and a brown foam will rise up in the bucket. This is accompanied by a wholesome smell as well. This gives you an idea of how active your yeast are and how active the other dry yeast you will add are as well.

Another reason to propagate at least some of your yeast is so they can go to work right away in the mash as the shock troops of the fermentation.

Yeast can be stable for long periods if kept refrigerated or in the freezer and dry. Keeping the yeast dry is a must. Superstart is rated by the manufacturer as having a shelf life of 24 months. Over that time some yeast will die off. The rate of loss is variable but strongly influenced by temperature. One manufacturer lists the viability decline as around 7% per month at room temperature but less than 10% per year at 4° C (39° F).

The following worksheet shows the decline in yeast viability over time (Table 39):

Show Yeast Viability Count decline on account of aging			
Months since yeast manufactured or purchased	6.00		
Type of Storage	Refrigeration	Room Temp	
Yearly Loss Rate	10.00%	7.0%	Monthly Loss Rate
Loss per Month	0.83%		
% Loss of Viability	5.0%	42%	
Original Estimate of Cell Count per Gram	18,000,000,000	18,000,000,000	
Calculated Loss per Gram	900,000,000	7,560,000,000	
Remaining Viable Cells per Gram	17,100,000,000	10,440,000,000	

TABLE 39—Link to Yeast 2 Worksheet

As your yeast ages you will need more and more of it to achieve a sufficient inoculation of your batch to start a vigorous fermentation. This is why it is important to start about half your yeast during the cooking run, several hours before they are needed. This way you can gauge the vitality of the yeast you are using and can adjust the quantity of the remaining dry yeast you will need to start the fermentation.

In my experience, I have been able to use two-year-old yeast that was stored at room temperature that was still viable. This is contrary to the calculations above in which the cell count would go to zero at around 14 months when stored at room temperature. As to refrigerated yeast, I have been able to use three-year-old yeast that was still viable. You really should refrigerate your yeast and your enzymes too. It will extend their useful life.

3.2 Fermentation Time and My Production Cycle

My usual production cycle tries to run on a weekly basis. I begin with cooking on Monday and set the batch by about 5 PM. Because my fermentations take at least 72 hours that means that the earliest the batch will be done is at 5 PM on Thursday. Of course it is too late in the day on Thursday to start an 8-hour distillation run, but I have occasionally pulled a night shift at the distillery to get the alcohol distilled. Usually I will wait till Friday morning which is just over 84 hours of fermentation time. After the stripping run on Friday, let the mash cool overnight till Saturday morning, then pump out the mash and clean the still on Saturday and then take Sunday off.

Hopefully the batch is done by Friday morning but usually there is some residual activity and I have to determine if it is really "done" or should wait another 12 or 24 hours before being distilled. I do this by checking the sugar levels with my hydrometer and refractometer and also by measuring the pH of the batch.

If I determine that the sugar levels and pH indicate that more fermentation can take place I really have to wait 12 hours and then pull a night shift stripping run on Friday night or wait 24 hours till Saturday morning which means the batch runs a total of 108 hours or 4 1/2 days till completion.

It is a judgment call on how long to let the batch ferment. While additional fermentation is occurring there are bacteria in the mash that are eating and digesting the alcohol produced into lactic acid. Also, alcohol is evaporating from the mash tank because it is volatile. Just like a glass of wine that is left out overnight loses its alcohol content, the batch, if left alone, will lose its alcohol very quickly. Meanwhile the yeast are continuing to use sugar to make alcohol. At some point the loss of alcohol exceeds the production and it is no longer efficient to let the batch continue to ferment.

This cooking, fermenting and distillation cycle goes on for four weeks in a row and then with 100 gallons of alcohol from each stripping run I accumulate 400 gallons of single run spirits to put back in the still along with 100 gallons of heads and tails left over from the last double run in order to have 500 gallons in the still for the double run. From this double run I recover almost all of the alcohol, but only about 250 gallons of 150 proof alcohol are the final product that is useable as corn whiskey. The remainder are heads and tails that can be set aside and re-run at a later time.

3.3 Yeast Nutrition

The last thing we need to consider adding to our batch are nutrients for the yeast to use in their metabolism. I use Fermaid K which I obtain from White Labs.[27] Following is the manufacturer's description of the qualities of Fermaid K. It summarizes what one is looking for when adding nutrients to a fermentation.

In general yeast nutrient additives are a blended complex yeast nutrient that supplies ammonia salts (DAP), alpha amino nitrogen (derived from yeast extract), sterols, and unsaturated fatty acids, to the batch. The major ingredients are magnesium sulfate, thiamin, folic acid, niacin, biotin, calcium pantothenate, and inactive yeast. It is supplied as a powder and is diluted with water (hydrated) before adding to an active fermentation to avoid CO_2 release and overflowing of tanks or barrels.

When the batch is depleted of 1/3 of its original sugar content some nitrogen is needed for protein synthesis and to maintain cellular growth. Nitrogen from the alpha amino acids contained in Fermaid is utilized much more efficiently than nitrogen derived from ammonia salts. The product also contains unsaturated fatty acids and sterols. These are important for the survival of yeast and are needed to maintain alcohol resistance and permease activity. They also help keep volatile acidity levels low. The cell wall fractions (inactive yeast) absorb medium chain fatty acids that are toxic to the yeast. They also provide nucleation sites to help keep the yeast in suspension.

For best results, the manufacturer recommends that Fermaid K should be used in conjunction with another product, GO-FERM, in order to assure proper nutrition of cultured yeast from rehydration through completed fermentation. This is a product that I have not tried.

The dosage rate is 2 lbs. per 1,000 gal. (25 g/hL). Some yeast strains may require extra feeding at two-thirds sugar depletion (i.e. yeast strains CY3079, BM45).

It is possible to use too much of this product. By mistake I killed a batch by adding a second large dose to a batch that was stuck. The reason is that these are nutrients and enough is a benefit to the batch and too much is really poisonous. I was fooled because when I added more the batch seemed to revive in a vigorous way. It

27 White Labs: http://www.whitelabs.com/.

made carbon dioxide and fizzed audibly. Had I actually read the directions they would have informed me that I should hydrate the product before adding to an active fermentation. The activity I was seeing was really their death throes because I was overloading the batch with these nutrients. After a short while, say 30 minutes, the batch slowed down to a crawl. I added more nutrients with the same result, a brief flurry of activity then, nothing. I just kept adding it till the batch was dead. There were so many "nutrients" in the batch it could not even be restarted by adding fresh yeast. It was a lesson learned.

3.4 Yeast and Bacteria Size and Concentrations

It is very difficult to find information about how many yeast are necessary to achieve an efficient fermentation. The material I have surveyed is inconsistent and does not converge to any kind of consensus. In order to gain some understanding I have really had to get down to basics to accomplish any kind of synthesis. My primary resource for this analysis is *The Alcohol Textbook*, 4th Edition.[28] In Chapter 9, "Understanding Yeast Fundamentals," the author, Inge Russell, cites several values for yeast size and concentrations that we will use as our starting point for calculating how many yeast will fit inside a given volume. This will also give us a chance to compare the size of yeast to that of bacteria. The value we will be using is the micron, which is one millionth (1/1,000,000) of a meter.

First we find the cubic microns per cubic centimeter. The simple way to do this is to simply cube the number of microns per meter but we will work it out the long way, just to be sure that the answer is one trillion cubic microns per cubic centimeter (Table 40).

I found a picture of adult yeast with a micron scale on page 86 of *The Alcohol Textbook* and from this I assigned a value for adult yeast size as having a dimension of 7 microns in diameter.

As a starting point we will use that value as a cubic value rather than as a spherical one and use that value to calculate a simple square approach to the total number of adult yeast that could fit into our cubic area. We can also assign a value for the size of an average bacteria to see the relationship between the number of yeast that can live in a batch and the number of bacteria that could do so (Table 41, next page).

Find Cubic Microns per Cubic Centimeter	
Meter length	1.0
Microns per meter	1,000,000
Centimeters per Meter	100
Microns per Meter/Centimeters per meter = Microns per Centimeter	10,000
Microns per Centimeter Squared = Microns per Square Centimeter	100,000,000
Microns per Sq Cm * Microns per Centimeter = Cubic Microns	1,000,000,000,000
Scientific Notation Equivalent	1.00E+12
	Or
Microns per Cm Cubed = Cubic Microns per CC	1,000,000,000,000
Scientific Notation Equivalent	1.00E+12

TABLE 40—Refer to Yeast 1 Worksheet

The conclusion is that almost 2.9 billion cubic yeast could fit into one cubic centimeter and that almost thirteen times as many bacteria, 37 billion of them, could squeeze into the same space.

Each yeast cell has a surface area that is in contact with the surrounding mash. The following calculations show that the contact area for the yeast is 0.857 square meters per cubic centimeter, while the bacteria have a contact area of 2 square meters which is 2.3 times as large as the surface area of our yeast. The lesson here is that not only can more bacteria live in our mash but they have a much larger surface area in the mash than the yeast do and so have more opportunity to soak up sugar for their metabolism (Table 42, next page).

---

28 My primary resource for this analysis is *The Alcohol Textbook*, 4th Edition, edited by KA Jacques and TP Lyons and DR Kelsall, published by Nottingham University Press, 2003, ISBN 1-897676-13-1.

	Yeast Square	Bacteria Square	
Microns of Yeast Length	7.0	3.0	Microns of bacteria Length
Microns of Yeast Height	7.0	3.0	Microns of bacteria Height
Microns of Yeast Depth	7.0	3.0	Microns of Bacteria Depth
Cubic Microns per Square Yeast	343	27.0	Cubic Microns per Square Bacteria
Cubic Microns per CC (1 Trillion)	1.0.E+12	1.0.E+12	Cubic Microns per CC
Number of "Cubic" Yeast per CC	2,915,451,895	37,037,037,037	Number of "Cubic" Bacteria per CC
Scientific Notation Equivalent	2.92E+09	3.70E+10	Scientific Notation Equivalent
		12.7	Ratio of number of Bacteria per Yeast organism.
		7.87%	Percentage Ratio.

TABLE 41—Refer to Yeast 1 Worksheet

Find Surface Area (Contact Area)	Yeast Area	Bacteria Area
Square Yeast per CC	2.92E+09	3.70E+10
Surface Area per Yeast (Square Microns)	294.00	54.00
Total Square Micron Area.	8.57E+11	2.00E+12
Square Microns to Square Meters	1.0E+12	1.0E+12
Surface Area/10 to the 12th = Sq. Meters	0.857	2.000
	2.3	Ratio
	42.86%	% Ratio.
1 cubic meter/surface area = Area to Vol. Ratio	1.167	0.500
	0.43	Ratio
	233.3%	% Ratio.

TABLE 42—Refer to Yeast 1 Worksheet

Dividing one cubic meter by the surface area gives the ratio of our yeast and bacteria volumes to their surface area. The point here is that volume goes up by the cube and area increases by the square and that bacteria have an area that is twice as large as their volume while yeast have a surface area that is close to that of their volume. Again, this simply demonstrates that bacteria have a large surface area with respect to their volume and consequently more opportunity to absorb sugar from the mash.

Now we can improve our approach by calculating the spherical area of our yeast as well as our bacteria. The results show that by changing to a spherical approach we have roughly doubled the number of yeast and also bacteria that can occupy one cubic centimeter of volume to a total of 5.5 billion yeast and 70.7 billon bacteria (Table 43, next page).

The reason we are finding the surface area is to compare it with *The Alcohol Textbook* value of 153 cubic microns, which matches our calculations,[29] and to assist us to calculate the total contact area. The more important value is the volume of each yeast which we will solve by two different methods.

This spherical approach is somewhat flawed and is, like the square approach, for demonstration purposes only. The square yeast can occupy all the area but the yeast are not really square. The round yeast cannot occupy all the area because there will be space between them on their curved surfaces. We could conduct a spherical packing analysis but that would not change the results sufficiently to affect the general conclusions we are looking for.[30]

---

29 *The Alcohol Textbook* 4th Ed. Page 86 value for surface area of 7 micron yeast is 153 square microns.

30 This spherical packing issue is a problem that a qualified reader might solve so I could improve the calculations.

	Spherical Yeast		Spherical Bacteria
Avg. Yeast Diameter In Microns	7.0	Linear Microns	3.0
Diameter/2 = Yeast Radius	3.5	Linear Microns	1.5
Pi	3.14159		3.14159
Find Surface Area per organism			
Sphere Surface Area = (4 π r2)	153.94	Square Microns	28.27
Find Volume			
Sphere Volume = (4/3 π r3)	179.59	Cubic Microns	14.14
Sphere Volume = 1/6 Pi *d3	179.59	Cubic Microns	14.14
Ratio of Surface Area to Volume	0.857		2.000
# of Cubic Microns per CC	1.0E+12		1.0E+12
Cubic μ per CC/Yeast Vol. = Yeast per CC	5,568,102,972		70,735,530,344
Scientific Notation Equivalent	5.57E+09		7.07E+10
Ratio of number of Bacteria per Yeast organism.		12.7	
		7.87%	Percentage Ratio
Ratios of Cubic yeast to Spherical Yeast			
Cubic Yeast to Spherical Yeast %	52.4%		52.4%
Cubic Yeast to Spherical Yeast ratio	1.91		1.91

TABLE 43—Refer to Yeast 1 *Worksheet*

Find Surface Area (Contact Area)	
Spherical Yeast per CC	5.57E+09
Surface Area per Yeast in sq microns	153.94
Total Surface area in sq microns	8.57E+11
Square Micron to Square Meters	1.0E+12
Surface Area/microns per Meter = Square Meters	0.857
Spherical Yeast * Sur. to Vol Ratio = Yeast, per CC	4,772,659,690
Percentage reduction in yeast	14.3%

TABLE 44—Refer to Yeast 1 *Worksheet*

Calculating the square meter area of our spherical yeast again yields a value of 0.857 square meters per cubic centimeter (Table 44).

The only remaining information from page 86 of *The Alcohol Textbook* that we need to verify is the author's claim that "one gram of dry weight yeast equates to 4.87×10^{10} number of cells or 48.7 billion cells per gram. According to my calculations this value on page 86 is incorrect by an order of magnitude and is in conflict with other values in *The Alcohol Textbook* as well as with manufacturer specifications indicating roughly 20 billion yeast per gram. We will examine this in subsequent calculations.[31]

3.5 Dried Yeast

We need to make some effort to determine how many dried yeast per gram we are starting in order to determine how much yeast to use in our fermentations.

The spherical calculations above indicate that about 5.5 billion 7-micron-round yeast can fit into a cubic centimeter. I have been unable to find any data on the micron size of dried yeast so we will have to infer it from other data that we do have.

---

31   The odd fact to note is that taking our yeast per cc value of 5.57 billion and multiplying it by the surface to volume ratio leads to a value suspiciously close to the value on page 86 of 4.87. But I don't think this is a valid result because it is simply the % difference between 0.857 and 1.0 expressed as the number of yeast.

My measurements of the weight of dried yeast yielded a value of 0.71 kilograms per liter which is equivalent to 0.71 grams per cubic centimeter.

Manufacturers' publications and other public sources indicate that dried yeast have a density of about 18 to 22 billion dried yeast per gram.[32]

Using the Alltech Superstart advertised value for their yeast of 18 billion CFU (Cell Forming Units) per gram we find that about 12.78 billion cubic dried yeast can occupy a volume of 1 cubic centimeter. We also find that taking the dried yeast per cubic centimeter and dividing by the total cubic microns per cc gives a cubic value per dried yeast and the cube root of that value is the length per side (Table 45).

Find Dried Yeast per CC	
Yeast per gram	18,000,000,000
Measured Grams wt. of yeast Per CC	0.71
Dried Yeast per CC	12,780,000,000
Cubic Microns per CC	1.0E+12
Cubic Microns per yeast	78.2
Cube Root = Cubic size per Yeast in Microns per side	4.277

TABLE 45—Refer to Yeast 1 Worksheet

Using this 4.277 microns as the diameter of dried yeast we can apply our square and spherical methods of calculating the number of yeast in a given volume.

The first column shows the result of cubing the length per side and confirming our cubic calculations. The other column shows number of spherical yeast it is possible to fit in the space of one cubic centimeter (mL) (Table 46).

Yeast Square Approach for Dried Yeast		Yeast Spherical Approach for Dried Yeast	
Microns of Yeast Length	4.277	4.277	Avg. Yeast Diameter In Microns
Microns of Yeast Height	4.277	2.14	Diameter/2 = Yeast Radius
Microns of Yeast Depth	4.277	3.14159	Pi
Cubic Microns per Square Yeast	78.2	40.97	Sphere Volume = $(4/3 \pi r3)$
Cubic Microns per CC	1.0E+12	40.97	Sphere Volume = 1/6 Pi *d3
Scientific Notation Equivalent	1.00E+12	1.0E+12	# of Cubic Microns per CC
Number of "Cubic" Yeast per CC	12,781,512,504	24,410,890,770	Cubic Microns per CC/Vol. = Yeast per CC
Scientific Notation Equivalent	1.28E+10	2.44E+10	Scientific Notation Equivalent
Actual Grams per CC	0.71	0.71	Actual Grams per CC
Increase to value per gram	1.290	1.290	Increase to value per gram
Yeast per CC * Grams per CC = Cells per Gram	16,488,151,130	31,490,049,094	Yeast per CC * Grams per CC = Cells per Gram
			Find Surface Area
Ratio of number of Spherical dried yeast to cubic dried yeast.	1.91	3.14159	Pi
Percentage Ratio. (Volume Ratio)	52.36%	57.47	Sphere Surface Area = $(4 \pi r2)$

TABLE 46—Refer to Yeast 1 Worksheet

Dividing by the total cubic microns available gives the same relative answer of roughly double the number of spherical yeast as cubic yeast per cubic centimeter. Having scaled down to find the number of yeast per cubic centimeter we need to scale back up to find the number per gram. The results indicate that between 16 billion square yeast and 31.5 billion spherical yeast can occupy one gram of active dried yeast.

---

32 See Page 97 of *The Alcohol Textbook*, 4th Ed.

While this only gives us an order of magnitude estimate for the number of yeast per gram it does contradict the value of 48.7 billion (4.87×10^{10}) yeast cells per gram of dry weight yeast cited by the chapter author on page 86 of *The Alcohol Textbook*.

There are other values for yeast density that are cited in *The Alcohol Textbook* that also indicate that the value of 48.7 billion yeast per gram is inaccurate (Table 47).

Compare Yeast Data by Type per Gram	Super Start - WV Distilling	Page 97 Active Dry Yeast	Outlier Value
			Page 86 Dry Yeast
Ten to the Tenth Power Yeast per Gram	1.80	2.20	4.87
Ten to the Tenth Power = Ten Billion	1.000E+10	1.000E+10	1.000E+10
Yeast Per Gram	18,000,000,000	22,000,000,000	48,700,000,000

TABLE 47—Refer to Yeast 1 *Worksheet*

Some distilleries make their own yeast slurry or purchase compressed yeast. The cell amounts per gram will vary but fall in the following range (Table 48).

	Low Range	Mid Range	High Range	
	Compressed Yeast	Compressed Yeast	Compressed Yeast	Yeast Slurry
Ten to the Tenth Power Yeast per Gram	6.00	9.50	13.00	3.00
Ten to the Tenth Power = Ten Billion	1.00E+09	1.00E+09	1.00E+09	1.00E+09
Yeast Per Gram	6,000,000,000	9,500,000,000	13,000,000,000	3,000,000,000

TABLE 48—Refer to Yeast 1 *Worksheet*

These values will help us determine the amount of yeast to use to properly inoculate our batches.[33]

Now that we have calculated the yeast concentration in various mediums we can apply these values to determine just how much of each product we will need to achieve an efficient fermentation of our mash.

3.6 Calculating Yeast Inoculation Values

We will start by calculating some yeast application values using active dry yeast. My yeast supplier, Alltech, has a rather simple formula as their application directions: "1 or 2 pounds per 1,000 gallons of Mash."

Applying these values shows that the recommended application is somewhere between 2.1 and 4.3 million yeast per cubic centimeter (Table 49, next page).

The disadvantage of using this straightforward method is that it does not take into account the sugar content of the batch. The more sugar one has in their batch the more opportunity there is for bacteria to also thrive in the sugar rich environment. The inoculation of yeast needs to be sufficient so that it is the yeast that will metabolize the sugar before the bacteria can multiply and consume a significant portion of it.

---

33   The values are derived from page 97 of *The Alcohol Textbook* 4th Ed.

Gallons of Mash Batch Volume	1,000.00	
Gallons to Liters	3.7854	
Batch Liters	3,785.41	
Lbs. of Yeast	1.00	2.000
Lbs. to Kg.	0.45359237	0.45359237
Kg. of Yeast	0.45	0.91
Grams of Yeast	453.59	907.18
Yeast Per Gram	18,000,000,000	18,000,000,000
Total Yeast organisms	8,164,662,660,000	16,329,325,320,000
Total Yeast as scientific Notation	8.16E+12	1.63E+13
Yeast per Liter	2,156,875,683	4,313,751,365
Yeast per ml (cubic centimeter)	2,156,876	4,313,751

TABLE 49—Refer to Yeast 2 Worksheet

Returning to *The Alcohol Textbook*, on page 97, it is recommended that the inoculation be tied to the degrees of Plato/Brix at the rate of 1 to 2 million viable cells per mL per degree of Brix. With a good conversion of starch to sugar I often achieve 22° Brix and we will use that value for this example (Table 50).

Find Yeast Cell inoculation values	Low Range	High Range
Yeast Cell Inoculation Value per mL per Degree of Plato/Brix	1,000,000	2,000,000
Degrees of Plato/Brix of Wort or Mash	22.00	22.00
Cells per mL Desired Inoculation	22,000,000	44,000,000
Total Liters In Batch	3,785.41	3,785.41
Milliliters Per Liter	1,000.00	1,000.00
Total Milliliters	3,785,412	3,785,412
Desired Starting Yeast Concentration per mL	2.20E+07	4.40E+07
Yeast Per Liter	2.20E+10	4.40E+10
Total Number of Yeast Needed to Start	8.33E+13	1.67E+14
Yeast Per Gram	18,000,000,000	18,000,000,000
Grams Needed	4,626.61	9,253.23
Kilograms	4.63	9.25
Kilograms to Pounds Avdp	2.20462260	2.20462260
Pounds of Yeast Needed	10.20	20.40
Grams / Liters = Grams Per Liter	1.22	2.44
Liters / Grams = Liters per gram	0.82	0.41

TABLE 50—Refer to Yeast 2 Worksheet

Applying this method results in an application rate of between 10 and 20 pounds of yeast and these values are 10 times the manufacturer's recommended values for either low dose or high dose inoculation values.

I don't see how an ordinary distiller could afford to inoculate at these high values. The cost would just be prohibitive.

It is possible to propagate yeast to increase their numbers prior to inoculation into the mash as we have discussed above and will again *infra*.

I certainly did not have this information available to me when I started my distillery. My practice has been to add double the manufacturer's recommended high dose value to my batches, which works out to 2 lbs. per 500 gallon batch and 4 lbs. per 1,000 gallon batch. This system has worked adequately for me.

Find Yeast per ml based on Lbs. used	
Lbs of Yeast	2.00
Pounds Avdp to Kilograms	0.45359237
Grams of Yeast	907.18
Yeast Per Gram	18,000,000,000
Total Yeast	1.63E+13
Gallons of Mash Batch Volume	500.00
Gallons to Liters	3.7854
Batch ml.	1,892,706
Yeast per ml.	8,627,503
Degrees of Plato/Brix of Wort or Mash	22.00
Yeast per ° of Brix per ml.	392,159

TABLE 51—Refer to Yeast 2 Worksheet

Find Yeast required to inoculate a given volume	
Gallons of Mash Batch Volume	500.00
Gallons to Liters	3.7854
Batch Liters	1,892.71
Total Milliliters	1,892,706
Desired Starting Yeast Concentration per Ml	10,000,000
Yeast Per Liter	10,000,000,000
Total Number of Yeast Needed to Start	1.9E+13
Yeast Per Gram	18,000,000,000
Grams Needed	1,051.50
Kilograms	1.05
Kilograms to Pounds Avdp	2.20462260
Pounds of Yeast Needed	2.32
Degrees of Plato/Brix of Wort or Mash	22.00
Yeast per ° of Brix per ml.	454,545

TABLE 52—Refer to Yeast 2 Worksheet

Find Yeast Cell Multiplication over time.		
Starting Cells per ML	10,000,000	20,000,000
1st Multiplication	20,000,000	40,000,000
2nd Multiplication	40,000,000	80,000,000
3rd Multiplication	80,000,000	160,000,000
4th Multiplication	160,000,000	320,000,000

TABLE 53—Refer to Yeast 2 Worksheet

Solving for the values that I have customarily used shows an inoculation rate of 8.67 million yeast per mL and 392 thousand yeast per degree of Brix. This latter value is still only 1/3 of the recommended low dose shown (Table 51).

I don't know why yeast manufacturers would encourage the use of less of their product than is required but apparently they do.

Rearranging the formula we can find the quantity of active dry yeast that is required to achieve an initial dose of ten million yeast per mL (Table 52).

On average, distiller's yeast, as opposed to brewer's yeast, are capable of producing four generations of offspring.[34]

From this beginning inoculation we hope and trust that our yeast will each divide four times and increase our yeast density by a factor of 16 times the initial cell density.

Using our initial inoculation of 10 million cells per mL and a comparison of 20 million we find that 4 multiplications are required to reach 160 million per mL on the low side but only three multiplications are required for the high dose value (Table 53).

This shows that our proposed yeast dosing results in the same yeast concentrations as are shown in the graph on page 94 of *The Alcohol Textbook*, which shows the growth curve for yeast over the course of a fermentation. The graph begins with 10 million yeast per mL and tops out at somewhere above 170 million yeast per mL.[35]

The last example for inoculation values that I can cite is some information disclosed in a History Channel program on the distilling industry and relates to the practices of Jameson's whiskey. The

---

34   See the bottom of page 94 and the top of page 95 of *The Alcohol Textbook*. This assumes no mortality, and using an average of 3.5 multiplications yields 120 million per mL with the yeast dose I have traditionally used.

35   Assuming no mortality. So you never reach 200 million yeast cells per mL, even with four multiplications. (*See* Page 127 of *The Alcohol Textbook*.) If you want that high a dose use more yeast. Graph in book assumes four multiplications and tops out at 160 million viable; later the author says only 3.5 are possible in anaerobic conditions. Temperature affects amount of reproduction.

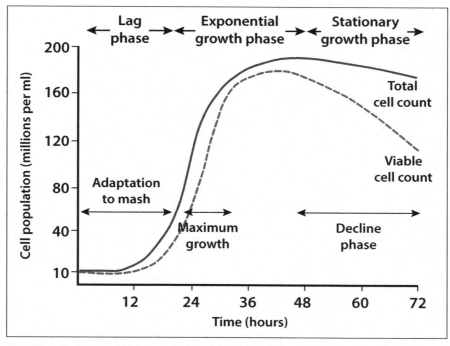

Yeast Multiplication. From KA Jacques, TP Lyons and DR Kelsall, The Alcohol Textbook, *4th Edition, pg. 94.*

information given was that a batch of 60,000 liters (15,850 gallons) required 215 kilograms of yeast (474 lbs.) to ferment an 8.5% beer/wort in 48 hours. The yeast they used was compressed yeast about the consistency of butter. I'm assuming a mid-range of yeast density for this yeast. Applying our method to find the initial concentration of yeast per liter shows that the value is about 2.65 million yeast per mL (Table 54).

This value is in line with the low dose of the recommended value that we started with for Superstart yeast at 1 lb. per 1,000 gallons. That value was 2,156,876 yeast cells per milliliter (see Table 49).

As I mentioned in the introduction the information in the industry is not consistent and it is difficult to find any consensus. Like many aspects of the distilling industry everyone does what works for them.

Keep in mind that as yeast ages in storage the viability count goes down and one must adjust the value per gram accordingly to continue achieving the same inoculation per cubic centimeter in later batches.

Jameson's History Channel Program Description	
Total Liters In Batch	60,000.00
Kilo's of Yeast Applied	215.00
Grams of Yeast Applied	215,000.00
Grams / Liters = Grams Per Liter	0.279
Liters / Grams = Liters per gram	3.58
Assuming Compressed Yeast mid range	
Cell Forming Units per Gram	9,500,000,000
Yeast per mL	2,651,163

TABLE 54—Refer to Yeast 2 Worksheet

3.7 Yeast Lebensraum

It is just amazing to me that so much life can occupy such a small volume. I'm going to try to give it some scale so we can see, in human terms, how much volume each yeast cell has to operate in.

Using a standard inoculation value of 10 million yeast per mL, we see that I allocated each yeast 100,000 cubic microns of volume and that this volume works out to be a cube 46 microns on each side (Table 55, next page).

Yeast per CC Initial Dose Desired	10,000,000
# of Cubic Microns per CC as Value	1.0E+12
Desired Yeast per CC / microns per CC = Cubic Microns per Yeast	100,000
Cube Root = Cubic Room size per Yeast Scale in Microns per side	46.416

TABLE 55—Refer to Yeast 3 Worksheet

Microns of Yeast Length	7.0
Microns of Yeast Height	7.0
Microns of Yeast Depth	7.0
Cubic Microns per Cubic Yeast	343
Cubic Microns per Yeast/Volume of Yeast = # of Cubic Yeast that can fit in the space allotted for one Yeast at dose rate	291.5

TABLE 56—Refer to Yeast 3 Worksheet

Now we need to determine how large the yeast organism is with respect to this cubic volume. Returning to our cubic yeast volume calculations we see that each yeast cell occupies a volume of 343 cubic microns and that 291 of them could fit in the cubic space assigned to one yeast. For spherical yeast these values would be about double those for our imaginary cubic yeast (Table 56).

In order to relate this to a human scale we are going to determine how large a room each yeast organism is allocated for their living area or "lebensraum." I for one do not easily relate a cubic space to a living area so we will pretend that our yeast are in a room or greenhouse with a ceiling eight feet high (Table 57).

Calculate Room size in square area assuming a height for the ceiling			
Total Cubic Microns restated as Feet	100,000		
Room Height	8.0		
Cubic Feet/Room Height = Square Feet of Room	12,500	0.30480	Feet to Meters Converter
Square Root of Square Feet of Room = Length per Side	111.8	34.1	Meters of Length & Breadth
Square Feet per Square Yard	9.0		
Square Yards	1,388.9	1,161.3	Square Meters
Square Feet per Acre	43,560	0.4046870	Acres to Hectares
Fraction of an Acre	28.7%	11.6%	Fraction of Hectare

TABLE 57—Refer to Yeast 3 Worksheet

At our initial dose each yeast could "live" in a 12,500-square-foot house or farm of about 1/4 (28.7%) acre of land.

At the end of the fermentation, after four multiplications, with 160 million yeast per cc, each yeast cell will still have a room-sized environment of 28 x 28 feet (Table 58, next page).

They would each still occupy a room 28-feet wide and long. If there is plenty of food in it, there is no reason they can't occupy it. The total volume of the yeast is still only 5.49% of the total volume. The rest of the medium is water, food, solids and waste products that the yeast have to wade through.

Just for completeness we should look at our spherical analysis and its multiplication over time. Applying it we see that there are roughly twice as many yeast that can occupy the same area and that regardless of whether one considers them cubic or spherical the percentage of the space they occupy is negligible with respect to the medium (Table 59, next page).

One other analysis we can perform is to evaluate the total surface area of the yeast in the batch at various concentrations. Using our values that we have previously calculated for active dry yeast we can get a rough idea of contact area between the yeast and the medium (Table 60, next page).

Yeast cell count after multiplication	160,000,000
# of Cubic Microns per CC as Value	1.0E+12
Desired Yeast per CC / microns per CC = Cubic Microns per Yeast	6,250
Cube Root = Cubic Room size per Yeast Scale in Microns per side	18.420
Calculate Cubic Microns per Yeast Organism	
Microns of Yeast Length	7.0
Microns of Yeast Height	7.0
Microns of Yeast Depth	7.0
Cubic Microns per Cubic Yeast	343
Cubic Microns per Yeast/Volume of Yeast = # of Cubic Yeast that can fit in the space allotted for one Yeast at dose rate	18.2
Cubic Microns per Cubic Yeast	343
Total number of Cubic Yeast that could ft. in one mL	2,915,451,895
Fraction of space taken up by yeast	5.49%
Calculate Room size in square area assuming a height for the ceiling	
Total Cubic Microns restated as Feet	6,250
Room Height	8.0
Cubic Feet/Room Height = Square Feet of Room	781
Square Root of Square Feet of Room = Length per Side	28.0

TABLE 58—Refer to Yeast 3 Worksheet

Spherical Volume	
Yeast Diameter in Microns	7.00
Diameter/2 = Yeast Radius	3.50
Pi	3.14159
Sphere Volume = (4/3 π r3)	179.59
Sphere Volume = 1/6 Pi *d3	179.59
Total number of Spherical Yeast that could ft. in one mL	5,568,102,972

	1.91	Ratio of Spheres to Cubes

Find Yeast Cell Multiplication over time	**Cubic**	**% of Volume**	**Spherical**	**% of Volume**
Cells per ML	10,000,000	0.34%	10,000,000	0.18%
1st Multiplication	20,000,000	0.69%	20,000,000	0.36%
2nd Multiplication	40,000,000	1.37%	40,000,000	0.72%
3rd Multiplication	80,000,000	2.74%	80,000,000	1.44%
4th Multiplication	160,000,000	5.49%	160,000,000	2.87%

TABLE 59—Refer to Yeast 3 Worksheet

Find Surface Area of Yeast	**Hydrated Yeast**	**Dried Yeast**
Yeast per CC or ml	5,568,102,972	12,780,000,000
Yeast Sphere Surface Area in sq. microns	153.94	57.47
Total Square Microns	8.57E+11	7.35E+11
Reduce to Meter Scale	1.00E+12	1.00E+12
Square Meter result	0.857	0.735
Sq. Meters to Sq. ft.	10.76	10.76
Square Feet of Surface Area	9.23	7.91

TABLE 60—Refer to Yeast 3 Worksheet

To make this calculation more meaningful we can apply it to the actual inoculation of yeast per mL to find the total surface area of the yeast contained in the batch as well as the total yeast organisms in the batch, which comes out to 18.9 trillion (Table 61).

Find Total Yeast and Surface Area			
Gallons of Mash Batch Volume	500.00		
Gallons to Liters	3.7854		
Batch Liters	1,892.71	Total Yeast Organisms	
Milliters	1,892,706	1.89E+13	
Yeast per ml	10,000,000	10,000,000	Yeast per ml
Yeast Sphere Surface Area in sq. microns	153.94	57.47	Dried Yeast Surface area
Total Square Microns	1,539,380,399	574,728,371	
Reduce to Meter Scale	1.0E+12	1.0E+12	
Square Meter result per ml	0.0015	0.00057	
Sq. meters per ml * Tot. ml = Tot. Sq. meters	2,914	1,088	
Sq. Meters to Sq. ft.	10.76391	10.76391	
Square Feet of Surface Area	31,362	0.0062	
Square meters to Acres	0.000247105	0.000247105	
Acres	0.72	0.27	

TABLE 61—Refer to Yeast 3 Worksheet

The result is about 2,914 square meters or 0.72 acres of area. A companion version using the dried yeast surface area is also set out for comparison. Not all yeast are large yeast and the true value is somewhere between the two. What we can say about this is that we have increased our initial surface area of contact with the medium by a factor of three by hydrating our yeast before we put them to work.

Finally, we can look at the total area of the yeast in the batch over time (Table 62).

Find surface area over time	Total yeast	As Scientific	Surface Area	Total Sq. microns	Sq. Meters	Hectares	Sq. m. to Acres	Acres of Area
Total Yeast Cells at inoculation	18,927,059,000,000	1.89E+13	153.94	2.91E+15	2,913.59	0.29	0.0002471	0.72
1st Multiplication	37,854,118,000,000	3.79E+13	153.94	5.83E+15	5,827.19	0.58	0.0002471	1.44
2nd Multiplication	75,708,236,000,000	7.57E+13	153.94	1.17E+16	11,654.38	1.17	0.0002471	2.88
3rd Multiplication	151,416,472,000,000	1.51E+14	153.94	2.33E+16	23,308.75	2.33	0.0002471	5.76
4th Multiplication	302,832,944,000,000	3.03E+14	153.94	4.66E+16	46,617.51	4.66	0.0002471	11.52

TABLE 62—Refer to Yeast 3 Worksheet

Re-arranging the equations we have developed allows us to solve from the quantity of yeast employed at the time of inoculation. Back checking this value determines the inoculation value per mL and this number is close to the ten million yeast per mL that we have previously used as our assumption (Table 63, next page).

Find total area and inoculation density using or hydrated yeast or dry yeast			
Lbs. of Yeast	2.32	Total Yeast Organisms	
Kg. of Yeast	1.05	1.89E+13	
Find Total Surface Area of Yeast	**Dried Yeast**		
Yeast per Gram	18,000,000,000	18,000,000,000	
Dried Yeast Sphere Surface Area in sq. microns	57.47	153.94	Hydrated Yeast Area
Total Square Microns	1.03E+12	2.77E+12	
Reduce to Meter Scale	1.00E+12	1.00E+12	
Square Meter result per Gram	1.03451	2.77088	
Total Square Meters	1,089	2,916	
Sq. Meters to Sq. ft.	10.76391	10.76391	
Square Feet of Surface Area	11,718.147	31,386.453	
Sq. m. to Acres	0.0002471	0.0002471	
Acres of Area	0.27	0.72	
Find Total Yeast and Surface Area			
Gallons of Mash Batch Volume	500.00		
Gallons to Liters	3.7854		
Batch Liters	1,892.71		
Milliters	1,892,706		
Initial Inoculation of Yeast per ml	10,007,903		

TABLE 63—Refer to Yeast 3 Worksheet

3.8 Sugar Molecules per Yeast

From a biological standpoint I was interested in how many sugar molecules each yeast cell had at its disposal as food.

The numbers I have calculated are so fantastically large that I doubted their accuracy, but several people more qualified than I have looked at them and agreed that they adequately represent the quantities involved.

To begin we simply find the cubic microns per yeast at our inoculation value (Table 64).

Then we calculate how many pounds of sugar are required to create a 10% by weight sugar and water solution using 500 gallons of water as the water weight reference value (Table 65).

Find sugar values per yeast	
Yeast Cell inoculation per ml	10,000,000
# of Cubic Microns per CC as Value	1.0E+12
Cubic Microns per Yeast	100,000

TABLE 64—Refer to Sugar & Yeast Worksheet

Gallons of Water	500.00	3.7854	Gallons to Liters
Lbs. of Sugar	462.50	1,892.71	Water Liters
Water Weight per US Gal.	8.3282	13.50	Sugar lbs. per gal.
Water Weight Lbs.	4,164.12	34.26	Total "Gal" sugar
Total Lbs.	4,626.62	534.26	Total Gal. "Volume"
Total Kilograms	2,098.6	2,022.39	Batch Liters
% Sugar by Total Wt.	10.00%	129.69	"Sugar Liters"
		6.85%	% sugar volume

TABLE 65—Refer to Sugar & Yeast Worksheet

In order to adjust our volume we use the TTB recommended value of 13.5 lbs. of sugar per gallon of displacement.[36] Next we find the total sugar molecules using the average of the molecular weight per gram of glucose and sucrose and assume that is the mixture of sugar we added (Table 66).

Find total sugar molecules			
Pounds Avdp to Kilograms	0.45359237	Sugar Wt. Values	
Grams of Sugar	209,786.47	180.16	Glucose Molecular wt.
Sugar Molar Density (Grams per Mole)	261.08	342.00	Sucrose Molecular wt.
Moles of Sugar	803.53	261.08	50 50 Sugar Mix Molecular Wt.
Avogadro's Number per Mole	6.02E+23		
Total Molecular Units	4.84E+26		
Molecular Units per Liter	2.39E+23		
Moles of Sugar per Liter	0.40	28	Grams per Oz.
Grams per Liter	103.73	3.70	Ounces per liter

TABLE 66—Refer to Sugar & Yeast *Worksheet*

The result is 4.84 to the 26th molecules and also confirms that about 10% of the batch mass is our sugar at 103 grams per liter.

Then using the total number of yeast we calculate the number of sugar molecules per yeast (Table 67):

Yeast Per CC @ Inoculation Restated	10,000,000			
Total CC in Batch	2,022,391		6.02E+23	Avogadro's Number per Mole
Total Yeast @ Inoculation	20,223,913,042,593	2.02E+13	3.97E-11	Moles Per Yeast
Total Sugar Molecules Restated	4.84E+26		1.04E-08	Grams per Yeast
Sugar Molecules per Yeast at Inoculation	23,927,077,761,412	2.39E+13		

TABLE 67—Refer to Sugar & Yeast *Worksheet*

The answer turns out to be almost 24 trillion sugar molecules per yeast cell. So, 20.2 trillion yeast will each have 23.9 trillion molecules of sugar—an insanely large number—available to metabolize

Accounting for the multiplication of yeast during fermentation and applying them as inoculation values does not appreciably affect the fantastic nature of the results (Table 68).

Molecules per Yeast after each Yeast Multiplication			10,000,000	Cells per mL
1st Multiplication	11,963,538,880,706	1.20E+13	20,000,000	1st Multiplication
2nd Multiplication	5,981,769,440,353	5.98E+12	40,000,000	2nd Multiplication
3rd Multiplication	2,990,884,720,177	2.99E+12	80,000,000	3rd Multiplication
4th Multiplication	1,495,442,360,088	1.50E+12	160,000,000	4th Multiplication

TABLE 68—Refer to Sugar & Yeast *Worksheet*

In order to provide a time component to our calculation we will apply a standard number of hours for fermentation and apply that to the total number of sugar molecules in the batch and assume that they are metabolized evenly throughout the fermentation by an average number of yeast per mL (Table 69, next page).

The results are an astronomical 33.2 billion molecules per hour, per yeast, and 9 million reactions per second.

---

36   Value per 27 *Code of Federal Regulations*, Chapter I Part 24 Subpart F Sec 24.181

One fact we can back-check is the amount of yeast necessary for the initial dose (Table 70). This value checks out and lets us know at least some of our basic math is right.

Hours of Fermentation	96.00
Total Sugar Molecules Restated	4.84E+26
Sugar Molecules Metabolized per Hour	5.04E+24
Average number of Yeast per ml	75,000,000
Total ml of batch restated	2,022,391
Average yeast population in batch	1.52.E+14
Molecules per hour metabolized per Yeast	33,232,052,446
Average Molecules processed per minute	553,867,541
Average Molecules processed per second	9,231,126

TABLE 69—Refer to Sugar & Yeast *Worksheet*

Yeast Per Gram	18,000,000,000
Total Yeast @ Inoculation	20,223,913,042,593
Kg. of Yeast	1.124
Lbs. of Yeast	2.48

TABLE 70—Refer to Sugar & Yeast *Worksheet*

One can even take the numbers we generated on the way down to the molecular level, and by adding in a reasonable molecular size, build the entire batch back up and find a reasonable percentage of sugar based on the volume of each molecule[37] (Table 71–1).

Calculate Cubic Volume of Sugar Molecules			
Avg. Nanometers of Molecule Length	0.770		
Nanometers of Molecule Height	0.770		
Nanometers of Molecule Depth	0.770		
Molecular Vol. in Cubic Nanometers	0.45653		
% of a cubic nanometer	45.65%		
Max Fit of Cubic Sugar molecules per cubic Nanometer	2.19		
Calculate Spherical Volume			
Sugar Molecule Diameter In Nanometers	0.770	Linear Nanometers	
Diameter/2 = Yeast Radius	0.39	Linear Nanometers	
Pi	3.14159		
Sphere Volume = $(4/3\ \pi r^3)$	0.239	Cubic Nanometers	
Sphere Volume = $1/6\ \pi d^3$	0.239	Cubic Nanometers	
% of a cubic nanometer	23.90%		
Max Spherical Sugar molecules per cubic Nanometer	4.18		
Build Back Up			
Total Sugar Molecular units restated	4.84E+26		
Cubic Volume per Sugar Molecule	4.57E-01		
Total Sugar Vol. = Cubic Vol. per Unit * Units	2.21E+26	1.16E+26	Total Sugar Vol. = Spherical Vol. per Unit * Units
Cubic Nanometers in Batch Restated	2.02E+27	2.02E+27	Cubic Nanometers in Batch Restated
Sugar Molecules % of the batch	10.92%	5.72%	As percentage of Batch
Max Cubes per batch	4.43E+27	8.46E+27	Max spheres per batch
Max Cubes per Liter	2.19E+24	4.18E+24	Max spheres per Liter
Molecular % Result	10.92%	5.72%	As percentage of Batch

TABLE 71–1—Refer to Sugar & Yeast *Worksheet*

---

37   http://en.wikipedia.org/wiki/Table_of_permselectivity_for_different_substances. 0.330, Glucose Effective molecular Radius 0.440 Sucrose Effective Molecular Radius Effective molecular radius is the size a molecule displays in solution. 0.74 Angstroms is the size of diatomic hydrogen. One Angstrom is 1/10 of a nanometer

Using the assumed size for a molecule of sugar we have confirmed that the sugar molecules will occupy 10.92% per liter on a cubic basis and one half of that or 5.72 percent on a spherical basis of the 1,892 liter batch size (as specified in Table 65, *supra*). I am not qualified to determine if this is an accurate representation of what occurs at the molecular level. I was aware that biology is a busy place, but if my explanation is accurate, even to an order of magnitude, it is a far busier place than I ever imagined.

I am reminded of a Mr. Tomkins story that physicist and science writer George Gamow wrote about the activity level inside a cell. It is very vivid in describing just how hectic a cell really is. We think of them as just sitting there munching away like us but it is quite more active at the cellular level.[38]

Sugar Energy

One last set of calculations we can undertake involves quantifying the amount of energy that is liberated by metabolizing the sugar in our batch. Sticking with our 10% sugar batch we will use the same 209,786 grams of sugar as in the last section and apply a standard value of 3.87 kilocalories per gram of sugar. The results indicate that over three million BTU's are liberated by fermentation of the batch and that his energy averages 33,560 BTU's per hour over a ninety six (96) hour fermentation.

Sugar Energy	Yeast Scale	Human Scale	
Grams of Sugar in Batch	209,786	209,786	Grams of Sugar in Batch
Kilocalories per Gram	3.870	3.87	Kilocalories per Gram
Kilocalories in Batch	811,874	811,874	Kilocalories in Batch
		2,500	Calories per Human per Day
Kilocalories to Kilojoules	4.1868	324.7	Days of Human Nutrition
Kilojoules in Batch	3.4.E+06	0.89	Years of Human Nutrition
Kilojoules to KW.h	0.00027778	4.1868	Kilocalories to Kilojoules
Kw Hrs. in Batch	944.21	3.4.E+06	Kilojoules in Batch
Kw. Hrs. to BTU's	3,412.14	0.00027778	Kilojoules to KW.h
BTU's in Batch	3,221,775	944.21	Kw Hrs.
Hours of Fermentation	96.00	2.91	Kw Hr. per human per day
BTU's per Hr.	33,560.16	121.15	Avg. Watts per Hr. Bulb Equivalent
		3,412.14	Kw. Hr. to BTU's
Glucose Molecular Wt.	180.16	9,920.80	Avg. Human BTU's per Day
Moles of Sugar	1,164.45	413.37	Avg. Human BTU's per Hr. Equivalent
Avogadro's Constant	6.0221E+23	150.00	Avg. Human Wt. in Lbs.
Molecules of Sugar	7.01E+26	2.76	BTU's per Lb. per Hr.
Energy per completed reaction	**Calculated Values**	1.16E-18	Gram Calories per Molecule
Joules per molecule	4.847E-18	4.59E-21	BTU's per Molecule
Aerobic Fermentation Textbook Values		**Aerobic Fermentation Energy**	
Joules per Molecule of Glucose	4.5399E-18	2,734.00	kJ/mol Glucose
Total Joules	3.18E+09	1,164.45	Moles of Sugar
Tot. Kilojoules	3,183,584	3,183,594	Kilojoules
Kilowatt Hours	884.33	884.33	Kilowatt Hours
Kw. Hrs. to BTU's	3,412.14	3,412.14	Kw. Hrs. to BTU's
BTU's in Batch	3,017,456	3,017,464	BTU's in Batch
Joules per molecule Agreement	93.7%		
BTU's % Agreement	93.7%		

TABLE 71–2—Refer to Sugar Energy Worksheet

---

38   If we can define the average amount of heat generated by each reaction we could determine how much heat the vessel must radiate and compare that with experience to see if they matched.

The second column is a human scale comparison indicating that the sugar available in the batch would provide the energy required to feed a person for 324 days and that the average human generates about 413 BTU's per hour, or burns with the equivalent energy of a 121.15 watt incandescent light bulb (Table 71-2, previous page)

By taking the number of molecules and dividing by the kilojoules in the batch we can derive a value for joules per molecule for glucose. Comparing the calculated joules per molecule value to textbook values shows substantial agreement of 93.7 % in the value of energy that is liberated by aerobic metabolism and verifies our starting value of 3.87 kilocalories per gram.

The flaw in this approach is that not all fermentation that takes place in our batch is accomplished by aerobic metabolism. This is fortunate because 33,000 BTU's per hour is a lot of heat that would need to be removed from the batch and would require active cooling throughout the fermentation.

For much of the fermentation process the amount of carbon dioxide being released creates an anaerobic environment that suppresses bacteria growth. Anaerobic metabolism of glucose liberates far less energy than aerobic metabolism does, amounting to only 2.7% of the heat generated by aerobic means[39] (Table 71-3).

Anaerobic Fermentation Textbook Values		Anaerobic Fermentation Energy	
Joules per Molecule of Glucose	1.2354E-19	74.40	kJ/mol Glucose
Total Joules	8.66E+07	1,164.45	Moles of Sugar
Tot. Kilojoules	86,632	86,635	Kilojoules
Kilowatt Hours	24.06	24.07	Kilowatt Hours
Kw. Hrs. to BTU's	3,412.14	3,412.14	Kw. Hrs. to BTU's
BTU's in Batch	82,111	82,114	BTU's in Batch
Hours	96.00		
BTU's per Hour	855.3		
Aerobic BTU's in Batch	3,017,456		
Anaerobic BTU's in Batch	82,111		
Anerobic Energy % of Aerobic	2.72%		
Aerobic Metabolism %	10.0%		
Aerobic BTU's	301,746		
Anaerobic BTU's	8,211		
Total BTU's	309,957		
Hours	96.00		
BTU's per Hour	3,228.72		

TABLE 71-3—Refer to Sugar Energy Worksheet

If entirely anaerobic fermentation was occurring then the batch would only be radiating 855 BTU's per hour. This is also not the case. In cold weather the batch would not be able to maintain its temperature and would fall to close to ambient levels. This is clearly not the case. My batches stay warm, even get hot and occasionally need cooling to keep the yeast from becoming too stressed by the increased temperature.

Anaerobic fermentation is the most efficient means to produce ethanol and despite the lower energy released by this metabolic pathway is the preferred environment for our purposes.

---

39 The value of anaerobic fermentation energy is somewhat variable with a range of between 68 kj/mole to 101.43 kj/mol. Some sources indicate that 2,808 kj/mole is the aerobic energy released by aerobic fermentation. This value appears in the worksheet as well.

During fermentation the batch will actually roil slowly as carbon dioxide rising from the batch transports material up to the top where the bubbles escape and the material carried by them falls back down into the mixture. To some degree this allows atmospheric oxygen to come into contact with parts of the batch and by virtue of Henry's Law relating to the permeability of liquids to atmospheric gasses, some oxygen is introduced into the batch. There is a gradient in the batch with more oxygen in the upper regions of the tank and less in the bottom.

Since I have no way of actually measuring the oxygen content of my batch during fermentation all we can do is to assign a percentage to the aerobic metabolism and calculate the BTU's per hour from that assumed value. Assuming 10% of each type of reaction produces an average of 3,228 BTU's per hour of energy liberated. The percentage function is variable in the workbook and users can chose the values that best suit their experiences.

3.9 Carbon Dioxide Production

Fermentation releases a significant amount of carbon dioxide. The carbon footprint of fermentation is carbon neutral since it derives from corn grown in the biosphere and not from burning fossil fuels. Let's look at just how much carbon dioxide is created during a fermentation. We will resume using my standard batch values for volume, percent sugar and total sugar produced (473.81 kg, and 1,044.56 Lbs.) in order to calculate the reactions that will take place during fermentation.

Sugar Produced and Used in Reaction			
Gallons of Water	390.00		
Water Weight per US Gallon	8.328230		
Water Weight Lbs.	3,248.01		
Corn Weight Lbs.	1,500.00		
Total Batch Weight Lbs.	4,748.01		
Kilogram Converter	0.453592		
Kilograms	2,153.66		
Grams of Solution	2,153,660.97		
% Sugar in Solution	22.00%		
Grams of Sugar	473,805.41		
Kilograms of Sugar	473.81	1,500.00	Lbs. of Corn
Pounds Converter	2.20	72.00%	% Starch in Corn
Pounds Lbs. Avdp	1,044.56	1,080.00	Lbs. of Starch

TABLE 72—Refer to CO₂ Footprint Worksheet

We are going to start with my standard batch and my standard Brix of sugar produced. We will define 22° Bx as 22% (w/w), with 22 grams of sugar per 100 grams of solution (Table 72).

We can roughly check the amount of sugar in our batch by comparing to the standard starch percentage of corn. While the quantity of sugar is less than that of the amount calculated from the starch base alone the value is not off by a significant amount.

We will be restricted to using just glucose in this example. The formula for glucose is $C_6H_{12}O_6$ with a molar mass of 180.16 g/mol.

In chemical nomenclature the glucose molecule has the configuration shown in the figure (right).

The biochemical reaction which converts sugar to ethanol is

$$Yeast + C_6H_{12}O_6 = 2\ C_2H_5OH + 2\ CO_2$$
$$Glucose \qquad Ethanol$$

Checking this value shows the constituent parts of glucose and a molecular weight sum of 180 (Table 73, next page).

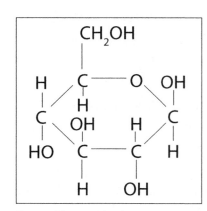

Figure 2: Glucose molecule.

Doing the same with carbon dioxide demonstrates its molecular weight of 44 (Table 74).

Atoms	Mass	Total	
6.00	12.00	72.00	Carbon
12.00	1.00	12.00	Hydrogen
6.00	16.00	96.00	Oxygen
		180.00	Total Molecular Wt.

TABLE 73—Refer to CO_2 Footprint Worksheet

Atoms	Mass	Total	
1.00	12.00	12.00	Carbon
2.00	16.00	32.00	Oxygen
		44.00	Total Molecular Wt.

TABLE 74—Refer to CO_2 Footprint Worksheet

Now we can calculate the amount of carbon dioxide produced by the batch if complete fermentation occurs (Table 75). Because of isotopes, the published molecular weight of sugar is 180.16 and that value is used in the worksheet.

Find Wt. of Fermentation products		
Kilograms of Sugar	473.81	
Grams of Sugar	473,805.41	
Sugar Molar Density (Weight per Mole)	180.16	Grams per Mole
Moles of Glucose	2,629.91	
Avogadro's Number per Mole	6.02E+23	
Total Molecular Units	1.58E+27	
Number of CO_2 Units per breakdown	2.00	Two Per Fermentation metabolism action
Total Co2 Molecules Possible	3.17E+27	If Complete Fermentation Occurs
Molar Weight of CO_2	44.00	Grams per Mole
Total Molar Weight	1.39E+29	Molecular Weight * Molecules produced
Avogadro's Number per Mole	6.02E+23	
Grams of CO_2	231,432.48	Total CO_2 Wt./Avogadro's Number
Kilograms of CO_2	231.43	
Pound Converter	2.20462	
Pounds of CO_2 Produced	510.22	
Net Batch Grams after Fermentation	4,237.79	

TABLE 75—Refer to CO_2 Footprint Worksheet

The result is that 510.22 lbs. of carbon dioxide is released. In large distilled spirit plants (DSPs) this carbon dioxide is captured and sold for carbonating beverages.

Because this mass of carbon dioxide leaves the batch as a gas, the fermented batch is lighter than it was in the beginning. If the batch was on load cells this would show up. It should also show in the amount of time it takes to heat the batch to boiling point for the stripping run. When conducting a stripping run and calculating the amount of time it will take to heat the batch to its vaporization point one should subtract the mass of carbon dioxide produced during the fermentation from the total batch weight. Because I add water to my fermentations to increase the water buffer available for the yeast I do not see a great difference in the amount of time it takes my batch to reach vaporization temperature.

3.10 Alcohol Produced

Now we will use the same general approach to determine the amount of alcohol (ethanol) produced by a fermentation; then we will total the products and see if it matches the batch totals.

The chemical formula for ethyl alcohol is C_2H_6O with a molecular weight of 46.07 grams per mole. Two molecules of alcohol are produced during the breakdown of sugar to alcohol for a total molecular weight of 92 per fermentation reaction (Table 76).

Atoms	Mass	Total	
2.00	12.00	24.00	Carbon
6.00	1.00	6.00	Hydrogen
1.00	16.00	16.00	Oxygen
		46.00	Total Molecular Wt.
		2.00	Molecules per Fermentation Reaction
		92.00	Total Molecular Wt.

TABLE 76—Refer to CO₂ Footprint Worksheet

Summing the reaction products balances with the input of 180 grams per mole (Table 77).

88.00	Carbon Dioxide Molecular Wt. per reaction
92.00	Alcohol Molecular Wt. per reaction
180.00	Total Wt. of By-products

TABLE 77—Refer to CO₂ Footprint Worksheet

Now we can calculate the amount of alcohol that can be produced by our starch and find the theoretical yield of absolute alcohol (200 proof) for the batch (Table 78).

Checking our calculations we find a close correlation between what we have calculated as a yield and the amount of starch initially employed (Table 79. **Tables 79–83 are on the next page**).

A second check beginning with the starch employed and subtracting the water and by-products yields satisfactory results as well (Table 80).

We can also calculate the theoretical yield based on Proof Gallons per bushel from our molecular analysis (Table 81).

Then we can compare that analysis to the industry goals for production found in *The Alcohol Textbook* 4th Edition (Table 82).

We see that the industry goals are reaching the limit of efficiency possible compared with our molecular yield calculations.

Finally, we can compare my experience of production and see how my fermentations compare to the industry standards (Table 83).

The Proof Gallons remaining in the still were calculated by proofing the remainder and gauging the volume in the still in gallons per inch of the

Find Wt. of Alcohol produced in Fermentation		
Molecules of Sugar Available for Fermentation		
Kilograms of Sugar	473.81	
Grams of Sugar	473,805.41	
Molar Density (Weight per Mole)	180.00	Grams per Mole
Moles of Glucose	2,632.25	
Avogadro's Number for Mole	6.02E+23	
Total Molecular Units	1.59E+27	
Number of Alcohol Units per breakdown	2.00	
Total Alcohol Molecules Possible	3.17E+27	
Molar Weight of Ethyl Alcohol	46.00	Grams per Mole
Total Molar Weight	1.46E+29	Molecular Weight * Molecules produced
Avogadro's Number for Mole	6.02E+23	
Grams of Ethyl Alcohol	242,167.21	Total Weight/ Avogadro's Number
Kilograms of Ethyl Alcohol	242.17	
Pound Converter	2.20462	
Pounds of Ethyl Alcohol	533.89	
Lbs. per Proof Gal. @ 200 Proof	3.3049	
Proof Gallon Theoretical Yield	161.55	
US Gal. of Absolute Alcohol Yeild	80.77	

TABLE 78—Refer to CO₂ Footprint Worksheet

Back Check	
Starting Grams	473,805
Co2 Grams	231,432
Ethyl Grams	242,167
Grams of Total Chemical By-products	473,600
Missing Grams	206
Missing Kilo's	0.21
Missing Lbs.	0.45

TABLE 79—Refer to CO_2 Footprint Worksheet

Back Check Through Weight	
Starch Employed	1,080.00
Water	3,248.01
Total Beginning Weight	4,328.01
Alcohol Weight	533.89
Carbon dioxide Weight	510.22
Total Reaction Products Weight	1,044.11
Water Weight Included	3,248.01
Sub total	4,292.12
Unaccounted for Wt.	35.89
% Wt. unaccounted for	0.8%

TABLE 80—Refer to CO_2 Footprint Worksheet

Calculate Theoretical yield in Proof Gallons per Bushel	
Corn Wt. Used	1,500.00
Lbs. per Bushel	56.00
Bushels of Corn	26.79
Theoretical yield Proof Gallons	161.55
Bushels / Proof Gal. = PG per Bushel	6.03
Divide by 2 for Anhydrous Absolute Alc. Per Bushel	3.02

TABLE 81—Refer to CO2 Footprint Worksheet

Industry Production Goals			
Proof Gal. per bushel of Corn Industry yield Fine Grind	5.70	2.85	Fluid Gal. Anhydrous Alcohol per Bushel w/fine Grind
Proof Gal. per bushel of Corn Industry yield w/ Coarse Grind	5.30	2.65	Fluid Gal. Anhydrous Alcohol per Bushel w/ Coarse Grind
Industry Goals % of Theoretical yield			
Find Grind	94.5%		
Coarse Grind	87.9%		

TABLE 82—Refer to CO2 Footprint Worksheet

Actual Experience of Recovery		
Proof Gallons Recovered in Barrels	109.00	
Proof Gallons Remaining in Still	20.00	
Total Proof Gallons Fermented	129.00	
Bushels Used	26.79	
Fermented Proof Gal. per Bushel	4.82	
Recovered Proof Gal. per Bushel	4.07	
Compared to Industry Goals Coarse Grind		
Efficiency of Fermentation	90.9%	Actual Proof Gallons/Industry Goals Proof Gallons
Efficiency of Recovery	76.8%	
Compared to Industry Goals Fine Grind		
Efficiency of Fermentation	79.85%	Actual Proof Gallons/Theoretical Proof Gallons
Efficiency of Recovery	67.47%	

TABLE 83—Refer to CO2 Footprint Worksheet

liquid in the still. The reason one does not recover 100% of the alcohol produced is that it is simply not energy efficient to drive off all the alcohol unless one is using a continuous process that never shuts off. For a small scale operation my fermentations and recovery are respectable if not outstanding.

3.11 Final Cooling Section

Returning to setting the batch for fermentation, we will look at the energy required to effect the temperature change. Staging your cooling is really a matter of deciding how long you want to stay in the shop that day. After I add the last dose of my glucoamylase sugar-making enzyme I allow the tank temperature to continue to fall naturally. At some point when I determine that I've made all the sugar I can at the operating temperature of the enzyme I will re-start the cooling water heat exchanger and begin taking heat out of the batch faster than natural processes would. If I have had a successful conversion of starch to sugar and the Brix and refractometer readings are both above 20% by weight, then it is time to start cooling as soon as possible. The enzymes in the batch will continue to be effective to convert the remaining starch to sugar, although operating more slowly, at lower temperatures.

Getting heat out of a batch is not quite as tough as getting it in to it but it still takes time. Cold weather is a help. Cold weather also means cold water in the pipes or in the ground to use as cooling water in a heat exchange system.

You want to get the temperature down under 100° F as quickly as possible because now you have a gigantic bowl of corn sugar that bacteria will eat as fast as they can. If you wait for nature to take its course and cool the batch from 149° F down to 100° F through radiation, conduction and convection to the atmosphere and ground, you might have to wait six hours or more. Bacteria can multiply at the rate of one division every half hour so six hours is enough time for twelve 30-minute bacteria life cycles. So for every 10 bacteria in the batch at the beginning of the cooling period, at the end of 6 hours one would find 10^{12} which is one trillion bacteria all munching happily away at your sugar.

Bacterial infection is a particular risk at temperatures below 140° F. We know this because pasteurization temperatures were originally in the neighborhood of 145° F, which was determined to be hot enough to kill bacteria and extend the shelf life of liquids but not so high as to change the taste or character of the underlying product.

People forget that Louis Pasteur originally developed his eponymous process for the purpose of keeping wine and mash from souring due to bacterial infections. Only later was it applied to milk. There is still a US FDA-legal alternative (typically for home pasteurization) to heat milk at 145° F (63° C) for 30 minutes. Modern commercial milk pasteurization typically finds the milk being heated to 161° F (71.7° C) for 15–20 seconds, or in ultra-high temperature processes to 275° F (135° C) for 1 second.

Unlike sterilization, pasteurization is not intended to kill all micro-organisms in the food. Instead pasteurization aims to reduce the number of viable pathogens to a low enough level that the product can be stored in a closed container for a reasonable period of time.

As to milk itself, the equipment that has been developed over the last century has enabled milk producers to implement high temperature short period processes and approach sterilization without changing the character of the milk.

For our purposes we know that any time the batch falls below the pasteurization temperature of 145° F then we are in danger of a bacterial infection. If the batch has a low pH this can inhibit but not stop the infection but I don't try to achieve a particularly low pH batch for the reasons outlined above. While backset stillage does have a low pH it will also generate bacteria at room temperature and this is why you do not want to let your backset stillage fall below pasteurization temperature before it is used. It should be kept hot or at least pasteurized before adding it to the next batch.

It is a fact that I can heat my batch faster than I can cool it. I can put more BTU's into it than I can take out in the same period of time. So while my temperature went up by 3/4 to 1° F a minute during the cooking phase, it will only fall at 0.5° F per minute during the cooling phase.

In the US the standard for measuring the ability to remove heat is referred to as a "ton" of cooling. This is an odd name for the value and like many English standards is confusing, similar to having fluid ounces and weight ounces. A ton of cooling is defined as 12,000 BTU's or British Thermal Units. The BTU is defined as the energy required to remove 1° F from one 16-ounce pound of water. So, one ton of cooling will reduce 12,000 lbs. of water by 1° F or 1,000 lbs. of water by 12° F. This is similar to the gram calorie or kilogram calorie which defines the temperature loss or gain in terms of the amount of energy to change the temperature of one gram or kilogram of water by 1° C. When adding a time unit to these values it is usually expressed in terms of energy transferred per hour. Since most of the world works in the metric system I've included conversions to kilowatt hours of energy required.

Making the value of 1,000 lbs. of water more meaningful shows an equivalent of 120 gallons changing temperature by 12° F (Table 84).

Turning the process around allows us to predict how many gallons of water will be affected by 1 ton of cooling (Table 85). Substituting your own numbers in the worksheet will allow you to predict how much cooling a given volume will require.

The reason the gallons of water are slightly over 120 is that our gallons are measured at 60° F and liters are measured at 4° C (39.2° F) which is the temperature at which water is densest.

Generally BTU's are referred to by the hour, but the unit itself is independent of time and so any time component can be associated with a BTU.

Not all BTU's are equal. Some water temperatures are slightly more receptive to temperature change than others. I have used "mean BTU's" for these calculations.

Predict effect of tons of cooling on mass of water	
Lbs. of Water	1,000.00
Water Wt. per Gal.	8.3282
Gal. at 60° F	120.07
Liters	454.53
Tons of Cooling	1.00
BTU's of Cooling	12,000.00
Degrees F Change	12.00

TABLE 84—Refer to BTU's Cool Worksheet

Predict effect of tons of cooling on gallons of water	
Gal. of Water	120.07
Water Wt. per Gal.	8.3282
Wt. of Water	999.97
Liters	454.51
Tons of Cooling	1.00
BTU's of Cooling	12,000.00
Degrees F Change	12.00

TABLE 85—Refer to BTU's Cool Worksheet

This discussion and the associated worksheet assumes that the specific heat of the corn and water mixture is the same as the specific heat as water itself. I have not been able to find any reliable data on the specific heat transfer rate of corn and so we will calculate our own value *infra*.

The following worksheet shows how many BTU's per hour are being transferred out of the batch by the cooling water, and it also includes the natural radiation of heat from the vessel itself. We are assuming water as our medium at the moment (Table 86, next page).

The cumulative effect is over 10.4 tons of cooling per hour delivered to the vessel. When measuring temperature decrease we are measuring the net effect and do not require an efficiency factor. If we are planning on installing a chiller unit to do the job we need to factor in an efficiency factor for the delivery of the cold water to the vessel. In that case, using an efficiency of 90% we would need to install a chiller rated at 11.57 tons of cooling per hour.

Measure Tons of Cooling		Predict Applied tons of cooling	
Degrees per Minute	0.50		
Gallons of Water	500.00		
Wt. per Gal	8.328230		
Total Wt.	4,164.12		
BTU's Needed for ° per Min.	2,082.06	**Predict Applied tons of cooling**	
BTU's Needed per Hour	124,923.45	11.57	Tons of Cooling Available
BTU's per "Ton" of Refrigeration	12,000.00	12,000.00	BTU's per Ton
BTU's required/ Tons Constant = Tons of Cooling	10.41	138,803.83	Total BTU's
		90.00%	Efficiency
Efficiency of Delivery	90.00%	124,923.45	Delivered BTU's
Scale up Value	1.111	13,880.38	Lost BTU's
Gross BTU's per Hr. Needed	138,803.83	1.16	Missing Tons of Cooling
Tons of Cooling Required	11.57	10.41	Applied tons of Cooling
BTU's to Kilogram Calories	0.2519958	0.2519958	BTU's to Kilogram Calories
Kilogram Calories Required	34,978	34,978	Kilogram Calories Required
Kilogram Cal. To Kw Hrs.	0.00116	0.00116	Kilogram Cal. To Kw Hrs.
Kilowatt Hours Required	40.68	40.68	Kilowatt Hours Required

TABLE 86—Refer to Degrees per Minute Worksheet

To digress slightly, the same holds true for heating a mixture. Boiler horsepower is rated at 33,475 BTU's per hour per boiler horsepower. The boiler's rated capacity must be adjusted to find the number of BTU's it will actually transfer to the destination (Table 87).

Measure Boiler Hp. Required	Scale Up	Predict Applied Boiler Horsepower	
Boiler Horsepower BTU's per Hour	33,475.00	4.15	Boiler Horsepower
Boiler Size in Boiler Horsepower	3.73	33,475.00	BTU's per Bhp.
Efficiency of Delivery	90.00%	138,803.83	Total BTU's
Scale up Value	1.111	90.00%	Efficiency of Delivery
Gross BTU's per Hr. Needed	138,803.83	124,923.45	Delivered BTU's
Boiler Horsepower Required	4.15	13,880.38	Lost BTU's
Increase in Boiler Horsepower (Bhp.)	0.41	0.41	Missing Bhp.
BTU's to Kilogram Calories	0.2519958	0.2519958	BTU's to Kilogram Calories
Kilogram Calories Required	34,978	34,978	Kilogram Calories Required
Kilogram Cal. To Kw Hrs.	0.00116	0.00116	Kilogram Cal. To Kw Hrs.
Kilowatt Hours Required	40.68	40.68	Kilowatt Hours Required

TABLE 87—Refer to Degrees per Minute Worksheet

In this case the original 125K BTU's required to heat the mixture at 0.5° per minute will require 3.73 boiler horsepower. Delivering those BTU's to the boiler will require an additional 1.11 boiler horsepower for a total of 4.15 boiler horsepower. The worksheet is also set up to run the equation in reverse to predict the amount of loss one will experience at any efficiency. On the cooling side we benefit from the fact that natural radiation from the vessel will assist us in cooling the vessel.

On the heating side we will not benefit from natural radiation from the vessel but it will in fact be a drag on our ability to heat it. Subsequently we will calculate this additional factor.

Returning to cooling the mash down to a temperature where we will be able to add our yeast to it, the temperature range we are concerned with is from 145° F to 95° F. At 0.5° F per minute it will take 100 minutes to cool. The reason I say 95° F is because that is the maximum temperature I feel comfortable adding my yeast to the batch.

Also, after we add the yeast we can top off the tank with cool unchlorinated water and it will quickly result in another 4° F fall in the temperature and reduce the temperature into the yeast's prime operating temperature range. When we add our water one must leave some freeboard because the yeast will start their metabolism vigorously and bubble up over the sides, but generally we can add 40 gallons or so of cold water at the end of the cooking process. Try not to use chlorinated water. Let it stand for a day or so before use to reduce the antimicrobial effects of the chlorine.

The second temperature is the final temperature at which we will cease cooling. For me that temperature is usually 84 to 86° F. The reason for the difference between the setting temperature and the yeast addition temperature is the discrepancy between what the yeast can tolerate for life and what their preferred metabolic temperature is. We must put our yeast to work as soon as possible in order to compete against the bacteria that are already multiplying in our mash so we add them at the highest safe temperature we can. Then we continue cooling down to the batch set temperature. Because, if we set the batch too hot, say 94° F, the yeast will add substantial heat by virtue of their metabolic processes and quickly kill themselves by generating too much heat for them to live. Particularly in the spring or summer you will find your batch creeping up past 92° F fermentation temperatures where the yeast will begin to become temperature stressed and start to metabolize different compounds other than alcohol in higher proportions. In these cases you must start the heat exchanger and take some heat out of the batch and bring it down to 88° F or so. If you cool the batch too much you can actually slow down the fermentation too much and the batch will never again reach its prime fermentation temperature. You just want to knock the temperature back a little, not put the batch to sleep. Throughout the entire fermentation process, but particularly in the first 48 to 72 hours, we must make sure that the batch does not overheat and cool it as necessary.

As the tank cools down you will find that the temperature gradient between the top and bottom of the tank reduces to less than 7° F. This gradient will show up again during fermentation but for now it is not a problem for you or the yeast.

So, once the top temperature at the top of the batch falls to 95° we can add in our yeast; at this point the bottom temperature will be about 7° F cooler, or around 88° F. According to the yeast manufacturer you can apply it at any temperature under 105° F but I don't add it at that high a temperature. We want to get the yeast into the batch as soon as possible but not push the yeast too hard. Therefore I choose between 100° F and 95° F as measured at the top of the tank. The bottom will always be cooler than that because of the temperature gradient in the tank.

When you pitch in your yeast you want to slow down your agitation. Don't beat your yeast to death by mixing them in too hard.

One other way to look at the energy required to cool the batch is to look at the total BTU's required to accomplish the change (18.4 tons, Table 88).

Find Gross Tons of cooling required to cool a mixture	
Gallons of water to change temp.	350.00
Weight per Gallon of Water	8.32823
Gal. * Lbs. per Gal. = H₂O Lbs. to change Temp.	2,914.9
Solids in Water - Corn Added to Mash	1,500.0
Total Pounds in mixture	4,415
Starting Temperature	145.00
Desired Ending Temperature	95.00
Temperature Difference	-50.00
Absolute Value of Temperature Difference	50.00
Pounds * Temp Dif.= BTU's required to Cool	220,744
Tons of Refrigeration required	
Total BTU's restated	220,744
Ton of Refrigeration Constant in BTU's	12,000
BTU's required/ Tons Constant = Tons of Cooling	18.40

TABLE 88—Refer to BTU's Cool Worksheet

Avg. Degrees F per Min.	0.50
Total Estimated Min.	100.00
BTU's per Minute	2,207
BTU's per Hour	132,446
Ton of Refrigeration Constant in BTU's	12,000
Ton's per Hour Required	11.04
Hours Required	1.67

TABLE 89—Refer to BTU's Cool Worksheet

Again, the reason we are using 350 gallons of water rather than 390 is that this cooling takes place before I add the last 40 gallons of water to the batch when I pitch in my yeast and water slurry.

If you want the batch to cool at 1/2 a degree F per minute it will take 100 minutes to cool it by the 50° required (Table 89).

Not all of this energy will have to come from our cooling water. We will attempt to account for radiation by finding the difference between what the water accomplishes and the remainder of the temperature change.

To find the amount of radiative cooling I measured how long it took to cool the batch with the equipment and water flow I had. By measuring the difference in time it took to do the job and the predicted time, I could infer the radiative energy of the tank over this temperature range from 145° F to 95° F (Table 90).

Cooling Water Heat Absorbing Capacity	
Water input Temperature	50.00
Water Output Temperature	95.00
Temperature Change	45.00
Absolute Value of Temperature Change	45.00
Weight per Gallon used as BTU's per ° of Change	8.32823
° of Change * Wt.per Gal.= Tot.BTU change per min	374.77
Gallon per Minute Flow	4.30
Total BTU's per minute	1,611.51
BTU's per Hour	96,691
Tons of Cooling per Hour	8.06
With Gal. Flow Predicted Min. to Cool Batch	136.98
Hours to Cool Batch	2.28
Actual Min. Required	105.00
Minutes Dif.	31.98
Hours Dif.	0.53
BTU's per Min.	1,611.51
Radiative BTU's	51,535
% Radiated BTU's	23.3%

TABLE 90—Refer to BTU's Cool Worksheet

Water Flow Through Condenser			
Find Water Flow per Min.			
Minutes	3.00	2.50	Minutes
Gallons	10.00	10.00	Gallons
Gal. per. Min	3.33	4.00	Gal. per. Min
Min per Hr.	60	60	Min per Hr.
Gal. per Hr.	200	240.00	Gal. per Hr.
Cost per Gal	$0.01	$0.01	Cost per Gal
Cost per Hr.	$2.00	$2.40	Cost per Hr.
		17%	% Change

TABLE 91—Refer to BTU's Cool Worksheet

What we see from this worksheet is that it took 32 minutes less time to cool the batch than the predicted time to do so and that the heat radiated was about 23% of the total.

I want to talk for a moment about how to run water through the heat exchanger. You want to get as much heat out of the batch for each gallon that is run through the heat exchanger. You don't want to just force water through as fast as possible. You want a flow rate that allows the water to pick up as much heat as possible while it is in the heat exchanger. If the temperature of the outflow is within 5 to 10 degrees of the bottom of the tank then you are probably picking up enough heat. At first you can run the water through at full flow without a problem but as the cooling progresses you can reduce the flow rate and use less water.

The following worksheet shows how one can calculate the cost savings associated with slowing down the rate of water flowing through the cooling coils. From this one can get a feel for cost vs. time efficiency in determining how fast to run water through the coils (Table 91, previous page).

Rounding out the BTU's to cool worksheet is a calculator which will allow one to predict how long it will take to reduce the temperature of a batch based on the tons of cooling available. In this worksheet we are including the weight of corn in the total mass and making the assumption that the corn will give up its heat the same as water does. This is not entirely accurate and we will address that particular issue a little later on (Table 92).

This worksheet allows one to include that parameter which is set tentatively at 23%. With five tons of cooling available and allowing for 23% additional heat loss through radiation, it will take 2.98 hours to reduce the temperature from 145 to 95 degrees. I ran into this problem because I bought a 5-ton chiller to do a 10-ton job, and three hours is about how long it took. The hot mash just overwhelmed that small chiller, even with a 55-gallon drum of cold water as a reservoir. After many attempts to get it to work, I had to go back to using city water as my cooling water source. Using city water allowed me to reduce the time it took to cool the batch down as well. I was using a lot of electricity to run that chiller unit and it turned out that the cost was the same for the electricity or the water, and the water was more effective. The

Tons of Refrigeration to Job Time Calculator	
Tons of Refrigeration Per Hour available	5.00
Gallons of water to change temp.	350.00
Weight per Gallon of Water	8.32823
Gal. * Lbs. per Gal. = Lbs. to change temperature	2,914.88
Solids in Water - Corn Added to Mash or other solids	1,500.00
Total Pounds in mixture	4,414.88
Starting Temperature	145.00
Desired Ending Temperature	95.00
Temperature Difference	50.00
Pounds * Temp Dif.= BTU's required	220,744.03
BTU Equivalent of Refrigeration Tons Restated	60,000.00
Efficiency of Deivery	95.00%
Net BTU's Available to Cool	57,000.00
BTU's Required/ BTU's delivered per Hr. = Hrs.	3.87
Percentage lost through Radiation	23.0%
Hours saved via heat radiated	0.89
Net Hours required to cool the mixture	2.98
Minutes	178.92

TABLE 92—Refer to BTU's Cool Worksheet

A five ton chiller to do a ten ton job.

Left: a close-up view of the two circulating pumps. Right: looking down into the evaporator.

Cooling Costs	
Gallon per Minute Flow	4.29
Minutes of Cooling	115.00
Total Gallons	493.35
Cost per Gallon	$0.01
Total Cost per Batch	$4.93
Batches per Month	4.00
Total Gallons	1,973.40
Total Costs	$19.73

TABLE 93—Refer to BTU's Cool Worksheet

only drawback is that if you cook in the summertime, the city water around my shop is about 72° F, and you don't get as much bang for the buck out of your cooling water. In the winter it is as low as 42° F which cuts down on the amount of water one has to use.

The last item we want to try to quantify is how much it is costing us to cool the batch and how we calculate what our water requirements are. My city water costs about 1 penny per gallon (Table 93).

3.12 BTU's Cool 2

Table 94 shows how many BTU's are required to cool our batch from 145° F down to 95° F.

	Water & Solids	Water Only	PF Corn Mash
Gallons of Fluid to change temp.	350.00	500.00	350.00
Weight per Gallon of Water (or Mash)	8.32823	8.32823	8.32823
Gal. * Lbs. per Gal. = H$_2$O Lbs. to change temp.	2,914.88	4,164.12	2,914.88
Solids in Water - Corn Added to Mash	1,500.00	0.00	1,500.00
Total Pounds in mixture	4,414.88	4,164.12	4,414.88
Starting Temperature	145.00	145.00	145.00
Ending Temperature	95.00	95.00	95.00
Temperature Difference	-50.00	-50.00	-50.00
Absolute Value of Temperature Difference	50.00	50.00	50.00
BTU's per Lb. to Change Temp (PF Constant)	1.00	1.00	1.080
Temp Dif. * BTU's per Lb. = Tot. BTU's per Lb.	50.00	208,205.75	54.00
Lbs. * BTU's per Lb. Value = Total BTU's	220,744.03		238,403.55

TABLE 94—Refer to BTU's Cool 2 Worksheet

This worksheet shows three methods of calculating the BTU's required to cool the batch. The first method assumes that the weight of the corn is included and added to the weight of the water to find the total batch weight. This assumes that the specific heat of corn is the same as that of water. Specific heat, or heat capacity, is the amount of energy required to change the temperature of a substance. As an example, it takes less energy to heat an aluminum pan to a given temperature than it does a cast iron skillet. The aluminum simply takes heat faster than the iron does. Conversely, it also radiates heat faster.

The second method assumes that the entire volume of the batch is water. In my experience this is not the correct way to gauge the energy required to heat or cool a corn and water mixture.

The third method uses a constant that I have developed regarding the specific heat of heating corn and water mixtures at the density that I cook with (1.08 BTU's per lb.). I have some data that indicates that it requires more energy to heat and cool a mixture of corn mash than it does to change the temperature of just the water and solids. It is not firm enough to base any conclusions on, but I have included it here as a tentative value.

I have not been able to find any data on the specific heat of corn or any vegetable substance other than wood, and wood is not a good comparison medium. Accordingly, I have left the BTU's per pound value as a variable in the *Distilling Manual* workbook.

What I can be certain of is that all the mass must be accounted for and using solely water applied to volume is not the correct method.

In order to get some sense of the amount of heat that is radiated from the cooking vessel I measured the temperature decrease on different occasions first, after I stopped my cooking and while I was re-configuring my heating coils to serve as cooling coils and subsequently by simply stopping the cooling process and recording the temperature fall over time (Table 95).

Calculate Radiative Cooling from Vessel over Time					
Starting Temperature	205.00	195.00	186.00	180.00	170.00
Time Elapsed (Minutes)	60.00	60.00	60.00	60.00	60.00
Ending Tank Temp	190.00	182.00	175.00	170.00	162.00
Absolute Value of Temperature Difference	15.00	13.00	11.00	10.00	8.00
°F per minute of change	0.25	0.22	0.18	0.17	0.13
Total Pounds in mixture Restated	4,414.88	4,414.88	4,414.88	4,414.88	4,414.88
BTU's per Lb. to Change Temp	1.00000	1.00000	1.00000	1.00000	1.00000
Total BTU's Radiated In Time	66,223.21	57,393.45	48,564	44,148.81	35,319.04
Ton of Refrigeration BTU's per Hr.	12,000.00	12,000.00	12,000.00	12,000.00	12,000.00
Total Tons of Radiative Cooling in Time	5.52	4.78	4.05	3.68	2.94
BTU's per Minute	1,103.72	956.56	809.39	735.81	588.65
BTU's per Boiler Hp.	33,475	33,475	33,475	33,475	33,475
Boiler Hp Equivalent of Radiative cooling	1.98	1.71	1.45	1.32	1.06
Terminal Temperature °F	90	90	90	90	90
Degrees from Terminal Temp	115	105	96	90	80
Total Energy to be removed	507,711	463,562	423,829	397,339	353,190
% of Radiated energy to total energy	13.04%	12.38%	11.46%	11.11%	10.00%

TABLE 95—Refer to BTU's Cool 2 Worksheet

The interesting part of this worksheet is that by translating the radiative BTU's to boiler horsepower one can see the radiative drag on trying to heat the batch during the last portion of the cooking phase (1.98 Boiler Hp., Column 1). The boiler must overcome this heat loss in order to raise the temperature at all. As you can see the radiative drag decreases with falling temperature as reflected in the tons of cooling equivalent at the declining temperatures (Columns 2–5).

I don't have much data on letting a batch under 145° F stand for an hour because the main goal at that point in the cooking run is to get the batch down under 95° F as fast as possible to avoid bacterial infection of the batch. Here is the one measurement I made (Table 96), resulting in 0.659 Boiler Hp. per hour of energy radiated.

Starting Temperature	145.00
Time Elapsed (Minutes)	60.00
Ending Temperature	140.00
Absolute Value of Temperature Difference	5.00
°F per minute of change	0.08
Total Pounds in mixture Restated	4,414.88
BTU's per Lb. to Change Temp	1.00000
Total BTU' Radiated	22,074.40
Ton of Refrigeration Constant in BTU's per Hr.	12,000.00
Total Tons of Radiative Cooling in Time	1.84
Hours of Cooling	1.00
Tons of Radiative Cooling per Hour	1.84
Boiler Horsepower of heat radiated	0.659

TABLE 96—Refer to BTU's Cool 2 Worksheet

The percent of energy radiated (13.04% in Table 95 above) is with respect to the total energy to be removed based on the mass and total degrees to be changed. This is not a measure of the radiated energy which we previously calculated at 23% in Table 90.

With respect to all these measurements I should have taken note of the ambient air temperature in the shop. Generally it is between 50 and 60° F in the shop when we are doing this work. If it is cold outside I will open up the doors and let in as much air as possible. I generally don't cook in hot weather because I don't want to ferment in hot weather. A large distillery in Virginia (A. Smith Bowman) whose staff served as my mentors actually shut their fermenting operations down in August because it was just too hot for the fermentations to run without constantly cooling them down and it was simply not cost effective to do it when cooler weather was coming in September.

One way to look at the increasing difficulty of taking heat out of the vessel as the temperature falls is to compare different output temperatures based on the same water temperature inputs (Table 97).

Cooling Water Heat Absorbing Capacity						
Average Tank Temp ° F	180	150	130	100		
Water input Temperature	60.00	60.00	60.00	60.00		
Time Unit in Minutes	30.00	30.00	30.00	30.00	120.00	Total Minutes
Average Water Output Temp.	150.00	120.00	100.00	80.00		
Temperature Change	90.00	60.00	40.00	20.00		
Absolute Value of Temperature Change	90.00	60.00	40.00	20.00		
BTU's per Lb. to Change Temp	1.00000	1.00000	1.00000	1.00000		
Weight per Gallon used as BTU's per ° of Change	8.32823	8.32823	8.32823	8.32823		
Temp Change * Wt. per Gal. = Tot. BTU change per min. Per Gal.	749.54	499.69	333.13	166.56		
Gallon per Minute Flow	4.29	4.29	4.29	4.29	514.80	Total Water Flow (Gal.)
Total BTU's per minute	3,215.53	2,143.69	1,429.12	714.56		
Time in Hours	0.50	0.50	0.50	0.50		
BTU's in Time	96,465.89	64,310.59	42,873.73	21,436.86	225,087	Total BTU's
Tons of Cooling in Time	8.04	5.36	3.57	1.79	18.76	Total Tons
If Left at that temp Dif for 1 Hour						
BTU's per Hour	192,931.78	128,621.18	85,747.46	42,873.73		
Ton of Refrigeration Constant in BTU's per Hr.	12,000.00	12,000.00	12,000.00	12,000.00		
Tons per Hr. Equivalent	16.08	10.72	7.15	3.57		

TABLE 97—Refer to BTU's Cool 2 Worksheet

This worksheet shows that as temperature falls we are taking less heat out of the batch despite using the same number of gallons of water flowing through the cooling pipes and also that the cooling water is not reaching the temperature of the mash in the tank before it is exiting. Slowing down the water would allow it to pick up more heat and use less water.

In terms of cost we find the following (Table 98):

Gallon per Minute Flow	4.29
Minutes of Cooling	120.00
Total Gallons	514.80
Cost per Gallon	$0.01
Total Cost per Batch	$5.15
Gal. per Hr.	257.4
Cost per Gal	$0.01
Cost per Hr.	$2.57

TABLE 98—Refer to BTU's Cool 2 Worksheet

Another way we can look at the problem is to use the tons of cooling available to calculate how long it will take to cool the mash down and to try to account for the help that natural radiation from the mash tank will assist in the process (Table 99).

Assuming 95% efficiency for the cooling unit transferring cold water to the tank, the advantage gained by radiation is 0.86 hours of cooling time that is saved.

Find Time to Cool with Equipment Available	
Tons of Refrigeration per Hour Available	5.00
Ton of Refrigeration in BTU's per Hr.	12,000.00
Total BTU's per Hour Available	60,000.00
Total BTU's Restated	220,744.03
Total BTU's/BTU's per Hour = Hrs. to change temp.	3.68
BTU's needed/Net Tons = Tot. Ton Hrs. of Cooling	18.40
Add Transfer Efficiency parameter	
Efficiency of Cooling	95.0%
Net BTU's Available	57,000
Tons Available * % = Net Tons of cooling	4.75
Net BTU's of Cooling	11,400.00
BTU's needed/Net Tons = Tot. Ton Hrs. of Cooling	19.36
Hours to change Temp	3.87
Restated as Minutes to change Temp	232.36
Recalculate Time and Tons of Cooling Needed	
Net Applied Total Tons per Hour Restated	4.75
Tons of Radiative Cooling per Hr. Restated	1.84
Total Tons per Hour Available	6.59
Total BTU's transferred per hour	79,074.40
Total BTU's to be transferred Restated	238,403.55
Total Hours to transfer energy	3.01
Initial Total Time required	3.87
Time saved by radiative cooling (Hrs.)	0.86

TABLE 99—Refer to BTU's Cool 2 Worksheet

The last calculation in this worksheet allows one to define the time and the BTU's required and then calculate the tons of cooling required to accomplish the job in that time frame (Table 100).

Find Tons of Refrigeration required to do job in X Hrs.	
Hours To Cool	2.00
Total BTU's restated	220,744.03
BTU's per Hr. Required	110,372.01
Ton of Refrigeration Constant in BTU's	12,000.00
BTU's required/ Tons Constant = Tons of Cooling per time unit entered	9.20

TABLE 100—Refer to BTU's Cool 2 Worksheet

Heat Exchanger Explanation

The following pictures are more closely related to my still than cooling a batch but the similar principals apply to both. With the chiller, one wants to pump from the bottom of the barrel and have the hot water return into the top to flow down past the evaporator. With the condenser for the still, one wants to keep the bottom of the condenser barrel cold and take the hot water off the top.

The pictures show how I took two hot water heater coils and adapted them to serve as cooling coils in a closed circuit heat exchanger for my still. Cold city water or chilled water flows to the bottom of the tightly wound coils where it picks up heat from the condenser barrel on its back to the top. The water in the condenser barrel simply transfers heat from the still coil to the cooling-water-filled coils. When condensing alcohol, one wants the cold water at the bottom of the barrel, not the top. So filling from the top is not the most water-efficient way to condense the alcohol. One way to overcome this problem would be to direct cold water to the bottom of the barrel but then one has the problem of hot water flowing out over the top. With this system one can pipe the cold water to the bottom of the coils, have it wind its way to the top and then exit as hot water. By using a water meter to observe the input flow, one can dial in the minimum amount of water necessary to keep the output temperature of the water below about 105° F. Even with this output temperature there will be a strong temperature gradient in the barrel and the bottom of the barrel will stay at or near the input temperature of the water.

CHAPTER 4 Energy and Efficiency

4.1 Combustion and Energy Transfer Efficiency ─────────────

Most appliances will state their efficiency of combustion somewhere in their documentation and on the machine itself. That value is determined by using a new unit under ideal circumstances that are rarely encountered in practice. Burner nozzles accumulate a varnish that reduces the orifice diameter and thus reduce the flow rate or just clog up entirely with stray particles in gas or pipes.

Over time ash accumulates on the boiler tubes, and this reduces the ability of the burned gasses to efficiently transfer heat energy to them. Chimneys also accumulate ash which prevents sufficient air flow through the system to achieve the most efficient burning. With all these uncertainties, that all reduce efficiency, one should be conservative about estimating the total heating capacity of any boilers or furnace acquired.

Once acquired it is easy to assess the heating value of equipment by doing timed runs of the equipment's ability to change the temperature of water or mash. In my practice, the results are usually disappointing because I've rarely achieved the power I had intended. However, taking data from timed runs and working out the power does allow a true efficiency to be established. Applying some reasonable efficiency assumptions about the applied energy will allow us to make predictive combustion calculations with some degree of certainty.

In addition to the efficiency of generating our heat in the boiler, we will need to add a parameter for how much energy is lost in transferring it through the pipes and into the vessel. This can be determined by measuring the temperature of the pipes at the boiler outlet and downstream at the point where the hot water is delivered to the tank. When making these measurements one should not measure the received temperature directly at the still interface. One must take the measurement six inches or a foot before the connection to the still itself. This is because the thermal mass of the still is at a much lower temperature than the pipes and one is trying to measure the pipe temperature and not the still temperature.

The pipes from my two boilers turned out to be longer than I wanted them to be given the proximity of my boilers to the still. The boilers are only six and ten feet respectively from the still but it turned out that I could not plumb them by the most direct route because of other equipment and uses of the space and because the pipes would be so hot one could not safely work around them. Because of these factors I had to run them along the wall and over to the still, and they turned out to be 22-feet long.

Because of the longer pipes I was losing a lot of heat energy in the transfer process. If the boiler was running at 200° F the temperature when entering the still was only 190° F. That was a 5% loss. So, I had to go back and buy a good deal of insulation and wrap all the pipes to reduce the loss of heat. After this remediation the loss rate was 5° F and was 2.5% of the total.

However, roughly the same 10° F difference still showed up when the boiler was operating at high temperatures from 180 to 200 degrees. Therefore the percentage loss was also varying from 2.5% to 5%. That put me in a pickle. The only thing to do was to average the loss percent before I applied it. The average is 3.75% and so the transfer efficiency averages 96.25% (Table 101).

Transfer Efficiency	
Degrees Start	5.0
Degrees Remediated	2.5
Total	7.5
Average Degrees	3.75
Average Efficiency	96.25

TABLE 101—Refer to Boiler Test Summary Worksheet

My natural gas boiler came with some documentation and tags on it that indicated it operated at an efficiency of 72.50% and I have used that value for it. With respect to the burning efficiency of my oil boiler, it came with no documentation on that point and I had to work backwards, as usual, from the actual measured heating capacity to the efficiency of combustion as we will see shortly.

Oil storage (left), natural gas boiler (center), oil boiler (right).

4.2 Energy Required to Heat Batch

I want to take a minute and talk about the energy required to heat the mash in a little more detail.

Table 102 (next page) demonstrates three different ways to determine how much heat I need to generate in order to cook my batch. The first method proceeds entirely from the mass of material added to the batch (water & solids) and assumes a heat input of 1.0 BTU's per pound for the entire mass.

The second method treats the batch a being comprised entirely of water occupying approximately the same volume of 460 gallons as the mass of water and solids. The third method modifies the water and solids method by assigning a value of 1.085 BTU's per pound value.

For the water and solids analysis we are using 350 gallons of water because that is the amount of water in use during the cooking phase, the cooked corn slurry is then diluted with 40 gallons of water and yeast slurry for the fermentation for a total of 390 gallons. The total batch is 500 gallons. For the water analysis we are subtracting the 40 gallons from the 500 total and heating just 460 gallons of water because that is the volume of the amount of solids and water amount being heated during the cooking phase before the addition of about 40 gallons of water at the end of the cooling phase.

Looking at the water only column of table 102 we see that if one heats 460 gallons of water it will require 616.7K BTU's to change effect the change from 44 to 205° F. Looking at column 1, we see that if one heats water and solids and treats the solids as if they were water it will require 710.7 K BTU's to effect the same temperature change.

Lbs. Dif.	583.89
Lbs. per Gal H₂0	8.32823
Gal. Equivalent of Lbs.	70.11
Total Gallons	460.00
Density increase %	15.2%

TABLE 103—Refer to BTU's to Heat Worksheet

Turning to Table 103 (left), we see that the corn is dissolved in the mixture to the extent of 70 gallons. This makes the density per unit of volume denser than that of water by 15.2%; although we compensate for this to some degree by including the weight itself in our total to which we apply BTU's per lb.

The difference in batch weight between water and the water and corn mixture is almost 584 lbs. One must treat the mass of the solids in the water as a participant in the heating process (Table 103).

	Water & Solids	Water Only	PF Corn Mash
Gallons of Fluid to change temp.	350.00	460.00	350.00
Weight per Gallon of Water (or Mash)	8.32823	8.32823	8.32823
Gal. * Lbs. per Gal. = H₂O Lbs. to change temp.	2,914.88	3,830.99	2,914.88
Solids in Water - Corn	1,500.00	0.00	1,500.00
Total Pounds in mixture	4,414.88	3,830.99	4,414.88
Starting Temperature	44.00	44.00	44.00
Ending Temperature	205.00	205.00	205.00
Temperature Difference	161.00	161.00	161.00
Absolute Value of Temperature Difference	161.00	161.00	161.00
BTU's per Lb. to Change Temp	1.000	1.000	1.085
Temp Dif. * BTU's per Lb. = Tot. BTU's per Lb.	161.00	161.00	174.63
Lbs. * BTU's per Lb. Value = Total BTU's	710,795.76	616,788.71	770,954.17
BTU's per Boiler Horsepower	33,475	33,475	33,475
Total Boiler Horsepower Required	21.23	18.43	23.03
Desired Cooking Time (Hrs.)	3.50	3.50	3.50
BTU's Per Hour Required	203,084.5	176,225.3	220,272.6
Applied Boiler Horsepower per Hr. Required	6.07	5.26	6.58
Boiler Transfer Efficiency	96.25%	96.25%	96.25%
Scale Up Value	1.039	1.039	1.039
Scaled up BTU's	210,996.9	183,091.3	228,854.7
Boiler Heat Generation Efficiency	72.5%	72.5%	72.5%
Scale Up Value	1.379	1.379	1.379
Scaled up BTU's per hour required	291,030.2	252,539.7	315,661.6
Boiler Hp Required	8.69	7.54	9.43

TABLE 102—Refer to BTU's to Heat *Worksheet*

There is something about cooking corn mash that requires more energy than the standard 1.0 BTU's per pound value. The mixture goes through a phase during cooking when it is very thick, and the energy transfer is impeded. One could say that the system efficiency of delivery has gone down or one could assume that the BTU's per lb. have changed because of the increased density per unit volume or simply that the mixture is passing through a phase were the resistance to temperature change has gone up. This condition seems to be confined to the portion of the cooking process where the batch is in its thickest state. Once the liquefying enzymes have done their work and the batch thins out the rate of temperature rise appears to increase; although this does not affect the overall density, at some point the solids do sink to the bottom of the batch and the fermented mixture is more like water than cooked oatmeal.

Using the ratio between corn and water and corn and solids as a reference, and by another method I will describe shortly, I have derived a value of BTU's per Mash Pound that reflects the amount of energy I find to be necessary to heat a mixture of corn and water mash at the density I work with. Using this value which is about 8.5% greater than that required for water, or 1.085 BTU's per pound, we find that a total of 770.9K BTU's are required at the mash density that I use for my standard batch, which is 14.5 gallon beer, which is a very dense mash. Thinner mashes would have a lower value for the constant I have derived.

I will cautiously be applying this derived value in subsequent worksheets but I will continue to research the specific heat of corn and water mixtures. One could weigh the weight of mash per gallon and use that value but it still assumes the specific heat of corn is 1.0.

The heat required to change the temperature of the batch is only the starting point. It is necessary to scale up that energy to arrive at the size of the equipment you will need in order to actually deliver that amount of heat to the mixture. I have included these calculations in this worksheet and we will discuss them more fully further on.

4.3 Boiler Test

The simplest way to test your boilers is to do a timed run with water and take the starting, intermediate and ending temperatures (Table 104).

Boiler Efficiency Test and Calculations				
Gallons of Water	400.0			
Weight per Gallon of Water	8.328			
Total Weight of Water	3,331.3			
	Water Temp in ° F.	Min. Boiler Run Time	° F. Temp Change	° F. Change per min.
	71.0	0.0		
	149.0	60.0	78.0	1.30
	198.0	60.0	49.0	0.82
Total ° F. of Temp Change	127.0	120.0	Total Min.	
Avg. temp change per min.	1.06			
Find BTU's Transferred				
BTU per lb. of Water	1.0			
BTU's per degree per Gal. of Water	8.328			
Gal.* BTU's per ° F. = Batch BTU per ° F.	3,331.3			
Total ° F. of Temp Change	127.0			
BTU per ° * Degrees = Tot. BTU	423,074			
Hours of Boiler Run Time	2.000			
Total BTU's/ Hours = BTU's per Hour	211,537			
Delivered BTU's after loss of energy due to boiler efficiency and heat exchange loss accounted for.				
BTU's per Hour per Boiler Hp.	33,475.00			
BTU per Hr. / BTU per Boiler HP = Boiler Hp. Per Hr.	6.32			

TABLE 104—Refer to Boiler Test Worksheet

The interesting part of this worksheet is that one can observe the decrease in effective heat transfer as the vessel becomes hotter since the same boiler input is resulting in fewer degrees per minute of change as the water temperature increases. Because the medium being heated is water we can apply our standard 1.0 BTU's per lb. with confidence and this is a direct test of the delivered boiler horsepower to the vessel.

This test was made from a cold start and very little agitation to assist in transferring energy from the coils to the water. This test mimics what occurs during a stripping run or double run when it is not possible to agitate the mixture during the process. Agitating the water does increase the effectiveness of heat transfer and draw more heat from the boiler. To some degree this does allow the boilers to burn more efficiently and generate more energy. It is a case of a rising tide floating all the boats. You pull the most energy out of the boilers when you give that energy a place to go. One would think that pulling more energy out by agitation of the water would simply suck energy out of the boiler and its temperature would go down. This does happen in some instances such as when one pre-heats the boiler and then puts it to work on the large and cold thermal mass of the tank. When I do this, boiler temperature decreases from 180° down to 145° and then slowly climbs back up. However, when you have already established some equilibrium and you add agitation, the effect on the boiler output temperature is much less noticeable, maybe 2° F or so and then one can get sustained increases in heat transfer because the agitation is pulling heat out of the boiler and the increased pull is allowing the boiler itself to operate more efficiently.

Another aspect of this worksheet is that it allows us to run the values from a desired degrees per minute change back through to the energy required. Taking the average degrees per minute and our efficiency ratings we can calculate the gross boiler horsepower of the system (Table 105).

Starting with average degrees per minute value from our test we find that it takes 9.06 boiler horsepower to deliver 6.32 of them to the still. This gives an efficiency of 69.78% and a scale up ratio of 1.433. Both of these numbers will be used subsequently.

One will notice in this process that we are using a two-step process to scale up the energy required to effect the temperature change. This method is used throughout the workbook because it is not possible to scale directly from the smaller number to the larger one since the energy loss in each stage affects the other.[40]

From Desired ° F per minute change to Boiler Size	
Degrees per Minute	1.06
Gallons	400.0
Wt. per Gal	8.328
Total Wt.	3,331.3
Wt.* ° per Min = BTU's Needed for those ° per Min.	3,525.6
BTU's Needed per Hour	211,537.0
Boiler Horsepower BTU's per Hour	33,475.00
Applied Boiler Hp. Per Hr.	6.32
Heat Exchange Efficiency	96.25%
Scale up to Gross BTU's for Transport	1.04
Scaled up BTU's	219,778.7
Boiler heating Efficiency	72.50%
Factor to find Gross BTU's Needed	1.379
Scaled up BTU's per Hr. Needed	303,143.1
Boiler Size in Boiler Horsepower	9.06
Delivered Energy/Gross Energy = Net Efficiency	69.78%
1/ Efficiency = Scale up Value	1.433

TABLE 105—Refer to Boiler Test *Worksheet*

4.4 Boiler Oil and Gas Use

Oil Boiler Energy Use	
Oil Quantity Used (Fluid Ounces)	24.00
Time Elapsed in Minutes	8.75
Min/60 = % of Hour	14.6%
Fluid Ounces per Gallon	128
Gal. Oz./Oz. used = % of Gallon	18.8%
1/% of Hour = Time Units Per Hour	6.86
% of Gal. *Time units = Gal. per Hr.	1.29
BTU's per Gal. of Oil used	140,000
BTU's per Gal. * Gal. per Hr. = Oil BTU per Hr.	180,000
BTU's per Hour per Boiler Hp.	33,475.00
BTU's per Hr./ BTU's per Boiler Hp = Boiler Hp. per hr.	5.38
Boiler Heat Generation Efficiency	72.5%
Net BTU's Available	130,500.00
Net Boiler Hp.	3.90
Transfer from Boiler Efficiency	96.25%
Net BTU's Available	125,606.3
Deliverable Boiler Hp. to Still Contents	3.75

TABLE 106—Refer to Boiler Oil & Gas Use *Worksheet*

Another way I can gauge how many BTU's my oil boiler is consuming is to take a known quantity of oil, assign an energy content to it, and measure the time it takes to consume that oil. I use a gravity feed for the oil to the boiler. Then that value is multiplied to obtain a gallon per hour value and from there, calculate the gross BTU's burned per hour (Table 106).

From these values I determined the gross heating capacity of my oil boiler at 5.38 boiler horsepower. Applying a discount for the efficiency of combustion and the transport efficiency, I was able to determine the net boiler horsepower was 3.90 boiler horsepower, and accounting for transmission loss from the boiler to the tank contents, the delivered boiler horsepower was 3.75.

I was really disappointed after I purchased my oil boiler. The manufacturer told me that this boiler would generate 450,000 BTU's per hour. I kept

---

40   See the Scale Up section (4.8) that demonstrates the problems encountered when trying to directly scale up.

cranking up the oil pressure and the compressed air to feed more oil to it. The only real result was that I was sending raw flames up my stack and the stack temperature gauge went up to 450° F. I try to keep my stack temperature somewhere around 350° F. Otherwise you are sending too much heat up the chimney. It is important to have a stack temperature gauge so you can keep track of the flue temperature. It is an inexpensive item and you just have to take it out when you clean the chimney periodically.

There is no sense in over-firing the boiler with more oil than it can effectively consume so I don't turn the oil boiler flames up and down during the heating process. Oil fired boilers can be finicky and once you get them adjusted to where they are burning well you should only check them every hour or so and keep an eye on the stack temperature.

Also, running the boiler rich rather than lean results in a lot of unburned hydrocarbons gumming up the firebox. Cleaning the boiler is a pain; the cleaner and leaner you run your boiler the less often you will have to open it up and scrape the residue off the firebox and boiler tubes. The residue builds up over time and decreases efficiency so it is important to perform this chore. On steam boilers it is even more important because one has to check for cracks and flaws regularly or risk a catastrophic failure. Water boilers are not as dangerous because they do not transfer steam around; they just circulate hot water. However, my water boiler runs at 50 pounds per square inch so there is a substantial amount of pressure behind it. It is a very heavy duty boiler but it came with a 30 lb. over-pressure valve. With the implied consent of the manufacturer I modified it to accept a 50 lb. over-pressure valve and have had no problems in ten years. I have run it at above 40 lbs. every time I cook or distill.

Sometimes I do crank up the boiler feed and drive the stack temperature up to 375° to force more heat into the system. It takes all I've got to cook the batch in 3.5 hours. You can get a leg up on the cook run by heating the water to 100° F the day before. This helps drive off chlorine. Because of the large thermal mass the batch will still be around 80° the next morning if you cover the top and insulate the tank. It is not energy efficient to do it this way but it is a way to shave a few minutes off the cooking time and does de-chlorinate the water for you but so does the cooking process itself.

4.5 Oil Specifications

Built into the prior worksheet is the BTU's per gallon value for the oil I use. It is difficult to obtain reliable data on the energy content of oil, or gasoline for that matter. For instance, the gasoline you run in your car has more BTU's in it in the winter than in the summer. Oil companies tailor their gas to the season. In order to ensure reliable starting in the wintertime the character of the gasoline is changed to be more volatile. You might even be able to notice that your car's miles per gallon increases slightly in the winter.

Table 107 lists some general values for oil energy content.[41]

No. 1 and No. 2 fuel are both used for residential heating purposes. No. 2 is slightly more expensive but the fuel gives more heat per gallon used.

No. 1 fuel oil is used in vaporizing pot-type burners. No. 2 is used in atomizing gun-type and rotary fuel oil burners.

The heavier the grade of fuel used in an oil burner, the greater the care must be taken to ensure that oil is supplied to the combustion process at the proper atomizing temperature. If the temperature is too low the fuel oil will not atomize properly, and the burner will not operate efficiently.

---

41   Data from the American Society for Testing and Materials (ASTM), http://www.astm.org. BTU content for important fuel oil types is summarized in Fuel Oil Primer.pdf, available at my business websites.

Energy Content of Various Fuel Oil Types	BTU's Per Gal		
Energy Content per Gallon	Low	High	
Fuel Oil No. 1	132,900	137,000	Small Space Heaters
Fuel Oil No. 2 #2	137,000	141,800	Residential Heating
Fuel Oil No. 4	143,100	148,100	Industrial Burners
Fuel Oil No. 5 (Light)	146,800	150,000	Preheating in General Required
Fuel Oil No.5 (Heavy)	149,400	152,000	Heating Required
Fuel Oil No. 6	151,300	155,900	Bunker C

TABLE 107—Refer to Boiler Oil & Gas Use *Worksheet*

The first thing we notice is that heavy oil has more BTU's per gallon than light oil does. That is why ships use heavy oil (bunker fuel); it packs more BTU's per volume and they can go farther on a given tank.

The problem with heavy oil is that it must be heated before it is fed to the boiler. Heavy oil will not aerosolize easily unless it is hot. My oil boiler has a pre-heater with an independent temperature control so I can adjust the temperature at which the oil is fed into the boiler.

This is useful because my oil is a hodgepodge of waste oils that I collect. What I have noticed over the last ten years is that cars are running on thinner oils. Where 10W40 oil used to be the norm, now 10W30 is more common and large numbers of cars now run 5W30. This reduces the energy content of the waste oil I obtain.

I have chosen a mean value of 140,000 BTU's per gallon as what my blend consists of. It is lots of heavy oil with about 15% of No. 2 fuel oil as a "sweetener" so that it will still flow at lower temperatures. This is probably a conservative estimate.

At my boiler's rate of consumption of that oil, the gross BTU's produced are 180,000 per hour and an equivalent 5.38 boiler horsepower.

4.6 Gas Boiler

My second boiler is a natural gas fired boiler and in order to measure how much gas it is actually using one can simply read the gas meter every hour to see how much gas has been metered through it (Table 108).

Natural gas is metered into my shop in cubic feet. The meter will register to a single cubic foot but I use 10-cubic-foot increments because that is the lowest value that registers in digits on the front of the meter. The heat content of my gas is about 1,000 BTU's for every cubic foot of gas. If I am using 100 cubic feet per hour then that is 100,000 BTU's. When I run my gas boiler it consumes 120 cubic feet per hour and so is consuming 120,000 BTU's gross. The effective heat transfer from the burning of gas to actual hot water is less, as we will see below.

Gas Boiler Energy Use	
BTU's per Cubic Foot of Natural Gas	1,000
Cubic Feet per Hour Used	120
BTU's per Hour Burned	120,000
BTU's per Hour per Boiler Hp.	33,475.00
Gross Hp.	3.58
Boiler Heat Generation Efficiency	72.5%
Net BTU's Available	87,000.00
Net Boiler Hp.	2.60
Transfer from Boiler Efficiency	96.25%
Net BTU's Available	83,737.5
Deliverable Boiler Hp. to Still Contents	2.50

TABLE 108—Refer to Boiler Oil & Gas Use *Worksheet*

My gas boiler is a standard household unit and is only rated for 30 psi. I would never modify it to accept a higher pressure safety valve. It is just not built for it. But it runs fine at 30 psi. It is great for helping kick-start the heating process and runs continuously for about 1 1/2 hours until the temperature reaches approximately 150° F. At that point the pressure in the circulating system reaches 30 lbs. per square inch and the over pressure valve on the gas boiler begins to open up. From this point on in the run the gas boiler only can cycle on for about 15 minutes per hour; so the effective BTU's delivered by it drop by 75%.

Total Heating Capacity of Two Shop Boilers	
Gross BTU's liberated per hour	300,000.00
Gross Boiler Hp. Both Boilers	8.96
Net Hp.	6.50
Net Deliverable Boiler Hp.	6.25

TABLE 109—Refer to Boiler Oil & Gas Use *Worksheet*

Taking all this into account shows that the two boilers generate 8.96 boiler horsepower; after taking into account the loss in transferring that energy to the still the net delivered horsepower is 6.25 (Table 109).

The worksheet also solves for kilowatt hours and two kinds of boiler horsepower (Table 110).

From kilowatt hours it is possible to determine the cost associated with generating the heat required and to do so for other sources of energy used in my shop (Table 111).

The worksheet concludes with a conversion table for oil to various other energy units (Table 112, next page).

Gross BTU's liberated per hour	300,000.0
BTU's to Kilogram Calories	0.2519958
Kilogram Calories Required	75,599
Kilogram Cal. To Kw Hrs.	0.00116
Kilowatt Hours Required	87.92
Find Horsepower Values	
Kw Hour to Hp. Hr. (Mechanical)	1.34102210
Kw. Hr. * Converter = Mech Hp. hours	117.90
Hp. Hrs. (Mech.) * Converters = Results	
Horsepower (Boiler)	8.96
Horsepower (Electric)	117.86

TABLE 110—Refer to Boiler Oil & Gas Use *Worksheet*

Find Energy Costs	
Electric Costs per Hr.	
Kilowatt Hours Restated	87.9
Electric cost per Kw Hr.	$0.10
Total Electric Cost	$8.79
Natural Gas Costs	
Cost Per 1,000 Cubic Feet (MCF)	$15.00
BTU's per cubic foot	1,000
BTU's per 1,000 cubic feet	1,000,000
Total BTU's applied (Consumed) per Hr.	300,000
Total MCF Used	0.30
Cost of Energy per hour run time	$4.50
Fuel Oil Costs	
Fuel Oil per Gal.	$3.75
BTU's per Gal. of Oil used	140,000
Total BTU's applied (Consumed) per Hr.	300,000
Gallons per Hour of Oil Use	2.14
Oil Costs per Hour	$8.04

TABLE 111—Refer to Boiler Oil & Gas Use *Worksheet*

Energy Content of Various Fuel Oil Types	BTU's Per Gal						
Energy Content per Gallon	Low	High	Average	BTU's to K Cal	Kilocalories	To Joules	Joules
Fuel Oil No. 1	132,900	137,000	134,950	0.2520	34,007.4	1,054.35	142,284,533
Fuel Oil No. 2	137,000	141,800	139,400	0.2520	35,128.8	1,054.35	146,976,390
Fuel Oil No. 4	143,100	148,100	145,600	0.2520	36,691.2	1,054.35	153,513,360
Fuel Oil No. 5 (Light)	146,800	150,000	148,400	0.2520	37,396.8	1,054.35	156,465,540
Fuel Oil No.5 (Heavy)	149,400	152,000	150,700	0.2520	37,976.4	1,054.35	158,890,545
Fuel Oil No. 6	151,300	155,900	153,600	0.2520	38,707.2	1,054.35	161,948,160

	To Ft. Lbs. Force	Foot Lbs. Force	To Hp. Hrs.	HP Hours	Horsepower (Boiler)	Boiler Hp. Hrs. per Gal.	
Fuel Oil No. 1	777.649	104,943,733	0.000393	53.04	0.076	4.0306866	
Fuel Oil No. 2	777.649	108,404,271	0.000393	54.78	0.076	4.1635992	
Fuel Oil No. 4	777.649	113,225,694	0.000393	57.22	0.076	4.3487808	
Fuel Oil No. 5 (Light)	777.649	115,403,112	0.000393	58.32	0.076	4.4324112	
Fuel Oil No.5 (Heavy)	777.649	117,191,704	0.000393	59.23	0.076	4.5011076	
Fuel Oil No. 6	777.649	119,446,886	0.000393	60.36	0.076	4.5877248	

TABLE 112—Refer to Boiler Oil & Gas Use *Worksheet*

4.7 Oil Boiler Test

Table 113 (below) is a test of my oil boiler from a cold start. The reason I am including it is because the data collected allows one to calculate the inferred increase in radiated energy as the temperature increases. We see here that the energy radiated with two data points increases with increasing temperature but the average is between 19% and 23% depending on how the numbers are treated.

Water Temp in °F	Minutes	Incremental Time	°F Temp Change	°F Change per min.	°Per Hr. Rise	BTU's per Hr.			
72.0	0.0	0.0							
97.0	30.0	30.0	25.0	0.83					
120.0	60.0	30.0	23.0	0.77	48.0	159,902.0			
141.0	90.0	30.0	21.0	0.70			Inferred Heat Exchange BTU Loss		
160.0	120.0	30.0	19.0	0.63	40.0	133,251.7	26,650.3	16.7%	Inferred Radiated BTU %
178.0	150.0	30.0	18.0	0.60					
188.0	180.0	30.0	10.0	0.33	28.0	93,276.2	39,975.5	30.0%	Inferred Radiated BTU %
Total °F of Temp Change	116.0							23.3%	Average Radiated BTU's
Avg. °F Change per Minute	0.644			128,810.0	Average BTU's per Hr.				
Total Hours of Boiler Run Time	3.00			31,092.1	Inferred Heat Exchange BTU Loss				
				19.4%	Avg. Inferred Radiated BTU %				

TABLE 113—Refer to Oil Boiler Test *Worksheet*

Find BTU's Transferred	
BTU per lb. of Water	1.0
BTU's per degree per Gal. of Water	8.328
Gal.* BTU's per ° F = Batch BTU per ° F	3,331.3
Total ° F of Temp Change	116.0
BTU per ° * Degrees = Tot. BTU	386,430
Hours of Boiler Run Time	3.000
Total BTU's/ Hours = BTU's per Hour	128,810
Delivered BTU's after loss of energy	
BTU's per Hour per Boiler Hp.	33,475.00
BTU per Hr. / BTU per Boiler Hp = Boiler Hp.	3.85
Calculate Gross Energy Required	
Scale up to Gross BTU's for Transport Loss	
Heat Exchange Efficiency	96.25%
1/ Efficiency = Scale up Value	1.0390
Total BTU's per Hour used	133,828.5
Boiler Generating Efficiency	72.50%
1/ Efficiency = Scale up Value	1.3793
Scaled up Boiler BTU's	184,591.1
BTU's per Hour per Boiler Hp.	33,475.00
BTU per Hr. / BTU per Boiler Hp = Boiler Hp.	5.51

TABLE 114—Refer to Oil Boiler Test *Worksheet*

Applying this data to calculate the boiler horsepower required shows that 3.85 boiler horsepower are being applied. This compares favorably with the 3.75 boiler horsepower from my measured oil consumption test (Table 114).

Scaling up the required horsepower shows that 5.51 boiler horsepower are required to generate the 3.85 of applied horsepower.

4.8 Scale Up

This worksheet describes the various problems one can run into when trying to scale up and down when two factors are involved (Table 115).

Scale up check for Energy Use	The order of scaling does not matter	
Gross Boiler Horsepower Available	5.83	5.83
BTU's per Hour per Boiler Hp.	33,475.00	33,475.00
BTU's Per Hour Available	195,159.3	195,159.3
Boiler Efficiency	72.50%	96.25%
Available BTU's * Efficiency = Net Boiler BTU's	141,490.46	187,840.78
Heat Transfer Efficiency from Boiler to Still	96.25%	72.50%
Actual BTU's Transferred to Contents of Vessel	136,184.56	136,184.56
Actual Energy Delivered % (Overall Efficiency)	69.78%	69.78%
Actual % Energy Lost	30.22%	30.22%
1/ Efficiency = Scale up Value	1.433	1.433

TABLE 115—Refer to Scale Up *Worksheet*

The first thing we notice is that the order of scaling does not affect the final result.

What does not work is to try to sum the percentage losses and then calculate the value of the energy applied (Table 116, next page).

Summing % Loss and Scaling down does not work	
Boiler Efficiency % Loss	27.50%
Transfer Efficiency % Loss	3.75%
Total Energy Loss %	31.25%
1-Tot. Energy Loss % = % Energy	68.75%
Invalid Value for Delivered Energy	134,171.98
Error as BTU's	2,012.6
Error as %	1.5%
Summing % Loss and Scaling Up does not work	
1 + Gross Change = Scaling Factor	1.313
Scaling factor from Net to Gross as %	131.3%
BTU's Per Hour Required Restated	136,184.6
Total Scaled up BTU's	178,742
Difference	16,417
% Off	8.41%

TABLE 116—Refer to Scale Up *Worksheet*

Summing the percentage losses and then scaling down or up results in a 1.5% error in the calculation. A greater error occurs when one sums the percentage losses and then attempts to scale back up from the required energy, which results in an error of 8.4%.

The only way one can scale directly from smaller to larger is if one already knows the net and gross and since one of those two values is generally the value to be determined this method is not useful except as means of verifying the two-step process we are using. The order does not matter. The problem is simply that one cannot sum the percentage losses and arrive at the correct result.

4.9 Relative Energy Costs

This worksheet compares the cost of various fuel sources to the cost per million BTU's of each fuel type actually applied to accomplish a given task. For natural gas the cost calculations are very easy; one simply uses the combustion and transportation loss that we have already calculated to determine how much it will cost to apply one million BTU's to our mash (Table 117).

Oil is a little more expensive, but since I use waste oil that I collect I only have my time and effort in it (Table 118).

Gas Cost per Million BTU's	
BTU's per cubic foot	1,000.0
BTU's per 1,000 cubic feet (MCF)	1,000,000
Efficiency of Combustion & Transport	65.25%
Net Available BTU's per cubic foot	652,500
Constant of 1,000,000	1,000,000
10^6/BTU's per MCF = MCF's per Million BTU's	1.53
Cost per MCF Cubic Feet	$15.00
Cost per Million BTU's	$22.99

TABLE 117—Refer to Relative Energy Costs *Worksheet*

Oil Cost per Million BTU's	
BTU's Per Gallon	140,000.00
Efficiency of Combustion & Transport	65.25%
Net Available BTU's per Gallon	91,350
Constant of 1,000,000	1,000,000
10^6/BTU's per Gal. = Gal. of Oil per Million BTU's	10.95
Cost per Gallon	$3.50
Cost per Million BTU's	$38.31

TABLE 118—Refer to Relative Energy Costs *Worksheet*

Electricity is far more efficient in the conversion of energy to heat. Accordingly I have only calculated a loss rate of 10% for the transportation loss and assumed 100% conversion on the heat side (Table 119).

Based on boiler horsepower one can directly compare the energy costs of different energy sources (Table 120).

Electricity Cost per Million BTU's	
BTU's per Kw. Hr.	3,414.40
Efficiency of Use	90.0%
Net Available BTU's per Kw. Hr.	3,072.96
Constant of 1,000,000	1,000,000
10^6/BTU's per Kw. = Kw per Million BTU's	325.42
Cost per Kw. Hr.	$0.11
Cost per Million BTU's	$35.80

TABLE 119—*Refer to* Relative Energy Costs *Worksheet*

Gross Size in Boiler Horsepower	10.00
Boiler Horsepower BTU's per Hour	33,475.00
Total BTU's per Hour	334,750.00
Constant of 1,000,000	1,000,000
Hours to consume 1,000,000 BTU's	2.99
Cost per Hour Natural Gas	$7.70
Cost per Hour Oil	$12.83
Cost per Hour Electric	$11.98

TABLE 120—*Refer to* Relative Energy Costs *Worksheet*

This is the table set up to calculate the cost per million BTU's of different energy sources. The cost values are slightly different from those generated in prior tables because in this case we have set the efficiency of application for each type of energy to 100% (Table 121).

	Gas Cost per Million BTU's	**Oil Cost per Million BTU's**		**Electricity Cost per Million BTU's**	
BTU's per cubic foot	1,000.0	140,000.00	BTU's Per Gallon	3,414.40	BTU's per Kw Hr.
BTU's per 1,000 cubic feet (MCF)	1,000,000	100.0%	Efficiency of Burning	100.0%	Efficiency of Use
Efficiency of Application	100.00%	140,000	Net Available BTU's per Gallon	3,414.40	Net Available BTU's per Kw Hr.
Net Available BTU's per cubic foot	1,000,000	1,000,000	Constant of 1,000,000	1,000,000	Constant of 1,000,000
Constant of 1,000,000	1,000,000	7.14	10^6/BTU's per Gal. = Gal. of Oil per Million BTU's	292.88	10^6/BTU's per Kw = Kw per Million BTU's
10^6/BTU's per MCF = MCF's per Million BTU's	1.000	$3.50	Cost per Gallon	$0.11	Cost per Kw Hr.
Cost per MCF Cubic Feet	$15.00	$25.00	Cost per Million BTU's	$32.22	Cost per Million BTU's
Cost per Million BTU's Applied	$15.00				
Boiler Size in Boiler Horsepower	10.00				
Boiler Horsepower BTU's per Hour	33,475.00				
Total BTU's per Hour	334,750.00				
Hours to consume 1,000,000 BTU's	2.99				
Cost per Hour Natural Gas	$5.02				
Cost per Hour Oil	$8.37				
Cost per Hour Electric	$10.78				

TABLE 121—*Refer to* Relative Energy Costs *Worksheet*

4.10 Cook Run Data

Now we can turn our attention to the process of cooking. Following is a summary of a cooking run that I made. First we will look just at the cooking and cooling temperature differential in the tank over the course of the cook run. (Table 122, next page).

Cook Run Data	Hrs.	Tank & Mash Top Temp	° of Change per 1/2 Hr.	Tank Bottom Temp	Tank Temp @ Top	Tank Top & Bottom Temp Dif.	Hot Water Delivery Temp To Bottom of Tank	Hot Water Return Temp From Top of Tank	Hot Water Dif.
Begin Cooking	0	44	0	44	44	0	44	44	0
	0.5	81	37	61	81	20	99	94	5
	1	113	32	109	113	4	122	113	9
	1.5	135	22	112	135	23	140	135	5
Adding Corn reduces temp dif.	2	156	21	130	157	26	160	156	4
	2.5	175	19	154	174	21	177	175	2
	3	191	16	167	190	24	193	190	3
End Cooking & Begin Cooling	3.5	205	14	181	204	24	205	197	8
Cooling Section									
Stand 1/2 hr. from 3.5 till hr. 4.	4	195	-10	177	195	18			
Cool with water circulation	4.5	143	-52	129	142	14			
End Water Cooling. 1 hr. total	5	109	-34	101	109	8			
Add 40 Gal Cold Water	5.5	104	-5	91	101	13			
Stand 1/2 Hour	6	103	-1	87	95	16			
Cool with water circulation 1/2 Hr.	6.5	91	-12	82	91	9			
End Cooling & Pitch in Yeast	7	86	-5	79	86	7			

TABLE 122—Refer to Cook Run Data Worksheet

What we can see from this chart is that the shop was very cold during this run because everything started out at 44° F. After I turned on the boiler I waited half an hour to add the corn until the top temperature had reached 81° F and 61° F at the bottom. You don't want to add your corn to cold water. It will clump up. By adding the corn and turning on the mixer it reduced the tank temperature differential to 4° F. As the heating continued the tank temperature differential shot back up and became greatest at the highest temperature reached. The tank bottom temperature just got into the really effective range of the liquefying enzyme, which is around 185° F, but it did get above the minimum temperature of 176° F. The pH was 4.9 after cooking so it was probably under 5.5 during cooking. The cooking process itself does lower pH. The top of the tank reached 204° F which was the top end of the liquefying enzymes effectiveness. Even with agitation I had a consistent 20° F plus tank differential during the cooking phase. This is unavoidable but makes it difficult to get the entire batch cooked. What we can say is that the average energy of the batch reached 192° F. It is not necessary to boil the corn to get it to cook. It takes too much energy and is not required in any event.

Using a modified version of our energy transfer equations we can see the total energy used to cook the batch and the size of the boilers in total. First we find the average temperature change per minute (Table 123, next page).

Using the average temperature change we can calculate the total energy required to cook the batch and then scale it up to find the gross energy required. The results indicate that around one million BTU's are required to cook the batch.

Total Boiler Cooking Hours	3.50
Total °F of Temp Change	161.0
Total Minutes of Run Time	210.0
Degrees per Minute	0.767
Gallons	350.0
Wt. per Gal	8.32823
Gal. * Lbs. per Gal. = H_2O Lbs.	2,914.88
Corn Meal Added to Mash	1,500.00
Total Pounds in mixture	4,414.88
BTU Value	1.000
Wt.* ° per Min = BTU's per ° per Min.	3,384.7
Applied BTU's Needed per Hour	203,084.5
Total Applied BTU's	710,796
Total Applied Boiler Hp.	21.23
Applied Boiler Hp. Per Hour	6.07
Scale up to Gross Boiler Hp.	
Heat Exchange Efficiency	96.25%
Scale up to Gross BTU's Transport	1.04
Scaled up BTU's	210,996.9
Boiler heating Efficiency	72.50%
Scale up to Gross BTU's Transport	1.379
Scaled up BTU's per Hr. Needed	291,030.2
Gross BTU's Required to Cook	1,018,606
Boiler Horsepower BTU's per Hour	33,475.00
Boiler Size in Boiler Horsepower	8.69

TABLE 123—Refer to Cook Run Data Worksheet

After 3.5 hours of cooking I shut of the boilers and shut off the pumps. I wanted to measure just the radiation of the vessel with the mixer paddle running. Of course I also took off the 1/2-inch foam insulation blanket and the stainless steel lid that helps keep heat in. At this point the shop becomes even more of a steam bath than it was during the last part of the cooking phase.

Table 124 (below, left) shows the energy transfer that occurred.

What this shows is that we are radiating about 3.68 tons of cooling in this half hour.

Then I applied water cooling for 1/2 hour, in addition to running the mixer paddles and achieved a 52° temperature drop with is a fivefold increase in the amount of temperature reduction; it went from 10° F per half hour to 52° F per half hour (Table 125, below right).

Calculate Radiative Cooling	
Gallons of water to change temp.	350.00
Weight per Gallon of Water	8.32823
Gal. * Lbs. per Gal. = H_2O Lbs.	2,914.88
Corn Meal Added to Mash	1,500.00
Total Pounds in mixture	4,414.88
Starting Temperature	205.00
Ending Temperature	195.00
Temperature Difference	-10.00
Absolute Value of Temp. Dif.	10.00
BTU's per Lb. to Change Temp	1.000
Temp Dif. * BTU's per Lb. = Tot. BTU's per Lb.	10.00
Lbs. * BTU's per Lb. = BTU's of Cooling	44,149
BTU's per Ton of Refrigeration	12,000.00
Tons of Refrigeration Equivalent	3.68
Degrees per Minute	0.3333

TABLE 124—Refer to Cook Run Data Worksheet

Calculate Cooling Water Heat Transfer	
Starting Temperature	195.00
Ending Temperature	143.00
Temperature Difference	-52.00
Absolute Value of Temp. Dif.	52.00
BTU's per Lb. to Change Temp	1.000
Temp Dif. * BTU's per Lb. = Tot. BTU's per Lb.	52.00
Batch Lbs. Restated	4,414.88
Lbs. * BTU's per Lb. = BTU's of Cooling	229,574
BTU's per Ton of Refrigeration	12,000.00
Tons of Refrigeration Equivalent	19.13
Degrees per Minute	1.73

TABLE 125—Refer to Cook Run Data Worksheet

The reason I could take off so many BTU's is that my water temperature was 44° F to start and the tank temperature was still high, so there was a strong temperature gradient that could be taken advantage of.

The worksheet shown in Table 126 uses an average water output temperature of 169°, midway between 195 and 145, to demonstrate how 6.0 gallons per minute can deliver 188K BTU's of cooling to the batch in 1/2 hour.

Using the average temperature has caused some uncertainty since we know that the batch shed 19.1 tons of energy of which 3 tons were radiative. Still the values line up reasonably well.

I continued cooling with the same water flow for another half hour with the results shown in Table 127.

I ended the cooling at hour 5 and added my 40 gallons of water. This reduced the water temperature in the tank by 5 degrees in that 1/2 hour. Then I let the batch just stand for 1/2 hour to see what would happen. Well, nothing happened. The temperature at the top of the tank only fell 1° F and that of the bottom only fell 4° F. In addition the gradient in the tank went from 13 to 16 degrees. The heat in the tank just re-arranged itself and went to the top (Table 128).

Clearly the remaining heat in the tank was not going to come out quickly unless it was encouraged. I ran the heat exchanger cooling water for a full hour from the beginning of hour 6 to the beginning of hour 7 and obtained 12° of cooling in the first 1/2 hour but only 5° of cooling in the second. Notice that I had to cut back on the water flow because it was just wasting water to run it through at 6 gallons per minute. In order to get the water to pick up sufficient heat in coursing through the coils I had to reduce the flow (Table 129, next page).

Cooling Water Heat Absorbing Capacity	
Gallon per Minute Flow	6.00
Water input Temperature	44.0
Average Water Output Temperature	169.0
Temperature Change	125.00
Wt. per Gal. as BTU's per ° of Change	8.32823
° of Change * Wt.per Gal.= Tot.BTU per Gal.	1,041.03
Minutes of Flow	30.00
Total BTU's per minute	6,246.17
BTU's per Time	187,385.18
Tons of Refrigeration Equivalent	15.62

TABLE 126—Refer to Cook Run Data *Worksheet*

Calculate Cooling Water Heat Transfer	
Starting Temperature	143.00
Ending Temperature	109.00
Temperature Difference	-34.00
Absolute Value of Temp. Dif.	34.00
BTU's per Lb. to Change Temp	1.000
Temp Dif. * BTU's per Lb. = Tot. BTU's per Lb.	34.00
Lbs. * BTU's per Lb. = BTU's of Cooling	150,106
BTU's per Ton of Refrigeration	12,000
Tons of Refrigeration Equivalent	12.51
Degrees per Minute	1.13

TABLE 127—Refer to Cook Run Data *Worksheet*

Standing .5 hr.	
Starting Temperature	104.00
Ending Temperature	103.00
Temperature Difference	-1.00
Absolute Value of Temp. Dif.	1.00
BTU's per Lb. to Change Temp	1.000
Temp Dif. * BTU's per Lb. = Tot. BTU's per Lb.	1.00
Lbs. * BTU's per Lb. = BTU's of Cooling	4,415
BTU's per Ton of Refrigeration	12,000.00
Tons of Refrigeration Equivalent	0.37
Degrees per Minute	0.03

TABLE 128—Refer to Cook Run Data *Worksheet*

Final Cooling	
Starting Temperature	103.00
Ending Temperature	86.00
Temperature Difference	-17.00
Absolute Value of Temp. Dif.	17.00
BTU's per Lb. to Change Temp	1.000
Temp Dif. * BTU's per Lb. = Tot. BTU's per Lb.	17.00
Lbs. * BTU's per Lb. = BTU's of Cooling	75,053
BTU's per Ton of Refrigeration	12,000.00
Tons of Refrigeration Equivalent	6.25
Minutes	60.00
Degrees per Minute	0.28
Cooling Water Heat Absorbing Capacity	
Water input Temperature	44.00
Water Output Temperature	80.00
Temperature Change	36.00
Wt. per Gal. as BTU's per ° of Change	8.32823
° of Change * Wt.per Gal.= Tot. BTU per Min.	299.82
Gallon per Minute Flow	3.50
Total BTU's per minute	1,049.36
BTU's per 1/2 Hr.	31,480.7
Tons of Cooling Equivalent	2.62

TABLE 129—Refer to Cook Run Data *Worksheet*

At the end of hour 7 the batch was cool enough to set by pitching in my yeast. Note that the final hour reduced the gradient in my tank from 16 degrees down to 7 degrees. Overall this was an efficient and good run and an example of a how you can get your work done in one full working day using time and temperature to best effect while still having time to take some data.

CHAPTER 5 Fermentations

5.1 Fermentation and Strip Run 1

Now we can turn our attention to how several fermentations proceeded and the alcohol produced by them. Following is a chart of my first fermentation run (Table 130).

Fermentation Run 1	Hours	Days	Shop Temp	Tank Top Surface	Tank Bottom Surface	Tank Temp Differential	Sugar % by Refractometer	Sugar % by Hydrometer (Balling)	SG @ 60	pH
	0	0.00	60	84	84	0	27	23	1.094	4.9
Insulation on	14	0.58	55	86	64	22	22	19	1.075	4.0
	26	1.08	54	88	73	15	17	17	1.067	4.0
	44	1.83	56	90	77	13	14	13	1.054	4.0
	67	2.79	54	88	70	18	12	7	1.028	4.0
	91	3.79	53	70	67	3	11	4	1.016	3.8
	112	4.67	50	65	65	0	10	2	1.008	3.6

TABLE 130—Refer to Ferment Runs *Worksheet*

The significant features of this fermentation run are that the pH did get to 4.9 by the time the batch was set. That means that the sugar making enzyme did reach its operational pH of below 5.1 at some time during the cooking and cooling process before the batch was set. The shop temperature dropped after the batch was set; the tank differential went up to 22° and the bottom surface was only 64°. The fermentation was not retaining enough heat to proceed quickly so I wrapped an insulation blanket of 3/8-inch Styrofoam around the outside of the tank. Twelve hours later the tank differential had dropped by 7° and the fermentation had speeded up. It reached a minimum after 44 hours and then began to increase again. The batch is completely fermented when the tank top and bottom temperatures converge again to only 3°. This means that the metabolic activity in the tank has reduced to the minimum consistent with bacterial infection rather than yeast metabolism. Because of the reduced production of carbon dioxide the batch is now able to support aerobic bacteria as well as anaerobic bacteria. These new aerobic bacteria will steadily reduce your alcohol yield.[42]

I like to keep my fermentations in the mid to high 80°s at the top of the batch, and with the insulation on this batch I was able to do so. The batch even got a little hot, up to 90°, but I decided to keep the blanket on rather than risk losing the ability to regain ground if it got cold again.

Still with insulation applied. The hydraulic mixer is stowed near the ceiling in this photograph.

---

42   Another consequence of aerobic metabolism in the tank is that any remaining yeast will switch over to respiration rather than fermentation metabolic pathways.

The picture above shows how my still is plumbed for a stripping run and also shows the 3/8-inch insulation I wrap around the tank to keep it warm during fermentations and also during distillation runs in order to cut down on radiation of heat out of the vessel. I will also lay insulation on the top as well. Note the hydraulic mixer over the condenser coils in its stored position on the trolley on the ceiling.

Let's look at the production figures from this batch (Table 131).

Calculate yield per Bushel				Calculate Metric yield	
Corn Wt. Used	1,500.00		390.00	Water Gal.	0.453592	Pounds Avdp to Kilograms
Lbs. per Bushel	56.00		14.56	Gal. per Bushel Beer	680.39	Kilograms of Corn
Bushels of Corn	26.79				0.154	Fermented Proof Gal. per Kilogram
Actual Experience for recovery					0.08	Anhydrous Alc. Gal. Per Kg
Proof Gallons Recovered in Barrels	84.84				77.04	Anhydrous Alc. Gal. per Metric Ton
Proof Gallons Remaining in Still	20.00				154.1	Proof Gal. per Metric Ton
Total Proof Gallons Fermented	104.84					
Fermented Proof Gal. per Bushel	3.91	1.96	Anhydrous Alc. Gal. Per Bushel		107.61	Wine Gallons Recovered
Recovered Proof Gal. per Bushel	3.17	1.58	Anhydrous Alc. Gal. Per Bushel		78.84	(P.G./W.G.)*100 = Average Proof of Run
Compared to Industry Goals Coarse Grind						
Efficiency of Fermentation	73.8%		Actual Proof Gallons/Industry Goals Proof Gallons			
Efficiency of Recovery Coarse Grind	59.8%					
Efficiency of Recovery Fine Grind	55.6%					

TABLE 131—Refer to Strip Run 1 *Worksheet*

This was a disappointing run. It started out so promising but didn't pan out. I only produced 84.84 Proof Gallons even though I ran the proof down to 30 on the stripping run. Below 30 proof it is simply not worth the energy cost to continue removing volatile products. The little bit of remaining alcohol is so contaminated with high boiling point compounds that there is no further use in trying to collect the distillate.

Collection data from the first stripping run is shown in Table 132 (next page).

At the end of the fermentation much of the corn has settled to the bottom of the still. We can't run the mixer paddles with the still lid on so there is no agitation of the mixture during the stripping run. The consequence is that it makes the transfer of heat from the coils to the mash more difficult and the corn can actually bake onto the coils, which is a job to scrub and hose off.

One really needs to preheat the boiler up to close to its operating temperature before putting it to work. Running the circulating pumps when the boiler is cold just prolongs the inefficient burning of your oil. With natural gas it is not so bad but an oil fired boiler needs to be at operating temperature to burn efficiently. Even bringing the boiler up to operating temperature before putting it to work will result in a drop in boiler temperature when you actually start the pumps. The large thermal mass that the boiler is trying to heat will just suck the heat out of the boiler and knock the temperature down. This is inevitable but having a hot boiler to start will keep the combustion going at a better rate than trying to start cold and heat everything at once.

Strip Run 1

	Elapsed Hours	Hot Water Return Temp	Tank Top Temp	Tank Bottom Temp	Tank Differential	Alcohol Wt. Collected	Lbs. per 1/2 Hr.	Trailing Lbs. per Hr.	Gallons Condensed	True Proof	Time
		58.0	82.0	65.0	17.0	0.0					8:20 AM
		130.0	87.0	88.0	-1.0	0.0					8:50 AM
	1.0	139.0	108.0	94.0	14.0	0.0					9:20 AM
		160.0	132.0	98.0	34.0	0.0					9:50 AM
	2.0	180.0	154.0	100.0	54.0	0.0					10:20 AM
		186.0	181.0	108.0	73.0	0.0					10:50 AM
Still Begins Running	3.0	196.0	194.0	110.0	84.0	44.0	44.0				11:20 AM
		198.0	195.0	112.0	83.0	114.0	70.0	114.0	15.1	125.0	11:50 AM
	4.0	201.0	199.0	110.0	89.0	175.0	61.0				12:20 PM
		203.0	203.0	106.0	97.0	240.0	65.0	126.0	16.5	115.0	12:50 PM
	5.0	206.0	205.0	107.0	98.0	314.0	74.0				1:20 PM
		205.0	205.0	105.0	100.0	386.0	72.0	146.0	18.6	90.0	1:50 PM
End Drum 1	6.0	207.0	207.0	115.0	92.0	446.0	60.0	132.0	16.7	82.0	2:20 PM
		207.0	205.0	111.0	94.0	92.0	58.0	118.0	14.9	78.0	2:50 PM
	7.0	208.0	205.0	121.0	84.0	146.0	54.0				3:20 PM
		209.0	206.0	113.0	93.0	196.0	50.0	104.0	13.0	65.0	3:50 PM
	8.0	209.0	207.0	124.0	83.0	250.0	54.0				4:20 PM
		210.0	208.0	124.0	84.0	282.0	32.0	86.0	10.6	42.8	4:50 PM
Boiler shutdown	9.0	210.0	209.0	128.0	81.0	305.0	23.0				5:20 PM
End Drum 2	9.5	209.0	209.0	136.0	73.0	335.0	30.0	53.0	6.5	30.7	5:50 PM
						122.2	Proof Sample Returns and transition jugs.				
						457.2	Wt. Drum 2				

TABLE 132—Refer to Strip Run 1 Worksheet

As to my condenser water, I don't waste a lot of cold water trying to keep my condenser cold during the stripping run. I let it float up to 110° or so. During a double run or finishing run I will slow the still down, so it does not overwhelm the condenser, and keep the condenser itself around 80° F. But the object of a stripping run is to get the raw alcohol out of the batch as quickly as possible, not to make potable whiskey. Also, keeping the condenser cold back feeds that cold into the still. So the colder you keep your condenser, the more heat the still will need. Thus it costs you on both ends: more energy to heat and more water to cool. This is a typical distilling business pitfall—like many others I encounter. In terms of heat I drove the tank almost to boiling and then drove the bottom of the tank temperature up towards the top temperature.

What we see is that the pounds condensed per hour rises to a peak of 146 pounds per hour and then trails off to only 53 pounds per hour despite adding the same amount of energy to the still during the entire run. When you are using the same amount of energy and driving off less and less weight, at some point you have to decide the run is over.

One would think that the most weight and volume of alcohol would come off of the still at the beginning of the run. That is when the fermented batch is the most volatile and when heated to vaporization temperature would generate the highest mass of output. Countering this assumption from a mass perspective is the fact that the alcohol derived would weigh less per unit of volume than the mass condensed later in the run. However, the relationship holds true even when measuring volume.

What we see is that both mass and volume rise from the beginning of the run and reach a peak about 2 1/2 hours into the run. I can't explain this bulge in the middle of the run but it is a recurring and predictable phenomenon. The batch seems to gather itself in the early stages and at some point when the entire thermal mass of the batch has reached an equilibrium of sorts the alcohol fairly leaps off of the mash and the flow increases dramatically. This peak of flow is also when the pressure in the still is greatest as well.

One has to be careful in decreasing the energy input into the batch at this point. If you back off too much then the batch will cease to flow alcohol and you will spend a long time getting it back up and running. You also run the risk of overshooting and making the pressure problem worse the second time you get it up and running. However, prudence requires that some backing off of the energy input is advisable but not so much as to keep the still from running. The practical effect of this increase in flow is that one will require the most cooling water in the middle of the run in order to condense this alcohol, even though the energy input is constant.

Some of the data at the end of the run is a little skewed by the fact that one must let the condenser continue to weep alcohol after the boiler had been turned off. It will run for a while and you may as well collect it into a jug. Also in order to proof alcohol properly I had to cool the samples below 100° so the alcohol tables will provide a true proof. This allowed me to track the proof of the run as it proceeded. I returned the weight of these samples at the end to prevent further skewing of the lbs. per 1/2 hour data. This accumulated weight was added to the batch total at the end, all in a lump.

Summarizing the collected alcohol shows (Table 133).

Alcohol Collected	Lbs.	Time	Lbs. per Hr.
Drum 1 net Lbs.	425.0	3.00	141.7
Drum 2 net Lbs.	436.2	3.50	124.6
Drum 3 net Lbs.	0.0	0.00	
Total Lbs. Condensed	861.2	6.5	Total Hrs. Condensing Time
Hours of Condensing Time	6.5	132.5	Avg. Lbs. Per Hour
Total Wine Gallons	107.6	16.6	Avg. Wine Gallons Per Hour
Total Proof Gallons	84.84	13.1	Avg. Proof Gallons Per Hour
Proof Gal./Wine Gal. * 100 = Avg. Proof	78.84	125.0	Highest Proof During Run
% By Vol. @ 60° F.	39.4	30.7	Ending, Lowest, Proof

TABLE 133—Refer to Strip Run 1 *Worksheet*

Looking at the energy required shows the following (Table 134, next page):

Now, we can make a determination of how many BTU's per Wine Gallon and Proof Gallon we have applied so that we can compare the values derived to calculations made from physical constants for alcohol and water mixtures. We will use these values to confirm the accuracy, to the extent we can, of the digital stills we will build a little further on.

Some uncertainty will attend these calculations. In this case we are applying known quantities of energy that are measured in BTU's per lb.; however, since we are heating an alcohol and water mixture, that decreases the amount of BTU's per pound required and that lowers the BTU's per lb. required to vaporize the mixture. This is the same principle we covered in the distillation section whereby the vaporization temperature varies with the alcohol content of the fluid, and since the fluid has a specific gravity of less than 1.0 it requires less than 1 BTU, per lb. to reach its vaporization temperature. In effect it is more volatile.

Calculate Energy					
Boiler Run Time Full Power	3.0	6.0	Condensing Hrs.	3.0	Hours of Gas. Run time
BTU's From Oil Boiler per Hr. (Full BTU's)	180,000	180,000	Condensing BTU's	120,000	BTU's From Gas Boiler per Hr.
Total Oil Boiler BTU's to Get Still Running	540,000	1,080,000	Tot. Condensing Oil BTU's	360,000.0	Total Gas. BTU's
Total Gas BTU's to Get Still Up and Running	360,000	1.1	Hrs. Gas Boiler Run Time		
Total BTU's to Get Still up and Running	900,000.0	132,000.00	Total Condensing Gas BTU's	**Condensing Gas. Boiler Run Time**	
BTU's per Hr.	300,000.0	1,212,000	Total Condensing BTU's	11.0	Min per Hr.
Gross Hp. Per Hr. To get Still Running	8.96	202,000.0	Condensing BTU's per Hr.	66.0	Total Min
		6.03	Average Condensing Boiler Hp.	1.1	Total Hrs.
Total Oil BTU's	1,620,000				
Total Gas BTU's	492,000				
Total BTU's applied	2,112,000				
	Gross	**Condensing**			
BTU's per Wine Gal. Condensed	19,628.3	11,263.9	BTU's per WG		
BTU's per Proof Gal. Condensed	24,893.9	14,285.7	BTU's per PG		
Gross BTU's per Condensing Hr.	202,000.0	69.78%	System Efficiency		
Applied BTU's per Condensing Hr.	140,958.1	7,860.1	Applied BTU's per WG		
Applied Boiler Hp. per Condensing Hr.	4.21	9,968.8	Applied BTU's per PG		

TABLE 134—Refer to Strip Run 1 *Worksheet*

The mass of the batch has changed since it was set. We calculated in our carbon dioxide worksheet that the batch dissipated 510 pounds of carbon dioxide that we no longer have to change the temperature of. This reduces the total BTU's we need to apply to get the batch up to running temperature but does not affect the rate of energy supplied. Countering this loss of mass is the 40 extra gallons of water we added when we pitched in our yeast slurry, which amounts to 333 lbs. The net effect is about 177 lbs. lighter which is about at the limit of what we could measure given the equipment I have. Accordingly it can't really be considered a measurable factor from which conclusions can be drawn.

Finally we have to account for the fact that no agitation can be applied to the mixture since the still lid is on the tank and all the corn residue has settled to the bottom. This impedes energy transfer and would affect the system efficiency on the input side.

Taking these considerations into account leaves us able to make only general deductive calculations about the number of BTU's required to distill each Wine and Proof gallon.

The batch fermented to 12% alcohol by volume. By using an average of 6% alcohol by volume for the mash during the entire run we can calculate the predicted BTU's per gallon of condensed alcohol and compare that value to the energy supplied by our boilers using the following formula:

(water energy calories x water % of mixture) + (alcohol energy calories x alcohol % of mixture) = calories required to vaporize one gram

Embodying this formula in a worksheet shows these results (Table 135):

Surprisingly the BTU's per gallon are within 2% of those we calculated on the input side. But I want to state that this is only a rough and ready calculation of averages and it is most useful as a guide to operations rather than a precision tool.

The boiler was shut down after nine hours, but the still continued to flow alcohol for another half hour. As I mentioned earlier, I had not handled the collection of heads and tails very well and had about 120 lbs. of alcohol that had to be added to drum 2 as well. Still, I did not make very many Proof Gallons, only 84.84.

Rounding out this discussion we can calculate the quantity of alcohol fermented and recovered by several different methods.

First we take the percent by volume from the batch as fermented and calculate the potential Proof Gallons to be distilled and compare them to the recovery to find the unrecovered Proof Gallons.

What is significant about this calculation is that one must use only the gallons of water used in the batch rather than the total volume of the batch. Apparently only the water counts towards the total and not the solids that are obscured. The solids, even though they contribute to the volume do not appear to participate in the equation. Further complicating things is the fact that the water is not water any longer; it is water and alcohol. The best results are obtained if one simply assumes the original water component is the amount that is the volume upon which to base your calculations (Table 136).

Then we take the distilled gallons and the proof of the remaining contents of the still and find the Proof Gallons remaining in the still. The way I calculate the Proof Gallons remaining in the still is to proof a sample of the remaining material in the still. It generally proofs out to around 5 to 8 proof which is 2.5 to 4% alcohol by volume. Having started with 390 gallons of water and distilled out 107.6 gallons of alcohol and water, the remainder is 282.4 gallons of fluid. (Table 137). Checking the remaining contents of the still revealed that they were 5 proof which equates to an alcohol content of 2.5 percent. This indicates that 14.12 Proof Gallons are remaining in the still.

Find BTU's to Vaporize Alcohol & Water Mixtures	
Alcohol % of Mixture	6.00%
Avg. Proof of Mixture to Be Vaporized	12.00
Water % of Mixture	94.00%
Energy to Vaporize Water Calories Per Gram	539.55
Energy Required to Vaporize Alcohol	200.87
Find Latent Heat of Vaporization (LHV)	519.23
Calories per Kg	519,229
Calories to Joules	4.1868
Kilojoules per Kg	2,173.91
Kilojoules to BTU's	0.947817
BTU's per Kg	2,060.47
Kg to Lbs.	0.4535924
BTU's per Lb.	934.61
Lbs. per Gal. @ Proof	8.2576
Lbs. per Gal. * BTU's per Lb. = BTU's per Gal.	7,717.69
Compare to Calculated BTU Value per Gal.	7,860.12
Correspondence %	101.85%

TABLE 135—Refer to Strip Run 1 Worksheet

% Alcohol at 60° F	12.50%
Volume of Fermented Alcohol in Still	390.00
Proof of Liquid	25.00
Proof Gallons in Still	97.50
Proof Gallons Recovered	84.84
Proof Gallons not Recovered	12.66

TABLE 136—Refer to Strip Run 1 Worksheet

Find Proof Gal. Remaining in Still	
Start Gal.	390.0
Distilled Gal.	107.6
Remaining Gal.	282.4
Proof of Remaining	5.0
% Alc	2.5%
Absolute Alcohol Gal.	7.06
Proof Gal. Remaining	14.12

TABLE 137—Refer to Strip Run 1 Worksheet

While the comparison is in agreement to within 1.5 Proof Gallons, which is roughly 1.5% of the total, this is still a fairly rough calculation but does contain enough predictive power to be useful as a guide.

Converting the energy required per gallon into other energy units for both gross and net shows the following units (Table 138).

Find Gross kW per Liter	Gross	Net
Liters per Gal.	3.7854118	3.7854118
BTU's per Liter	5,185.2	2,076.4
Kilowatt Hrs. per Liter	1.5	0.61
Gallons per Liter §19.722	0.264172	0.264172
BTU's per Liter	5,185.2	2,076.4
1 BTU to Calories =	252.00	252.00
Calories per Gal	19,376.3	7,608.1
Gal. to Liters	3.78541	3.78541
Calories per Liter	5,118.7	2,009.9
BTU to Watt Seconds (Joules) =	1,054.35	1,054.35
Watt Seconds (Joules)	20,695,048	8,287,316
Divisor to kW hours	3,600,000	3,600,000
Kilowatt Hours per Gal.	5.75	2.30

TABLE 138—Refer to Strip Run 1 *Worksheet*

Now we can address costs (Table 139) which shows the cost to be about three dollars ($3.01) per Proof Gallon:

Cost Per Wine Gallon Condensed		Cost Per Proof Gal. Condensed	
Cost Per MCF	$15.00	$15.00	Cost Per MCF
BTU per Wine Gal./1,000,000 BTU's per MCF = % of MCF Per Wine Gal	1.96%	2.49%	% of MCF Per Proof Gal.
Cost Per Wine Gal. Condensed	$0.29	$0.37	Cost Per Proof Gal.
Total BTU's applied	2,112,000.0		
Total MCF	2.11		
Total Energy Cost	$31.7		
Corn Costs per Proof Gallon			
Lbs. per Bag of Corn	50.0		
Corn Cost per Bag	$8.50		
Lbs. Per Bushel	56.0		
Bags per Bushel	1.12		
Cost per Bushel	$9.52		
Bushels used	26.79		
Total Corn Cost	$255.00		
Proof Gallons Produced	$84.84		
Cost per Proof Gallon	$3.01		

TABLE 139—Refer to Strip Run 1 *Worksheet*

5.2 Fermentation and Strip Run 2

Moving on to the second fermentation run we will see that it was a better run all around (Table 140).

Fermentation Run 2	Hours	Days	Shop Temp	Tank Top Surface	Tank Bottom Surface	Tank Temp Differential	Sugar % by Refractometer	Sugar % by Hydrometer
	0.0	0	60	84	81	3	26.0	25.0
	18.0	1	54	89	84	5	22.0	19.0
Insulation On	50.0	2	56	85	80	5	18.00	16.0
	72.0	3	51	85	72	13	16.0	13.0
	96.0	4	49	82	67	15	15.0	9.0
	117.0	5	46	76	62	14	13.0	6.0
	144.0	6	43	74	57	17	10.0	2.0
	168.0	7	43	70	55	15	8.0	1.0

TABLE 140—Refer to Ferment Runs Worksheet

The fermentation shown in Table 140 ran for seven full days. I could probably have distilled it off after six days but I wanted to see what another day would bring. By this time the shop temperature was so cold that the ground was sucking heat out of the bottom of the tank at a rate faster than the metabolic activity was generating heat.

Strip Run 2	Hrs.	Hot Water Delivery Temp	Hot Water Return Temp	Temp Dif.	Tank Top Temp	Tank Bottom Temp	Tank Differential	Lbs. per 1/2 hour	Net Cumulative Alc. Lbs.	Trailing Lbs. per Hr.	Gallons Condensed	True Proof	Oil Boiler Pressure	Still Lid Pressure	Spout Temp
	0.0	45.0	45.0	0.0	71.0	60.0	11.0								
		152.0	81.0	71.0	152.0	81.0	71.0								
Running @ 3 1/2 Hours	3.5	193.0	192.0	1.0	192.0	92.0	100.0		0.0			15.0			
		194.0	194.0	0.0	194.0	92.0	102.0	17.2	17.2		10.2	102.0	30.0		
	4.5	199.0	196.0	3.0	197.0	100.0	97.0	62.0	79.2	79.2					48.0
		200.0	193.0	7.0	200.0	100.0	100.0	72.0	151.2	134.0	17.7	125.0	40.0		
	5.5	197.0	191.0	6.0	200.0	101.0	99.0	71.0	222.2	143.0	18.7	115.0	45.0		52.0
		203.0	191.0	12.0	204.0	101.0	103.0	72.0	294.2	143.0	18.7	115.0	45.0	1.0	
	6.5	203.0	192.0	11.0	207.0	101.0	106.0	73.4	367.6	145.4	18.7	102.0	45.0		70.0
Drum 1 Full 413 Lbs. net		205.0	196.0	9.0	208.0			45.4	413.0						
		207.0	203.0	4.0	210.0	109.0	101.0	77.0	31.6					2.0	83.0
	7.5	208.0	203.0	5.0	208.0	113.0	95.0	81.0	112.6	158.0	20.0	84.4	43.0		
		208.0	203.0	5.0	208.0	113.0	95.0	87.6	200.2	168.6	21.2	73.5	42.0	1.0	
	8.5	208.0	204.0	4.0	207.0	117.0	90.0	72.0	272.2	159.6	19.9	64.5	41.0	1.0	80.0
		212.0	206.0	6.0	209.0	124.0	85.0	73.6	345.8	145.6	18.0	54.0	41.0	1.0	
Drum 2 full 421 lbs. net	9.5	212.0	210.0	2.0	210.0	125.0	85.0	75.2	421.0	148.8	18.4	50.5	41.0	1.0	79.0
		214.0	212.0	2.0	211.0	130.0	81.0	61.6	61.6	136.8	16.9	42.8	41.0	1.0	
Drum 3 149 lbs. net	10.5	215.0	213.0	2.0	211.0	134.0	77.0	65.6	127.2	127.2		35.5	41.0	1.0	79.0
End Drum Wt. w/remaining flow after shutdown and transition jugs.									149.0						
Total Alcohol Wt. Collected		983.0													

TABLE 141—Refer to Strip Run 2 Worksheet

What this means is that I did not see the top and bottom tank temperatures converge towards each other. The batch might have been able to run another day, and if it had been warmer in the shop or I could have heated the batch gently with the boiler I might have been able to get another day's fermentation out of it. But it had already run seven full days and I couldn't wait any longer given that I had several more fermentations and stripping runs to make before the double run.

In this run I tracked the boiler pressure and the still lid pressure in PSI (Table 141, previous page). You can see that the most pressure was generated in the middle of the run and that even though the temperature continued to climb towards the end of the run the overall boiler pressure was dropping. In this run I ran the batch up to 215° which is as high as I can get it. Even though I was still condensing fluid at a brisk pace the batch was depleted of alcohol content. Also, we see again the bulge in the middle of the run where the most pounds and gallons are distilled each hour. There is a small break in the middle where the first drum filled up and I had to take a 15-minute interval rather than 30 minutes but the overall pattern is of increasing flow to peak of around 80 proof distillate and then a decline as the proof falls to 35 and the run ends.

Looking at the alcohol collected shows that the Proof Gallons collected has shot up from 84.84 on the first run to over 109 Proof Gallons which is a 22% improvement over the first fermentation and strip run (Table 142).

Strip Run 2					
Alcohol Collected	**Lbs.**	**Hours**	**Lbs. per Hr.**		
Drum 1 net Lbs.	413.0	3.00	137.7		
Drum 2 net Lbs.	421.0	2.75	153.1		
Drum 3 net Lbs.	149.0	1.25	119.2		
Total Lbs. Condensed	983.0	7.0	Total Hrs. Condensing Time		
Hours of Condensing Time	7.0	140.4	Avg. Lbs. Per Hour		
Total Wine Gallons	125.2	17.9	Avg. Wine Gallons Per Hour		
Total Proof Gallons	109.1	15.6	Avg. Proof Gallons Per Hour		
Proof Gal./Wine Gal. * 100 = Avg. Proof	87.14	125.0	Highest Proof During Run		
% By Vol. @ 60° F	43.6	35.5	Ending, Lowest, Proof	**Gas Boiler Run Time**	
				11.0	Min per Hr.
Total Hours - Boiler Run Time	10.5	7.0	Condensing Hrs.	77.0	Total Min
BTU's From Oil Boiler per Hr.	180,000.0	180,000.0		1.3	Total Hrs.
Total Oil BTU's	1,890,000.0	1,260,000.0		**Gas Meter Calcs**	
Total Hours Gas Boiler Run	5.0	1.3		850.0	Gas Boiler Calc. MCF
BTU's From Gas Boiler per Hr.	120,000.0	120,000.0		850,000	Gas BTU's
Total Gas BTU's	600,000.0	154,000.0			
Total BTU's applied	2,490,000.0	1,414,000.0			
Gross BTU per Wine Gal. Condensed	19,888.2	11,293.9	BTU's per WG	**Cycle Time Gas Boiler**	
Gross BTU per Proof Gal. Condensed	22,823.1	12,960.6	BTU's per PG	11.00	Min per Hr. Run
		202,000	Avg. BTU's per Condensing Hr.	18.33%	% of Hour
		6.03	Avg. Boiler Hp.	120,000	Boiler BTU Per Hr.
				22,000	Actual Use per Hr.
		69.78%	System Efficiency		
Gross BTU's per Condensing Hr.	202,000.0	7,881.0	Applied BTU's per WG		
Applied BTU's per Condensing Hr.	140,958.1	9,044.1	Applied BTU's per PG		
Applied Boiler Hp. per Condensing Hr.	4.21	986,707	Total applied BTU's		

TABLE 142—Refer to Strip Run 2 Worksheet

Another noticeable feature of this run is that the average proof has shot up from 77 proof on the first strip run to 87.14 on the second one.

Looking at the yield per bushel from this run also shows a substantial improvement over the first one (Table 143).

Calculate yield per Bushel				Calculate Metric yield	
Corn Wt. Used	1,500.00	390.00	Water Gal.	0.453592	Pounds Avdp to Kilograms
Lbs. per Bushel	56.00	14.56	Gal. per Bushel Beer	680.39	Kilograms of Corn
Bushels of Corn	26.79	8.32826	HCP 72nd Lbs. per Gal. Air 15.556	0.182	Fermented Proof Gal. per Kilogram
Actual Experience for recovery		3,248.02	Water Wt.	0.09	Anhydrous Alc. Gal. Per Kg.
Proof Gallons Recovered in Barrels	109.10	4,748.02	Total Batch Wt.	91.20	Anhydrous Alc. Gal. per Metric Ton
Proof Gallons Remaining in Still	15.00			182.4	Proof Gal. per Metric Ton
Total Proof Gallons Fermented	124.10				
Fermented Proof Gal. per Bushel	4.63	2.32	Anhydrous Alc. Gal. Per Bushel		
Recovered Proof Gal. per Bushel	4.07	2.04	Anhydrous Alc. Gal. Per Bushel		
Compared to Industry Goals Coarse Grind					
Efficiency of Fermentation (Coarse Grind)	87.4%	Actual Proof Gallons/Industry Goals Proof Gallons			
Efficiency of Recovery Coarse Grind	76.9%				
Efficiency of Recovery Fine Grind	71.5%				

TABLE 143—Refer to Strip Run 2 *Worksheet*

Find BTU's to Vaporize Alcohol & Water Mixtures	
Alcohol % of Mixture	7.00%
Avg. Proof of Mixture to Be Vaporized	14.00
Water % of Mixture	93.00%
Energy to Vaporize Water Calories Per Gram	539.55
Energy Required to Vaporize Alcohol	200.87
Find Latent Heat of Vaporization (LHV)	515.84
Calories per Kg	515,842
Calories to Joules	4.1868
Kilojoules per Kg.	2,159.73
Kilojoules to BTU's	0.947817
BTU's per Kg	2,047.03
Kg to Lbs.	0.4535924
BTU's per Lb.	928.52
Lbs. per Gal. @ Proof	8.2467
Lbs. per Gal. * BTU's per Lb. = BTU's per Gal.	7,657.24
Compare to Calculated BTU Value per Gal.	7,881.05
Correspondence %	102.92%

TABLE 144—Refer to Strip Run 2 *Worksheet*

Part of the increase in yield is by virtue of the number of Wine Gallons I condensed. This, despite the fact that I was still collecting some alcohol at 35 proof at the end of the run rather than driving it down to 30 proof like in the first batch. This was a long day and frankly I was ready to quit. After I turn off the boiler and stop collecting alcohol there is still 2 to 3 hours of work to do to safely shut down the shop and clean up before I can leave.

Looking at the BTU's applied versus the mathematical calculation of energy required shows a close correspondence (Table 144).

Again, there is some relationship between our energy input estimates and the formulas for the transformation. We are applying slightly more energy per gallon than the formula indicates, but given the uncertainties involved in calculating our energy inputs the correspondence is at least satisfactory.

Then we calculate the alcohol in the tank by our two different methods and see how well they match. (Table 145, next page).

Find Alcohol Values for Batch	
% Alcohol at 60° F	15.00%
Gallon Volume	390.00
Proof of Liquid	30.00
Proof Gallons in Still	117.00
Proof Gallons Recovered	109.10
Proof Gallons not Recovered	7.90
Find Proof Gal. Remaining in Still	
Start Gal.	390.0
Distilled Gal.	125.2
Remaining Gal.	264.8
Proof of Remaining	5.0
% Alc	2.5%
Absolute Alcohol Gal.	6.62
Proof Gal. Remaining	13.24
Total Proof Gallons	122.34

TABLE 145—Refer to Strip Run 2 *Worksheet*

Again, there is some relationship between the starting percentage alcohol and the Proof Gallons remaining in the still as it relates to the 390 gallons of water that we used to begin with.

Summarizing the costs shows that the cost per Proof Gallon is only $2.34 for this run (Table 146).

Strip Run Cost Per Gallon Condensed if using all natural gas for heat			
Cost Per Proof Gal. Condensed		**Cost Per Wine Gallon Condensed**	
Cost Per MCF	$15.00	$15.00	Cost Per MCF
% of MCF Per Proof Gal.	2.28%	1.99%	BTU per Wine Gal./1,000,000 BTU's per MCF = % of MCF Per Wine Gal
Cost Per Proof Gal.	$0.34	$0.30	Cost Per Wine Gal. Condensed
Total BTU's applied	2,490,000.0		
Total MCF	2.49		
Total Energy Cost	$37.4		
Total Cooling Costs Restated	$16.50	$16.50	
Cost Per Proof Gal.	$0.15	$0.13	Cost Per Wine Gal. Condensed
Total Energy Costs per Proof Gal.	$0.49	$0.43	Total Energy Costs per Wine Gal.
Corn Costs per Proof Gallon			
Lbs. per Bag of Corn	50.0		
Corn Cost per Bag	$8.50		
Lbs. Per Bushel	56.0		
Bags per Bushel	1.12		
Cost per Bushel	$9.52		
Bushels used	26.79		
Total Corn Cost	$255.00		
Proof Gallons Produced	109.10		
Cost per Proof Gallon	$2.34		

TABLE 146—Refer to Strip Run 2 *Worksheet*

5.3 Fermentation and Strip Run 3 —————

Moving on we can look at a third fermentation and stripping run (Table 147).

Fermentation Run 3

	Hours	Days	Shop Temp	Tank Top Surface	Tank Bottom Surface	Tank Temp Differential	Sugar % by Refractometer	Sugar % by Hydrometer	Mash Temp Top
	0	0.00	44	86	79	7	24	23	86
Insulation On	17	0.71	39	86	75	11	19	16	88
	72	3.00	41	85	62	23	11	3	87
	96	4.00	42	80	59	21	10	0	80
	120	5.00	47	74	59	15	10	0	75
	144	6.00	47	70	57	13	9	-1	70
	160	6.67	47	65	57	8	9	-1	65

TABLE 147—Refer to Fermentation Runs *Worksheet*

Strip Run 3

	Elapsed Hours	Hot Water Delivery ° F.	Hot Water Return	Temp Dif.	Tank Top Temp	Tank Bottom Temp	Tank Differential	Lbs. of Alcohol	Lbs. per 1/2 hr.	Lbs. per Hr.	Gallons Condensed	Boiler Pressure Lbs.	Still Pres.	True Proof
Start		56	56	0	71	60	11							
		107	103	4	152	81	71							
Running @ 3.75 Hours	3.5	143	137	6	193	92	101	0				15		
	4.0	196	193	3	194	92	102	17	17	34				102
	4.3	197	194	3	197	100	97	79	62	124	16.2			115
	4.8	198	195	3	200	100	100	151	72	144	19.0			125
	5.3	202	197	5	200	101	99	222	71	142	18.6	45		115
	5.8	205	199	6	204	101	103	294	72	144	18.8	45	1	115
	6.3	208	201	7	207	101	106	368	73	147	18.9	45	1	102
		210	204	6				413	45					
	6.8	211	205	6	210	109	101	32	77	154	19.7	44	2	93
	7.3	211	205	6	208	113	95	113	81	162	20.5	43	2	84
		211	206	5	208	113	95	200	88	175	22.0	42	1	74
	8.3	212	208	4	207	117	90	272	72	144	18.0	41	1	65
	8.8	212	208	4	209	124	85	346	74	147	18.2	41	1	54
		212	209	3	210	125	85	415	69	138	17.0	41	1	51
	9.8	210	210	0	211	130	81	62	62	123	15.2	41	1	43
	10.3	210	210	0	211	134	77	127	66	131	16.1	41	1	36
								954.8	Total Drum Wt.					
Total Wt.			954.8											
Empty Weight of Each Drum (Tare)			23.0											
Number of Drums			3.0											
Total Drum Wt.			69.0											
Net Alcohol Wt.			885.8											

TABLE 148—Refer to Strip Run 3 *Worksheet*

This was a middling batch. I did make a good bit of sugar, and the fermentation did OK, but the low shop temperatures held it back. I had to let it ferment 6.6 days in order to get it to complete.

The stripping operation is summarized in Table 148 (previous page).

The only good thing about this run is that I was able to collect the optimal amount of alcohol in the least amount of time. The output in lbs. per hour was about as good as my still will produce. You can see the bulge in weight per hour condensed in the middle of the run and that increase is also reflected in the gallons as well (Table 149).

Strip Run 3			
Alcohol Collected	**Lbs.**		
Drum 1 net Lbs.	397.0		
Drum 2 net Lbs.	373.8		
Drum 3 net Lbs.	85.0	131.7	Avg. Lbs. Per Hour
Total Lbs. Condensed	855.8	16.8	Avg. Wine Gallons Per Hour
Hours of Condensing Time	6.5	14.6	Avg. Proof Gallons Per Hour
Total Wine Gallons	109.00	125.0	Highest Proof During Run
Total Proof Gallons	94.96	35.0	Ending, Lowest, Proof
Proof Gal./Wine Gal. * 100 = Avg. Proof	87.12		
% By Vol. @ 60° F	43.6		
Total Hours - Boiler Run Time	10.3	6.6	Condensing Hrs.
BTU's From Oil Boiler per Hr.	180,000.0	180,000.0	
Total Oil BTU's	1,854,000.0	1,188,000.0	
Total Hours Gas Boiler Run	5.0	1.2	
BTU's From Gas Boiler per Hr.	120,000.0	120,000.0	
Total Gas BTU's	600,000.0	145,200.0	
Total BTU's applied	2,454,000.0	1,333,200.0	
Gross BTU's per Wine Gal. Condensed	22,513.8	12,231.2	BTU's per WG
Gross BTU's per Proof Gal. Condensed	22,513.8	14,039.6	BTU's per PG
		202,000	Avg. BTU's per Condensing Hr.
		6.03	Avg. Boiler Hp.
		69.78%	System Efficiency
Gross BTU's per Condensing Hr.	202,000.0	8,535.1	Applied BTU's per WG
Applied BTU's per Condensing Hr.	140,958.1	9,797.0	Applied BTU's per PG
Applied Boiler Hp. per Condensing Hr.	4.21	930,324	Total applied BTU's

TABLE 149—Refer to Strip Run 3 Worksheet

Despite the middling fermentation I was able to recover almost 95 Proof Gallons. Part of the decrease in yield is the number of Wine Gallons I condensed: only 109 gal. rather than 125, and I cut off at 35 proof instead of 30. I really just wanted two full drums out of this. I was running out of space to put drums and I didn't need another drum with just 10 gallons in it taking up space (Table 150, next page).

Comparing the energy inputs to the mathematical formulations showed less agreement than usual (Table 151, next page).

Probably the cold shop temperatures contributed to the increased number of BTU's required per gallon. The still was simply radiating more energy and the efficiency went down in a way that is difficult to measure.

Calculate yield per Bushel			Calculate Metric yield	
Corn Wt. Used	1,500.00		0.453592	Pounds Avdp to Kilograms
Lbs. per Bushel	56.00		680.39	Kilograms of Corn
Bushels of Corn	26.79		0.162	Fermented Proof Gal. per Kilogram
Actual Experience for recovery			0.08	Anhydrous Alc. Gal. Per Kg.
Proof Gallons Recovered in Barrels	94.97		80.81	Anhydrous Alc. Gal. per Metric Ton
Proof Gallons Remaining in Still	15.00		161.6	Proof Gal. per Metric Ton
Total Proof Gallons Fermented	109.97			
Fermented Proof Gal. per Bushel	4.11	2.05	Anhydrous Alc. Gal. Per Bushel	
Recovered Proof Gal. per Bushel	3.55	1.77	Anhydrous Alc. Gal. Per Bushel	
Compared to Industry Goals Coarse Grind				
Efficiency of Fermentation (Coarse Grind)	77.5%	Actual Proof Gallons/Industry Goals Proof Gallons		
Efficiency of Recovery Coarse Grind	66.9%			
Efficiency of Recovery Fine Grind	62.2%			

TABLE 150—Refer to Strip Run 3 *Worksheet*

If one uses the cost of natural gas as a benchmark you can compute the cost to vaporize a Proof Gallon or a Wine Gallon (Table 152). The lower corn costs for this run amount to $2.69 per Proof Gallon (Table 153).

Find BTU's to Vaporize Alcohol & Water Mixtures	
Alcohol % of Mixture	6.00%
Avg. Proof of Mixture to Be Vaporized	12.00
Water % of Mixture	94.00%
Energy to Vaporize Water Calories Per Gram	539.55
Energy Required to Vaporize Alcohol	200.87
Find Latent Heat of Vaporization (LHV)	519.23
Calories per Kg	519,229
Calories to Joules	4.1868
Kilojoules per Kg	2,173.91
Kilojoules to BTU's	0.947817
BTU's per Kg.	2,060.47
Kg to Lbs.	0.4535924
BTU's per Lb.	934.61
Lbs. per Gal. @ Proof	8.2576
Lbs. per Gal. * BTU's per Lb. = BTU's per Gal.	7,717.69
Compare to Calculated BTU Value per Gal.	8,535.08
Correspondence %	110.59%

TABLE 151—Refer to Strip Run 3 *Worksheet*

Cost Per Gallon Vaporized by Heat	
Cost Per 1,000 Cubic Feet (MCF)	$15.00
BTU's per cubic foot	1,000
BTU's per 1,000 cubic feet	1,000,000
Total BTU's applied	2,005,714
Total MCF Used	2.01
Cost of Energy	$30.09
Wine Gallons Restated	109.0
Proof Gallons Restated	95.0
Cost per Wine Gallon	$0.28
Cost per Proof Gallon	$0.32

TABLE 152

Corn Costs per Proof Gallon	
Lbs. per Bag of Corn	50.0
Corn Cost per Bag	$8.50
Lbs. Per Bushel	56.0
Bags per Bushel	1.12
Cost per Bushel	$9.52
Bushels used	26.79
Total Corn Cost	$255.00
Proof Gallons Produced	94.97
Cost per Proof Gallon	$2.69

TABLE 153—Refer to Strip Run 3 *Worksheet*

CHAPTER 6 Distillation Cooling Calculations

6.1 Distallation Cooling Calcs

Table 154 shows the water consumption and energy transfer for my two-circuit condenser system. (Continued in Table 155, next page)

Cooling Data & Calcs

Red Water Exchange Circuit

Condenser Water Input Temp   45.0

Time	Red Circuit Water Meter	Output Temp	Gal. per 1/2 Hr.	Gal. per Min.	BTU's per Gal.	BTU's per 1/2 Hr.	BTU's per Hr. Calc	Avg. Gal per Hr.
10:50 AM	4,390	45.0	0.0	0.00	0.0	0.0		
11:20 AM	4,430	114.0	40.0	1.33	574.6	22,985.3	45,970.6	80
11:50 AM	4,510	118.0	80.0	2.67	607.9	48,635.5	97,271.0	160
12:20 PM	4,610	106.6	100.0	3.33	513.0	51,300.5	102,601.0	200
12:50 PM	4,700	90.0	90.0	3.00	374.8	33,728.4	67,456.8	180
1:20 PM	4,770	95.0	70.0	2.33	416.4	29,148.0	58,296.0	140
1:50 PM	4,870	104.0	100.0	3.33	491.4	49,135.2	98,270.4	200
2:20 PM	4,970	100.0	100.0	3.33	458.0	45,804.0	91,608.0	200
2:50 PM	5,050	97.0	80.0	2.67	433.1	34,644.5	69,289.0	160
3:20 PM	5,130	101.0	80.0	2.67	466.4	37,309.4	74,618.9	160
3:50 PM	5,205	104.0	75.0	2.50	491.4	36,851.4	73,702.8	150
4:20 PM	5,280	110.0	75.0	2.50	541.3	40,599.0	81,198.0	150
Total Gallons Used	890.0	890.0	Total BTU's Exchanged			430,141		

	BTU's per "Ton" of Cooling	BTU's per Boiler Hp.			BTU's per "Ton"	BTU's per Boiler Hp.		
	12,000	33,475			12,000	33,475		

Time	"Tons" of Cooling per Hr.	Boiler Hp. Per Hr.	Trailing Gal. per Hr.	Trailing BTU's per Hr.	"Tons" of Cooling per Hr.	Boiler Hp. Per Hr.	Gal. per min.
10:50 AM							
11:20 AM	3.83	1.37					
11:50 AM	8.11	2.91	120.0	72,953	6.08	2.18	2.0
12:20 PM	8.55	3.07					
12:50 PM	5.62	2.02	190.0	71,204	5.93	2.13	3.2
1:20 PM	4.86	1.74					
1:50 PM	8.19	2.94	170.0	83,530	6.96	2.50	2.8
2:20 PM	7.63	2.74					
2:50 PM	5.77	2.07	180.0	77,950	6.50	2.33	3.0
3:20 PM	6.22	2.23					
3:50 PM	6.14	2.20	155.0	76,160	6.35	2.28	2.6
4:20 PM	6.77	2.43					

TABLE 154—Refer to Cooling Calcs Worksheet

Totaling the heat transfer accomplished by the two circuits and comparing them to the calculated heat input of my boiler indicates that I need about 19.5% fewer BTU's to cool the mixture than to vaporize it. I've assigned

Black Water Exchange Circuit

Condenser Water Input Temp   45.0

Time	Black Circuit Water Meter	Output Temp	Gal. per 1/2 Hr.	Gal. per Min.	BTU's per Gal.	BTU's per 1/2 Hr.	BTU's per Hr. Calc	Avg. Gal per Hr.
10:50 AM	8,860	45.0	0.0	0.00	0.0	0.0		
11:20 AM	8,890	114.0	30.0	1.00	574.6	17,239.0	34,477.9	60
11:50 AM	8,930	118.0	40.0	1.33	607.9	24,317.8	48,635.5	80
12:20 PM	8,950	106.6	20.0	0.67	513.0	10,260.1	20,520.2	40
12:50 PM	8,990	90.0	40.0	1.33	374.8	14,990.4	29,980.8	80
1:20 PM	9,030	95.0	40.0	1.33	416.4	16,656.0	33,312.0	80
1:50 PM	9,060	104.0	30.0	1.00	491.4	14,740.6	29,481.1	60
2:20 PM	9,090	100.0	30.0	1.00	458.0	13,741.2	27,482.4	60
2:50 PM	9,135	97.0	45.0	1.50	433.1	19,487.5	38,975.0	90
3:20 PM	9,180	101.0	45.0	1.50	466.4	20,986.6	41,973.1	90
3:50 PM	9,220	104.0	40.0	1.33	491.4	19,654.1	39,308.2	80
4:20 PM	9,260	110.0	40.0	1.33	541.3	21,652.8	43,305.6	80
Total Gallons Used	400.0	400.0	Total BTU's Exchanged			193,726		

	BTU's per "Ton" of Cooling	BTU's per Boiler Hp.			BTU's per "Ton"	BTU's per Boiler Hp.		
	12,000	33,475			12,000	33,475		

Time	"Tons" of Cooling per Hr.	Boiler Hp. Per Hr.	Trailing Gal. per Hr.	Trailing BTU's per Hr.	"Tons" of Cooling per Hr.	Boiler Hp. Per Hr.	Gal. per min.	Tot. Gal. per Min.
10:50 AM								
11:20 AM	2.87	1.03						
11:50 AM	4.05	1.45	70.0	42,556	3.55	1.27	1.2	3.2
12:20 PM	1.71	0.61						
12:50 PM	2.50	0.90	60.0	22,486	1.87	0.67	1.0	4.2
1:20 PM	2.78	1.00						
1:50 PM	2.46	0.88	70.0	34,395	2.87	1.03	1.2	4.0
2:20 PM	2.29	0.82						
2:50 PM	3.25	1.16	75.0	32,479	2.71	0.97	1.3	4.3
3:20 PM	3.50	1.25						
3:50 PM	3.28	1.17	85.0	41,765	3.48	1.25	1.4	4.0
4:20 PM	3.61	1.29						
						Total		19.6
						Avg. Gal per Min		3.917

TABLE 155—Refer to Cooling Calcs Worksheet

this percentage to BTU's radiated. Some of this could be uncertainties in the data but it seems plausible that this represents actual radiated BTU's (Table 156, next page).

Refer to Section 4.7 *supra*. Remember that we were seeing somewhere between 19% and 23% radiated energy based on the decrease in temperature of the water in the tank per unit of time.

In the Oil Boiler Test the radiation percentage actually increased to 30% as the vessel reached cooking and distillation temperatures.

Since the cooling data reported here was taken at the higher temperature associated with distillation, we might conclude that the radiation was more than 19% as well.

Total Time in Hours	5.5
Grand Tot. BTU's Exchanged	623,867.1
Avg. Total BTU's per Hr.	113,430.4
BTU's per "Ton" of Cooling	12,000
Avg. Tons Cooling per Hr.	9.45
BTU's per Boiler Hp.	33,475
Avg. Boiler Hp. Per Hr.	3.39
Grand Total Gallons Used	1,290.0
Avg Gal. per Hour	234.55
Avg. Gal. per Minute	3.909
Avg. BTU per Gal.	483.62
Compare to Still input values	
Still Input Net BTU's per Hr.	140,958.1
Net boiler Input in Boiler Hp.	4.21
Avg. Condensing BTU's per Hr.	113,430.4
Input to Output BTU Dif. = Gross Radiated BTU's per Hr.	27,527.7
% Cooling BTU's	80.47%
% Radiated BTU's	19.53%
BTU's per "Ton" of Cooling	12,000
Radiated Tons of Cooling per Hr.	2.29
Total Tons of Cooling Based on Input BTU's	
Total Tons of Cooling	11.75

TABLE 156—Refer to Cooling Calcs *Worksheet*

Find differential between vaporization energy and condensation energy		
Find BTU's to Vaporize Alcohol & Water Mixtures		
Alcohol % of Mixture	7.00%	40.00%
Avg. Proof of Mixture to Be Vaporized	14.00	80.00
Water % of Mixture	93.00%	60.00%
Energy to Vaporize Water	539.55	539.55
Energy Required to Vaporize Alcohol	200.87	200.87
Find Latent Heat of Vaporization (LHV)	515.84	404.08
Calories per Kg	515,842	404,078
Calories to Joules	4.1868	4.1868
Kilojoules per Kg	2,159.73	1,691.79
Kilojoules to BTU's	0.947817	0.947817
BTU's per Kg	2,047.03	1,603.51
Kg to Lbs.	0.4535924	0.4535924
BTU's per Lb.	928.52	727.34
	78.3%	
Percentage Fewer Calories per Lb.	21.7%	

TABLE 157—Refer to Cooling Calcs *Worksheet*

One other consideration needs to be addressed. The energy required to vaporize the alcohol in the still is substantially greater than that required to condense it. Taking the average alcohol concentrations of the batch we see that the energy required to condense is 21.7% less than that required to vaporize it (Table 157).

I can't be certain how the difference in energy required to condense related to the total radiated BTU's, but we will return to this topic in the Condensing BTU Advantage section *infra*.

For now, we can simply conclude that in my still setup the cooling requirements are somewhere between 9.45 and 11.75 tons of cooling per hour to handle the cooling load of my still.

In terms of the BTU's per gallon transferred by my condenser system, the data assembled for these calculations is confirmed by comparison to other data that I have collected (Table 158, next page).

The condenser barrel is a heat reservoir that can absorb some of the irregularities in heat output from the still. Calculating the heat buffer size of my condenser shows that there are about 1.56 tons of cooling buffer in each condenser barrel (Table 159, next page).

This means that if your water flow stops for any reason you have about 15 minutes of reserve cooling in the condenser before it becomes too hot to do its job effectively.

Condenser and cooler, both set up and ready.

I also need to explain the gradient in the condenser barrel. It is a convenient way to measure the amount of heat buffer, or in this case, cold buffer, one has. As the barrel heats up, the bottom will stay colder than the top. You will be able to feel with your hand where the transition is from cold to hot on the vertical face of the barrel. One wants to keep that transition interface as high up on the barrel as possible to retain the most cooling buffer in the barrel consistent with not using more water than is necessary to cool the batch.

Comparison to other worksheets	Cooling Calcs	Strip Run 2	2nd Data Set
Avg. BTU's	113,430	113,951	116,176
Avg. Tons	9.45	9.50	9.68
Avg. Gal. per Minute	3.91	3.93	3.88
Avg. BTU's per Gal	483.6	483.4	499.7

TABLE 158—Refer to Cooling Calcs *Worksheet*

Calculate Buffer size of condenser barrel water	
Find BTU's Exchanged	
Gallons of water to change temp.	50.00
Weight per Gallon of Water	8.32823
Gal. * Lbs. per Gal. = H_2O Lbs. to change temperature	416.41
Starting Temperature	45.00
Desired Ending Temperature	90.00
Temperature Difference	45.00
Pounds * Temp Dif. = BTU's required to Cool	18,738.52
Condenser Buffer Tons of Cooling	1.56

TABLE 159—Refer to Cooling Calcs *Worksheet*

6.2 Distillation Cooling Calcs 2

Table 160 is a somewhat simplified method of making cooling calculations.

Cooling Calcs 2				Red Water Circuit						Black Water Circuit				
Data from Strip Run 2	Hrs.	Time	Spout Temp	H2O Input Temp	1.25" Coil H2O Output ° F.	1.25" Coil Gal per Hr.	Cooling BTU's Per Hr.	Gal. per Minute	.75 in Coil H2O Output ° F.	.75 in Coil Gal. per Hr.	BTU's Per Hr.	Gal. per Minute	Total Gal. per Min
	0.0	5:00 AM											
		5:30 AM											
Running @ 3 1/2 Hours	3.5	8:30 AM											
		8:50 AM											
	4.5	9:20 AM	48.0	45	107	130	67,124	2.2	105	90.0	44,971	1.5	3.7
		9:50 AM											
	5.5	10:20 AM	52.0	45	114	130	74,702	2.2	99	90.0	40,474	1.5	3.7
		10:50 AM											
	6.5	11:20 AM	70.0	45	108	130	68,206	2.2	99	60.0	26,983	1.0	3.2
Drum 1 Full 413 Lbs. net		11:35 AM											
		11:50 AM	83.0	45	108	150	78,700	2.5	95	90.0	37,476	1.5	4.0
	7.5	12:20 PM											
		12:50 PM											
	8.5	1:20 PM	80.0	45	108	150	78,700	2.5	95	90.0	37,476	1.5	4.0
		1:50 PM											
Drum 2 full 421 lbs. net	9.5	2:20 PM	79.0	45	101	180	83,946	3.0	98	90.0	39,725	1.5	4.5
		2:50 PM											
Drum 3 149 lbs. net	10.5	3:30 PM	79.0	45	98	180	79,449	3.0	98	90.0	39,725	1.5	4.5
				1,050		530,827	Tot BTU's		600		266,829	Tot BTU's	

TABLE 160—Refer to Cooling Calcs 2 *Worksheet*

Condensing Hrs.	7.0
Tot. Cooling BTU's	797,656
Avg. BTU's per Hr.	113,951
Average "Tons" of Cooling per Hr.	9.5
Avg. BTU's per Gal	483.4
Total Water Gallons used for Cooling	1,650.0
Avg. Gal. per Minute	3.93
Still Input Net BTU's per Hr.	140,958
Avg. Condensing BTU's per Hr.	113,951
Input to Output BTU Dif.	27,007
% Cooling BTU's	80.84%
% Radiated BTU's	19.16%
Calculate Cooling Costs	
Total Water Gallons used for Cooling	1,650.0
Cost per Gal.	$0.01
Total Cooling Costs	$16.5

TABLE 161—Refer to Cooling Calcs 2 Worksheet

The results are very similar to the Cooling Calcs section above. The data was taken from Strip Run 2. Note that I had to increase the gallon per minute flow as the batch went along to keep the spout temperature, which is the temperature of the alcohol as it exits the condenser, within a reasonable limit. Even on a strip run one should not let the whiskey run too hot out of the condenser, except at the end of the run when you are just trying to get the last alcohol out.

Table 161 shows that the average gallons per minute and BTU's per gallon are about the same as in the first cooling calculations worksheet and that the percentage radiated is in the same percentile at 19% of the total.

6.3 Distillation Cooling Calcs 3

Table 162 (next page) shows an even more simplified method to calculate the amount of cooling energy supplied to the still. In this method one simply takes the beginning and ending gallon value from the water meters and applies an average temperature to the output value after the water has served its purpose of acquiring heat from the condenser.

Cooling Calcs 3

Red Water Exchange Circuit

								BTU's per "Ton" of Cooling	BTU's per Boiler Hp.
Water Meter Start Reading	3,480								
Condenser Water Input Temp	45.0							12,000	33,475

Time	Red Circuit Water Meter	Avg. Output Temp	Total Gal	BTU's per Gal.	Total BTU's	BTU's per Hr. Calc	Avg. Gal per Hr.	"Tons" of Cooling per Hr.	Boiler Hp. Per Hr.
2:00 AM									
8:00 AM	4,230	105.0	750.0	499.7	374,760	62,460	125	5.21	1.87
Total Gallons Used	750.0	750.0							
Total Hours	6.0								
Total Minutes	360.0								
Gallons per Minute	2.1								

Black Water Exchange Circuit

								BTU's per "Ton" of Cooling	BTU's per Boiler Hp.
Water Meter Start Reading	8,690								
Condenser Water Input Temp	45.0							12,000	33,475

Time	Red Circuit Water Meter	Avg. Output Temp	Total Gal	BTU's per Gal.	Total BTU's	BTU's per Hr. Calc	Avg. Gal per Hr.	"Tons" of Cooling per Hr.	Boiler Hp. Per Hr.
2:00 AM									
6:00 AM	9,120	105.0	430.0	499.7	214,862	53,716	108	4.48	1.60
Total Gallons Used	430.0	430.0							
Total Hours	4.0								
Total Minutes	240.0								
Gallons per Minute	1.8								

TABLE 162—Refer to Cooling Calcs 3 *Worksheet*

Water meters for filling the still.

Combining the data and calculating the costs (Table 163).

Combined Cooling Data			
Avg. Gallons per Minute	3.88		
Grand Total Gallons Used	1,180.0		
Avg. BTU per Gal.	499.68		
Grand Tot. BTU's Exchanged	589,622.4		
Avg. Total BTU's per Hr.	116,175.6		
BTU's per "Ton" of Cooling	12,000	33,475	BTU's per Boiler Hp.
Avg. Tons Cooling per Hr.	9.68	3.47	Avg. Boiler Hp. Per Hr.
Applied BTU's per Condensing Hr.	140,958		
Net boiler Input in Boiler Hp.	4.21		
Avg. Condensing BTU's per Hr.	116,175.6		
Input to Output BTU Dif.	24,782.5	Gross Radiated BTU's per Hr.	
% Radiated BTU's	17.58%		
BTU's per "Ton" of Cooling	12,000		
Avg. Tons Cooling per Hr.	2.07	Radiated Tons of Cooling	
BTU's per Boiler Hp.	33,475		
Boiler Hp. Radiated	0.74		
Cooling Costs			
Total Gallons	1,180.00	4.00	Batches per Month
Cost per Gallon	$0.01	4,720.00	Total Gallons
Total Cost per Batch	$11.80	$47.20	Total Costs

TABLE 163—Refer to Cooling Calcs 3 *Worksheet*

The data is consistent with the other data reported above, showing in this case 499.68 BTU's per gallon of heat acquired per Table 163 above. The radiated BTU percentage of 17.58% of the input BTU's is less than the 19% value calculated previously. The cost per batch is also calculated.

Also included is the following algorithm (Table 164) which allows one to determine how much more water one needs to use to achieve the same amount of cooling when the water is at different temperatures. This is also included in digital still mass and digital still volume worksheets.

Find Gal. per Min. Flow to achieve same cooling at different water temps.		
Cooling Water Heat Absorbing Capacity		
Water input Temperature	45.00	63.00
Water Output Temperature	104.00	104.00
Temperature Change	59.00	41.00
Weight per Gallon used as BTU's per ° of Change	8.32823	8.32823
° of Change * Wt. per Gal. = BTU's per min.	491.37	341.46
Gallons per Hour Required	236.4	340.2
Gallons per Min. Flow Result	3.94	5.67
Total BTU's per minute	1,936.26	1,936.26
BTU's per Hour	116,175.60	116,176
Ton of Refrigeration Constant in BTU's	12,000.00	12,000.00
Tons of Refrigeration per hour Equivalent	9.68	9.68
Radiation %	16.0%	16.0%
Net Tons of cooling required per Hr.	8.1	8.1

TABLE 164—Refer to Cooling Calcs 3 *Worksheet*

6.4 Run Pause Ratio

Calculate Run Time % from Run Time to Pause Time Ratio			
Run Time Gas	2.0		
Pause Time	9.0		
Ratio	4.5		
One Minute % of Hour	0.01667		
Run % of hour for each cycle	3.3%	Minute Ratio	
Pause % of hour for each cycle	15.0%		
Total % per hour per cycle	18.3%		
1/% = Cycles per Hr.	5.45		
Run time * Cycles per Hr. = Min per hr.	10.91	18.2%	Run %
Pause Min	49.1	81.8%	Pause %
Total Min	60.0		
Find BTU's per hour based on run time			
Min per Hr. Run	10.91		
% of Hour	18.18%		
Boiler BTU Per Hr.	120,000		
Actual BTU Use per Hr.	21,818		

TABLE 165—Refer to Run Pause Ratio *Worksheet*

My gas boiler only runs part of the time. To calculate how much heat energy it contributes to the batch, I built the following run time to pause time worksheet (Table 165).

CHAPTER 7 Building a Digital Still

7.1 Water Heat

Now we will take everything that we have learned from making whiskey the old fashioned way and build a digital still. To do this we need to start with heating and vaporizing water and work our way up to vaporizing alcohol.

Since it is easier to think in volume rather than mass we will proceed with caution using volume. In order to do so, we need to make a few assumptions that do not appreciably affect the results.

We are assuming our water is starting at its freezing temperature. That is not the point where water is most dense. Water is most dense at 3.98° C. It actually expands, just a bit, from 3.98° C down to freezing point. This is understandable in that as water freezes its molecules arrange themselves as ice crystals which, when frozen, occupy about 10% more volume than they do in a liquid state. During this phase the water molecules, which are bipolar in their electrical charge, are starting to arrange themselves to cancel out the charge between them as they freeze.

Secondly, we are assuming that even at 3.98° C water has a mass of 1 kilogram per liter. This is also not quite true. The density of water at 3.98° C is 0.99975 kilograms per liter at C.[43] This difference amounts to 25 parts out of 100,000 or 0.25 parts out of 1,000, amounting to 25 grams per 1,000 kilograms.

The third assumption we are making is that the water has the specified density and mass in a vacuum rather than in the atmosphere. This topic is covered more fully in the ABS Software manual. In summary I offer the following for this assumption. Roughly speaking the atmosphere buoys up a mass of 1 metric ton of water by about 1.06 kilograms. Therefore a scale in the atmosphere indicating a reading of 1,000 kilograms has in fact been loaded with 1,001.06 kilograms to achieve that reading. This discrepancy of 1 part out of 1,000 is not significant enough to affect these calculations in a material way.

In terms of heating water to its vaporization temperature we are assuming the specific heat of water as follows (Table 166):

Specific Heat of Water	
1.0 BTU per pound mass per ° F	1.00
1.0 calorie per gram per ° C	1.00

TABLE 166—Refer to Vaporize H$_2$O 2 Worksheet

Table 167 (next page) demonstrates how much energy is required to heat water from its freezing temperature to its boiling temperature starting with 1,000 liters or one metric ton of mass, that mass being its mass in a vacuum as per the definition of a kilogram. We find that 396,832 BTU's are required to raise the temperature of 1,000 liters of water at 1 kilogram per liter.

Along the way we can check some of our converter values to other energy units and then back to BTU's and verify their efficacy.

---

43   See "History of the Liter" section and worksheet in the ABS software manual (included in the software package).

Water Heating			
Liters * Kg per Liter = Total Kilograms	1,000.000	2.20462260	Kg to Lbs.(Uconeer)
Find Energy to Change Water Temperature		2,204.6226	Lbs.
° C Starting Temperature	0.00	32.00	Starting Temperature ° F
° C Ending Temperature	100.00	212.00	Ending Temperature ° F
° C Temp Change	100.00	180.00	Temperature Change
Grams	1,000,000	396,832	Lbs. * Temp Change = BTU's to change Temp
Grams * ° C Change = Gram Calories	100,000,000	11.85	Heating Boiler Hp.
Find Joules to Heat Water			
Calories to Joules (Uconeer Value)	4.1868	1,055.0559	BTU to Joules Converter
Gram Calories * Joules per Calorie = Joules	418,680,000	418,680,015	BTU's * Converter = Joules Required
Find BTU's to Heat and Vaporize Water			
Gram Calories to BTU's (Uconeer Value)	0.003968321	251.99576	BTU's to Gram Calorie Converter
BTU's Required	396,832.07	99,999,999	Gram Calories of Energy to Change Temp
Joules/3,600 /1000 = Kw. Hrs.	116.30	0.00029287	BTU to Kw Hr.
Electric cost per Kw Hr.	$0.10	116.22	Kw Hrs. OK
Total Electric Cost	$11.63		
Kw Hrs. to Hp. Hours	1.3419	0.000393015	BTU's to Hp. Hrs.
Horsepower Hrs. (Mechanical & Electric)	156.06	155.96	Mechanical Hp. Hours
Kw Hrs. to Metric Hp. Hours	1.35985	0.0760	Hp. Hrs. (Mech.) to Hp. Hrs. Boiler
Metric Horsepower Hours	158.2	11.85	Boiler Horsepower Hrs.
Gram Cal. To BTU's	0.00396832		
BTU's	396,832		

TABLE 167—Refer to Water Heat *Worksheet*

7.2 Vaporize Water 1

Now that we have heated our water to its boiling point we need to determine how much energy is required to vaporize that water. In this worksheet we are working from the physical constants for water vaporization towards values per kilogram and gallon, and then finding other energy units from those values (Table 168, next page)

In this worksheet I also had to derive some of my own values so that my gram calories would match my joules per gram of water. You can see how I arrived at my values for joules per gram of water based upon 539.55 gram calories per gram of water which matches the value obtained from my reference book (*Pocket Ref,* page 108).

An important value derived in the above worksheet is the BTU's per lb. of water. The value adopted is 971.9 BTU's per lb. rather than the traditional value of 970. Using this value we can have a reciprocal relation between that value and our gram calories per gram.

Energy Required to Vaporize Water		Check Reciprocality				Gram Calories to Vaporize 1 Gram of H_2O Pocket Ref. P. 108
Gram Calories to Vaporize 1 Gram of H_2O	539.55	2,258.99	Joules per Gram			Traditional Calories per Gram to Vaporize Water
Calories to Joules (Uconeer Value)	4.18680	0.2388459	Joules to Cal. (Uconeer)			Traditional Value Gram Calories to Vaporize 1 Gram of H_2O
Gram Cal to Vaporize * Joules per Gram = Joules per Gram Vaporized	2,258.99	539.55	Gram Calories			
						Calories to Joules (Uconeer Value)
Kilojoules per Kg to Vaporize Water	2,258.99					Intl. Steam Table Gram Calorie= 4.1868 Joules
Kilojoules to Calories (Uconeer)	238.84590					Second Source One Mean Gram Calorie = 4.190 Joules
Calories per Kg	539,550					
Calories per Gram	539.550					
Grams per Lb.	453.59237					Joules per Gram Engineering Toolbox Source
Gram Calories per Lb.	244,736					Traditional Joules per Gram
Calories to Kilojoules	0.00418680					Derived Value from 539.55 G. Cal.
Kilojoules per Lb.	1,024.66					
Kilojoules to BTU's	0.947817120					Gram Calories to Vaporize 1 Gram of H_2O Pocket Ref. P. 108
BTU's per Lb.	971.19					Derived Value
Find BTU's per Lb. and Gal.						Traditional Calories per Gram to Vaporize Water
Kg to Lbs.	2.2046226					Traditional Value Gram Calories to Vaporize 1 Gram of H_2O
Cal per Kg/Kg to Lb. =Calories per Lb.	244,736					
Calories to BTU's (Uconeer)	0.0039683207					Traditional Value BTU's per lb.
BTU's per Lb.	971.19					BTU's per Lb. Dif.
Lbs. per Gal. (Air)	8.328198					
BTU's per Gal.	8,088.26					Compare to Vap Alc 2 when set to water
						BTU's per Gal Dif.
Find Kilojoules per Mole			**Compare Value**			
Kilojoules per Kg to Vaporize Water	2,258.99		2,258.99			
Kilojoules per Gram to Vaporize Water	2.25899		2.25899			
Atomic Wt. of Water Grams per Mole	18.0153		18.0000			Machinery's Handbook Value
Kilojoules per Mole	40.70		40.66			Wikipedia kJ/mol
Find Atomic Weight of Water						
Water Formula H_2O	Atoms	Mass	Total			
	2.00	1.00794	2.016	Hydrogen		
	1.00	15.9994	15.999	Oxygen		
			18.01528	Total Molecular Wt.		

TABLE 168—Refer to Vaporize H_2O 1 *Worksheet*

The sheet also contains a comparison between the kilojoules per mole required based upon two different assumed atomic weights for water, and compares them to values in published literature and online sources.

The worksheet portion (Table 169, next page) shows that assuming 1,000 grams per kilogram does not appreciably affect the moles per kilogram.

It also concludes, correctly, that there will be fewer moles per liter at 60° F (15.556° C) based on whether the water is measured in air or vacuum. Also, there is some difference in the values assigned to the mass of water, even by the TTB itself.

	Lbs. per Gal. Air	Lbs. per Gal. Vac @ 60° F.		Separate TTB Value for Lbs. per Gal. H2O	
Grams per Kilogram	1,000.00	999.75	Grams per Liter @ 4° C		
Atomic Wt. of Water	18.0153	18.0153			
Moles per Kilogram @ 4° C	55.508	55.495		0.014	Moles Dif.
Lbs. per Gal. Air Using 1/Table 4 Results	8.32820	8.33740	AlcoDens & Uconeer Lbs. per Gallon Value	8.328230	Pounds Per Gallon of Water @ 60° (15.56° C) § 5.47a
		-0.009202	TTB Dif. from AlcoDens TTB is Lighter. Air to Vac Density Dif.		
	Air	**Vac**			
Kilograms per Gal.	3.778	3.782			
Liters per Gal.	3.785	3.785			
Kilograms per Liter @ 60° F	0.99794	0.99904			
Grams per Liter	997.94	999.04			
Atomic Wt. of Water Grams per Mole	18.0153	18.0153			
Moles per Liter Air @ 60° F	55.394	55.455	Moles per Liter Vac @ 60° F	-0.061	Moles Dif.
				-0.053	Moles Dif. From 4° C Air
Liters per Gal.	3.785	3.785		-0.039	Moles Dif. From 4° C Vac
Moles per Gal. @ 60° F (Air)	209.69	209.92	Moles per Gal. @ 60° F (Vac)		

TABLE 169—Refer to Vaporize H₂O 1 *Worksheet*

Checking the derived BTU's per lb. (Table 170) shows that it is reciprocal with our starting calories per gram.

Heat of Vaporization for Water Cross Check		
Water Latent heat of Vaporization lb.	971.19	BTU's per Pound
BTU's to Gram Calories (Uconeer)	251.9958	
BTU's per lb. *Value= gCal per 1 lb.	244,735.7655	
Grams per Lb.	453.592370	Difference
g Cal./Grams per Lb.=gCal per gram	539.5500	0.00

TABLE 170—Refer to Vaporize H₂O 1 *Worksheet*

Using the assumed calories and the derived BTU's per lb. we can derive the same value for BTU's per gram (Table 171).

Find BTU's per Gram to Vaporize Water		
Cal. To Vaporize 1 Gram of H₂0	539.55	
Gram Calories to BTU's (Uconeer)	0.0039683207	
Gram Calories per Gram * Cal to BTU Converter = BTU's to Vaporize 1 Gram H₂O	2.1411	Derived Value
Using BTU's per Lb. Find BTU's per Gram to Vaporize Water		
BTU's to Vaporize 1 Lb. Water	971.19	
Grams per Lb. (Uconeer Value)	453.592	
BTU/Grams per Lb.=BTU's per Gram	2.14111	Derived Value

TABLE 171—Refer to Vaporize H2O 1 *Worksheet*

With these values determined we can proceed to create a water vaporization worksheet that begins from boiler horsepower and gives results in the mass vaporized.

7.3 Vaporize Water 2

Table 172 proceeds from units of boiler horsepower to determine the amount of water vaporized by that energy input.

Energy Required to Vaporize Water Based on Boiler Hp. Input				
Boiler Horsepower Available	1.00			
BTU's per Hour per "Boiler Horsepower"	33,475.00		**Find Joules of Energy**	
Total BTU's Per Hour Available	33,475.00	1,054.350		BTU to Joules Converter
Heat Transfer Efficiency from Boiler to Still/Cooker	100.0%	35,294,366.3		BTU's * Converter = Joules per Hour
Actual BTU's Delivered to Contents of Vessel	33,475.00	9.8040		(Joules/60)/60/1000 = Kilowatt Hours
BTU's to Gram Calories	251.996	$0.10		1 Kw. Cost
BTU's * Converter = Gram Calories Available	8,435,558.07	$0.98		Total Cost
Calories to Joules (Uconeer)	0.0041868			
Kilojoules	35,317.99			
Find Grams & Gallons per Hour Boil off Rate				
Gram Cal. to Vaporize 1 Gram of Water	539.55			
Gram Cal. Available/Cal. To Vaporize 1 Gram = Total Grams Vaporized per Hour	15,634.43	0.00029287		BTU to Kw Hr.
Grams Per Minute	260.57	9.8038		Kw Hrs. per Boiler Hp.
Grams to U.S. Pounds Converter	0.0022046			
Grams * Converter = Pounds per Hour	34.468			
Pounds Per Gallon (Air)	8.328198	**Gal. to Liters**	**Liters**	
Gallons Per Hour	4.139	3.785413	15.667	
Gallons Per Minute	0.07			
Weight per Gallon @ 60° F (Air)	8.328230	**Lbs. to Kg.**	**Kilograms**	
Total Lbs. of Water per Hour	34.47	0.4535920	15.634	
Pounds per Minute	0.57			
Find Derived Values and Compare				
BTU's per Gram (Derived)	539.5500			
BTU's per Gallon (Derived)	8,088.26			
Find BTU's per Lb.			**Closer to Std. Value**	
Lbs. per Gal. (Air)	8.32820		8.337400	Lbs. per Gal. (Vac)
BTU's per Lb. (Derived)	971.19		970.12	BTU's per Lb. (Derived)

TABLE 172—Refer to Vaporize H₂O 2 Worksheet

What is noticeable about this worksheet is that using the lbs. per gallon in a vacuum and at 60° F (15.556° C) derived from BTU's per gallon gives a value closer to the traditional value of 970 BTU's per lb. This is misleading in that we are using the mass of water per gallon in air as the starting point.

Most scientific research attempts to find the absolute vacuum values for the physical constants they are measuring. This makes is difficult for those of us who work in an atmosphere to determine the applicability of those measured constants. In this case we might label 917.19 as BTU's per lib in air for reference. What I did test was to substitute the vacuum value for the mass of one gallon of water and it just made the problem worse.

The worksheet is in substantial compliance with the following definition of a boiler horsepower: Boiler Horsepower = 33,475 BTU/h (9.8095 kW), which is the energy rate needed to evaporate 34.5 lbs. (15.65 kg) of water at 212° F (100° C) in one hour. The worksheet calculates the pounds per hour at 34.47.

7.4 Water, Heat and Vaporize

Now we will combine our heating and vaporization worksheets together to heat and vaporize water (Table 173).

Water Heating and Vaporization			
Kilograms of water	1,000.000	2.20462260	Kg to Lbs.(Uconeer)
Find Energy to Change Water Temperature		2,204.6226	Lbs.
° C Starting Temperature	0.00	32.00	Starting Temperature ° F
° C Ending Temperature	100.00	212.00	Ending Temperature ° F
° C Temp Change	100.00	180.00	Temperature Change
Grams	1,000,000	396,832	Lbs. * Temp Change = BTU's to change Temp
Grams * ° C Change = Gram Calories	100,000,000	11.85	Heating Boiler Hp.
Find Joules to Heat Water			
Calories to Joules (Uconeer Value)	4.1868	1,055.0559	BTU to Joules Converter
Gram Calories * Joules per Calorie = Joules	418,680,000	418,680,015	BTU's * Converter = Joules Required
Find BTU's to Heat and Vaporize Water			
Gram Calories to BTU's (Uconeer Value)	0.003968321	251.99576	BTU's to Gram Calorie Converter
BTU's Required	396,832.07	99,999,999	Gram Calories of Energy to Change Temp
Find Vaporization Energy			
Joules to Vaporize 1 g. of H_2O	2,258.99	971.19	BTU's to Vaporize 1 Lb. of H_2O
Grams * Joules per Gram = Total Joules	2,258,987,940	2,141,107	Lbs. * BTU's per Lb. = Tot BTU's
Find Gram Calories to Vaporize Water		63.96	Vaporization Boiler Hp.
Gram Calories for 1 Gram H_2O @ (212°) to steam	539.55	251.9958	BTU's to Gram Calorie Converter
Grams * Constant = Vaporization Gram Calories	539,550,000	539,549,992	Gram Calories of Energy to Change Temp
Find BTU's to Vaporize Water			
Gram Calories to BTU's	0.00396832	4.1868	Calories to Joules
BTU's Required to Vaporize Water	2,141,107.4	2,258,987,908	Joules to Vaporize
Find Totals			
Total BTU's to Heat and Vaporize	2,537,940	2,537,939	Total BTU's to Heat and Vaporize
Total Joules to Heat and Vaporize	2,677,667,940	2,677,667,922	Total Joules to Heat and Vaporize
Total Gram Calories to Heat and Vaporize	639,550,000	639,549,991	Total Gram Calories to Heat and Vaporize
		75.82	Total Boiler Hp.
% of energy in stage 1	16%	16%	
% of energy in stage 2	84%	84%	
Ratio of Energy to heat as to vaporize	5.40	5.40	

TABLE 173—Refer to Water Heat & Vape *Worksheet*

The primary lesson from this worksheet is to observe the ratio of energy required to heat the water in comparison to that required to vaporize it.

This worksheet demonstrates that it takes 5.4 times as much energy to vaporize water as to heat it from freezing temperature to boiling.

One caveat is that not all BTU's or gram calories are applied to equal effect. Water has a tendency to pick up heat more quickly at some temperatures than at others. Therefore one will see values for "mean calories" or "mean BTU's" that average this small discrepancy into the final value.

7.5 Fusion vs. Vaporization Energy

This is slightly off topic but I want to mention it. Using the heat of fusion for water and comparing it to the vaporization energy required shows that the heat of fusion is only 3.5% of that required to vaporize it. This points out that once water reaches its freezing temperature it requires a relatively small amount of additional energy to be removed in order to induce the phase change from liquid to ice, at least in comparison to the energy required to vaporize it (Table 174).

Specific Heat of Water		
1.0 BTU per pound mass per ° F	1.00	Per pound Mass per ° F
1.0 calorie per gram per ° C	1.00	Per gram per ° C
Water Heat of Fusion @ 0° C Calories per Gram. Pocket Ref.	79.71	
Vaporization Cal per Gram	2,257.00	
Percentage of fusion energy to vape energy	3.5%	

TABLE 174—Refer to Water Heat & Vape *Worksheet*

7.6 Vaporize Alcohol 1

In finding and verifying the values required to vaporize alcohol, we will follow the same path as we constructed for doing so with water. There are conflicting values in the literature relating to the number of joules per gram that are required to vaporize alcohol.[44]

I have adopted the value of 841 kilojoules per kilogram as our standard. We can derive various values and also check the results against the kilojoules per mole values against the *Handbook of Chemistry and Physics* (HCP) value given in kilojoules per mole.

We will start by finding reciprocal values for joules per gram and gram calories per gram, since these are the two most basic energy inputs we will use. Using the Uconeer conversion values, we find that in Table 175 the two energy values are reciprocal when using those values.

Energy Required to Vaporize Alcohol		Check Reciprocality	
Joules per Gram	841.00	200.87	Gram Calories to Vaporize 1 Gram of Alcohol
Joules to Cal. (Uconeer)	0.2388459	4.18680	Calories to Joules (Uconeer Value)
Gram Calories	200.869402	841.00	Gram Cal to * J per Gram = Joules per Gram Vape.

TABLE 175—Refer to Vaporize Alc 1 *Worksheet*

Using the value of 841 kilojoules per kilogram as our standard we then derive various subsidiary values and also check the results against the kilojoules per mole values provided by the *Handbook of Chemistry and Physics* (Table 176, next page).

The results for kilojoules per mole are not quite equal to the HCP value; however, they are sufficiently close for our purposes. Some of the difference may be attributed to the conditions under which the enthalpy of alcohol was determined for each constant.

The worksheet has additional comparisons built in that are not reproduced here.

---

44 841.00 Joules per Gram from *Machinery's Hand Book* 22nd Edition ISBN 0-8311-1155-0. 841.00 Kj Kg -1 Wikipedia Source (Enthalpy). LHV of Alcohol, Engineering Toolbox Values 846.00 kJ per kg and 364.00 BTU per lb.

Kilojoules per Kg to Vaporize Alcohol	841.00
Kilojoules to Calories (Uconeer)	238.84590
Calories per Kg	200,869
Calories per Gram	200.869
Grams per Lb.	453.59237
Gram Calories per Lb.	91,113
Calories to Kilojoules	0.00418680
Kilojoules per Lb.	381.47
Kilojoules to BTU's	0.947817120
BTU's per Lb.	361.56
Lbs. per Gal. (Air) @ 60° F	6.609910
BTU's per Gallon (Derived)	2,389.91
Find Kilojoules per Mole	
Kilojoules per Gram to Vaporize Alcohol	0.84100
Atomic Wt. of Alcohol in Grams per Mole	46.0684
Kilojoules per Mole	38.74
The HCP 72nd Ed. Lists 38.56 kJ/mol for Ethanol	38.56
Kj per Mole Dif.	-0.18

TABLE 176—Refer to Vaporize Alc 1 *Worksheet*

7.7 Vaporize Alcohol 2

Now that we have identified and verified the values we will use for the enthalpy of alcohol and water, we can apply them to determine the enthalpy of alcohol and water mixtures according to the following formula:

(water energy calories x water % of mixture) + (alcohol energy calories x alcohol % of mixture) = calories required to vaporize one gram of this mixture

From this equation we can then derive many other values with respect to the alcohol to be vaporized and verify that the same formula will work by substituting joules of energy for gram calories (Table 177, next page).

Find BTU's to Vaporize Alcohol & Water Mixtures				
Alcohol % of Mixture	50.00%	100.00	Proof Equivalent	
Water % of Mixture	50.00%			
Calories Per Gram to Vaporize Water	539.55		2,258.99	Joules per gram to Vaporize Alcohol
Calories Per Gram to Vaporize Alcohol	200.87		841.00	Joules per gram to Vaporize Alcohol
Find Latent Heat of Vaporization (LHV) of Mixture Expressed as Calories per Gram	370.21		1,549.99	Joules per Gram
Calories per Kg	370,210		0.2388459	Joules to Calories
Calories to Joules	4.1868		370.21	Calories
Kilojoules per Kg	1,550.00			
Kilojoules to BTU's	0.947817			
BTU's per Kg	1,469.11			
Kg to Lbs.	0.4535924			
BTU's per Lb.	666.38			
Lbs. per Gal. @ Proof	7.7803		7.78028	Lbs. per Proof Gal.
Lbs. per Gal. * BTU's per Lb. = BTU's per Gal.	5,184.61		5,184.61	BTU's per Proof Gal.
Liters to gal	0.2641721			
BTU per Gal. * Liters to Gal. = BTU's per Liter	1,369.629			
BTU's to kcal	0.251996			
Kilocalories per liter	345.141			

TABLE 177—Refer to Vaporize Alc 2 *Worksheet*

7.8 Vaporize Alcohol 3

The worksheet in Table 178 solves from gallons of alcohol to be vaporized to the energy required. It is a mezzanine worksheet that confirms by several approaches the values we have found in *Vaporize Alcohol 1* and *2*.

Find Energy to Vaporize Desired Gallons				
Gallons to be Vaporized	100.00	378.54	Liters	
Alcohol % of Mixture	100.00%	200.00	Proof Equivalent	
Water % of Mixture	0.00%			
Calories per Gram to Vaporize Water	539.55		2,258.99	Joules per gram to Vaporize Water
Calories per Gram to Vaporize Alcohol	200.87		841.00	Joules per gram to Vaporize Alcohol
Find Latent Heat of Vaporization (LHV) of Mixture Expressed as Calories per Gram	200.87		841.00	Joules per Gram
Calories per Kg	200,870		0.2388459	Joules to Calories
Calories to Joules	4.1868		200.87	Calories
Kilojoules per Kg	841.00			
Pounds Avdp to Kilograms	0.45359237			
Lbs. per Gal. @ Proof	6.6098			
Kg per Gal.	2.998			
Total Kg to Vaporize	299.82			
Total Kj Required	252,146.4			
Kilojoules to BTU's Converter	0.947817			
BTU's Required to Vaporize Volume	238,988.70			
System Efficiency	69.78%			
Scale up Value	1.43			
Total Kj Required	361,338			
Total BTU's Reqired at system efficiency	342,483			

TABLE 178—Refer to Vaporize Alc 3 *Worksheet*

7.9 BTU's to Heat and Vaporize Mass

This worksheet combines alcohol heating and vaporization into one algorithm.

The interesting part of this worksheet is the method of determining the energy needed to raise alcohol and water mixtures to their boiling point by using the specific gravity of the alcohol multiplied by the total BTU's required. Of course this could be joules or any other energy unit one chooses. One can find the vaporization temperature from Table 179-1, this page, and Table 179-2, next page.

Find Energy Values to Heat and Vaporize Mass			
Proof of Alc. Loaded in Still.	20.00	10.00%	Alcohol % of Mixture
Lbs. Loaded in Still	151.20	68.58	Kilograms
Start ° F Temp of Still	32.00		Gal. @ 60° Loaded
Vaporization temp	199.43		18.40
Temp change	167.43		
Find Energy to Raise to Vaporization Temperature			
Temp Change times Total Pounds = BTU's	25,315.42		
SG Air @ 60° F of Alcohol	0.98660	0.45359237	Pounds Avdp to Kilograms
BTU's Times Specific Gravity = BTU's	24,976.19	68.58	Kg Raised to Vaporization Temp
Energy to Raise to Vape Temp Results	**Results**	**Constants**	
Boiler Horsepower Required	0.746	33,475	BTU's per Hour per "Boiler Horsepower"
Kilowatt Hours	7.315	0.000293	BTU's to KW Hours =
Horse Power Hours	9.816	0.000393	BTU's to HP hours =
Gram Calories of Energy to Change Temp	6,294,000	252.00000	BTU's to Gram Calorie Converter
Joules or Watt Sec.	26,351,276	1,055.056	BTU's to Joules or Watt Seconds =
Kilojoules	26,351.28	1.0550559	BTU's to Kilojoules
Find Values per Unit of Mass			
Gross BTU's/Lbs. = BTU's per Lb.	165.19	384.22	Kilojoules/Kg = Kj per Kg
		91,772	Gram Cal./Kg = Gram Cal. Per Kg
Find Values per Unit of Volume			
Wine Gal. per Lb. @ 60	0.12170		
Wt. * WG per Lb. = Gal. @ 60 Loaded	18.4010		
Kilojoules/Gal. = Kj per Gal.	1,432.1		
Gallons to Liters	3.7854118	0.00418680	Gram Cal. To Kilojoules Converter
Kilojoules per liter	378.31	384.23	Kilojoules per Kg

TABLE 179-1—Refer to BTU's to Heat & Vape Mass Worksheet

Find Energy to Vaporize			
Alcohol % of Mixture	10.00%	0.947817	Kilojoules to BTU's Converter
Water % of Mixture	90.00%	2,006.71	BTU's per Kg
Calories per Gram to Vaporize Water	539.55	0.4535924	Kg to Lbs.
Calories per Gram to Vaporize Alcohol	200.87	910.23	BTU's per Lb.
Find Latent Heat of Vaporization (LHV) of Mixture Expressed as Calories per Gram	505.68	8.2169	Lbs. per Gal. @ Proof
Calories per Kg	505,682	7,479.27	BTU's per Gal.
Calories to Joules	4.18680	18.40	Gal. Equivalent of Lbs.
Kilojoules per Kg	2,117.19	137,626.41	Vape BTU's for Lbs. Entered
Energy to Vaporize Results	**Results**	**Constants**	
Boiler Horsepower Required	4.111	33,475	BTU's per Hour per "Boiler Horsepower"
Kilowatt Hours	40.3073	0.000293	BTU's to KW Hours =
Horse Power Hours	54.087	0.000393	BTU's to HP hours =
Gram Calories	34,681,856	252.00000	BTU's to Gram Calorie Converter
Joules or Watt Sec.	145,203,559	1,055.056	BTU's to Joules or Watt Seconds =
Kilojoules	145,203.56	1.0550559	BTU's to Kilojoules
Find Values per Unit of Volume & Mass			
Wine Gal. per Lb. @ 60	0.12170	2,117.19	Kilojoules/Kg = Kj per Kg
Wt. * WG per Lb. = Gal. @ 60 Loaded	18.4010	505,691	Gram Cal./Kg = Gram Cal. Per Kg
Kilojoules/Gal. = Kj per Gal.	7,891.1		
Gallons to Liters	3.7854118	0.00418680	Gram Cal. To Kilojoules Converter
Kilojoules per liter	2,084.60	2,117.23	Kilojoules per Kg
		0.45359237	Pounds Avdp to Kilograms
		960.4	Kilojoules per Lb.
		0.9478171	Kilojoules to BTU's
		910.2	BTU's per Lb.

TABLE 179-2—Refer to BTU's to Heat & Vape Mass *Worksheet*

What is a little troubling is that with water as an input the kilojoules per liter should match the kilojoules per kilogram (Table 180).

Find Values per Unit of Volume			
Wine Gal. per Lb. @ 60	0.12170		
Wt. * WG per Lb. = Gal. @ 60 Loaded	18.4010		
Kilojoules/Gal. = Kj per Gal.	1,432.1		
Gallons to Liters	3.7854118	0.00418680	Gram Cal. To Kilojoules Converter
Kilojoules per liter	378.31	384.23	Kilojoules per Kg
Percent Differential		1.541%	

TABLE 180—Refer to BTU's to Heat & Vape Mass *Worksheet*

They do not. This discrepancy of 1.54% may be converter imprecision or an air and vacuum density of water issue. It may also be related to the discrepancy between the definition of a liter, the definition of a cubic centimeter and the intersection between the two. It could also have to do with the calibration temperature of 4° C being the density at which a kilogram is defined. See the history of the liter in the ABS Software user's manual for a fuller discussion.

Find Density from energy relationship	
Kilojoules per liter to Vaporize	2,084.60
Kilojoules per Kg to Vaporize	2,117.23
Kj per liter/Kj per Kg = Kg per Liter (Air)	0.98459
Kg per m^3 (Air)	984.59
Air Kg per m^3 @ 60° F	1.0698
Kg per m^3 (Vac)	985.66
Kg per liter (Vac)	0.98566
Find SG and Compare to SG Air & SG Vac	
Alcohol Kg per Liter (Air)	0.98459
H$_2$O Kg. per Liter (Air) @ 60° F	0.99795
Alc. Density/H$_2$O Density = SG Air	0.98661
SG Air From Lookup	0.98660
Difference	0.00001
Alcohol Kg. per Liter (Vac)	0.98566
H$_2$O Kg. per Liter (Vac) @ 60° F	0.99902
Alc. Density/H$_2$O Density = SG Vac	0.98663
SG Vac From Lookup	0.98661
Difference	0.00002

TABLE 181—Refer to BTU's to Heat & Vape Mass Worksheet

Another interesting part of this worksheet is that it allows one to calculate the density of the material vaporized from the energy required to do so. Dividing the kilojoules to vaporize each liter by the kilojoules required to vaporize each kilogram one can derive the density of the material in air.

Using this inferred density value one can find its density in a vacuum by adding the kilograms of atmosphere displaced by one cubic meter of air at standard atmospheric pressure.

Then, using the density of water in air and vacuum, also at 60° F, one can find the relative density or specific gravity of the material in air and vacuum and compare each one to the TTB table values.

This is simply running the equations in reverse but provides some confirmation that the math is correct and all the converters are the proper ones to be using. The results appear to be valid to four decimal places. (Table 181.)

7.10 BTU's to Heat and Vaporize Volume

Just to cover all the bases I modified the mass worksheet to work as a volume worksheet. (Table 182-1 below; continued as Table 182-2, next page).

Find Energy Values to Heat and Vaporize Volume			
Proof of Alc. Loaded in Still.	20.00	10.00%	Alcohol % of Mixture
Gallons of Alcohol Loaded in Still	18.4000		
Lbs. per Gal. @ 60° F Value	8.2169		
Lbs. Loaded in Still Result	151.19	68.58	Kilograms
Start ° F Temp of Still	32.00		
Vaporization temp	199.43		
Temp change	167.43		
Find Energy to Raise to Vaporization Temperature			
Temp Change times Total Pounds = BTU's	25,313.99		
SG Air @ 60° F of Alcohol	0.98660	0.45359237	Pounds Avdp to Kilograms
BTU's Times Specific Gravity = BTU's	24,974.78	68.58	Kg. Raised to Vaporization Temp
Energy to Raise to Vape Temp Results	**Results**	**Constants**	
Boiler Horsepower Required	0.746	33,475	BTU's per Hour per "Boiler Horsepower"
Kilowatt Hours	7.314	0.000293	BTU's to KW Hours =
Horse Power Hours	9.815	0.000393	BTU's to HP hours =
Gram Calories of Energy to Change Temp	6,293,644	252.00000	BTU's to Gram Calorie Converter
Joules or Watt Sec.	26,349,787	1,055.056	BTU's to Joules or Watt Seconds =
Kilojoules	26,349.79	1.0550559	BTU's to Kilojoules
Find Values per Unit of Mass			
Gross BTU's/Lbs. = BTU's per Lb.	165.19	384.22	Kilojoules/Kg = Kj per Kg
		91,772	Gram Cal./Kg = Gram Cal. Per Kg
Find Values per Unit of Volume			
Wine Gal. per Lb. @ 60	0.12170		
Wt. * WG per Lb. = Gal. @ 60 Loaded	18.4000		
Kilojoules/Gal. = Kj per Gal.	1,432.1		
Gallons to Liters	3.7854118	0.00418680	Gram Cal. To Kilojoules Converter
Kilojoules per liter	378.31	384.23	Kilojoules per Kg
Percent Differential		1.541%	

TABLE 182-1—Refer to BTU's to Heat & Vape Vol *Worksheet*

As with the mass version of this worksheet, when using water as an input the kilojoules per liter should match the kilojoules per kilogram. They do not, as we noted above (Table 180).

Find Energy to Vaporize			
Alcohol % of Mixture	10.00%	0.947817	Kilojoules to BTU's Converter
Water % of Mixture	90.00%	2,006.71	BTU's per Kg
Calories per Gram to Vaporize Water	539.55	0.4535924	Kg to Lbs.
Calories per Gram to Vaporize Alcohol	200.87	910.23	BTU's per Lb.
Find Latent Heat of Vaporization (LHV) of Mixture Expressed as Calories per Gram	505.68	8.2169	Lbs. per Gal. @ Proof
Calories per Kg	505,682	7,479.27	BTU's per Gal.
Calories to Joules	4.18680	18.40	Gal. Equivalent of Lbs.
Kilojoules per Kg	2,117.19	137,618.63	Vape BTU's for Lbs. Entered
Energy to Vaporize Results	**Results**	**Constants**	
Boiler Horsepower Required	4.111	33,475	BTU's per Hour per "Boiler Horsepower"
Kilowatt Hours	40.3051	0.000293	BTU's to KW Hours =
Horse Power Hours	54.084	0.000393	BTU's to HP hours =
Gram Calories	34,679,896	252.00000	BTU's to Gram Calorie Converter
Joules or Watt Sec.	145,195,352	1,055.056	BTU's to Joules or Watt Seconds =
Kilojoules	145,195.35	1.0550559	BTU's to Kilojoules
Find Values per Unit of Volume & Mass			
Wine Gal. per Lb. @ 60	0.12170	2,117.19	Kilojoules/Kg = Kj per Kg
Wt. * WG per Lb. = Gal. @ 60 Loaded	18.4000	505,691	Gram Cal./Kg = Gram Cal. Per Kg
Kilojoules/Gal. = Kj per Gal.	7,891.1		
Gallons to Liters	3.7854118	0.00418680	Gram Cal. To Kilojoules Converter
Kilojoules per liter	2,084.60	2,117.23	Kilojoules per Kg
		0.45359237	Pounds Avdp to Kilograms
		960.4	Kilojoules per Lb.
		0.9478171	Kilojoules to BTU's
		910.2	BTU's per Lb.

TABLE 182-2—Refer to BTU's to Heat & Vape Vol Worksheet

7.11 Boiler Efficiency

This worksheet examines the efficiency of boilers from the energy consumed down through the efficiency of burning and efficiency of transportation, to the deliverable energy that is imparted to the mass to be heated. The reason it is included here is that this is the first time we are attempting to determine the mass of alcohol vaporized by the input of a specified boiler horsepower (Table 183, next page).

The results are consistent with my experience of production for distilling alcohol in my shop and with the prior worksheets for vaporizing mass and volume. This worksheet also contains a large number of converter tests and comparison values that are not reproduced here.

The worksheet also shows that the gallons per hour condensed are greater than those vaporized because the density of the concentrated alcohol is less than the base stock and accordingly the same mass in pounds occupies a greater volume.

Boiler Efficiency				
Gross Boiler Horsepower (Per Hr.)	5.89			
BTU's per "Boiler Horsepower"	33,475.00			
Total BTU's Generated	197,225.5			
BTU's to Joules Value	1,054.3500			
Joules per Hour or Watt Seconds per Hr.	207,944,697			
Divide by 3,600 = Joules per Sec Result	57,762.4			
Divide by 1k = Kilowatt Hours Result	57.7624			
Kw Hrs. to Hp. Hours	1.3419	1.35985	Kw Hrs. to Metric Hp. Hours	
Horsepower Hrs. (Mechanical & Electric)	77.51	78.5	Metric Horsepower Hours	
Boiler Efficiency	72.50%			
Available BTU's * Efficiency = Net Boiler BTU's	142,988.48		1.620	Boiler Efficiency Hp. Loss
			0.160	Transfer Hp. Loss
Heat Transfer Efficiency from Boiler to Still/Cooker	96.25%		1.780	Total Hp. Loss
Actual BTU's Transferred	137,626.41		4.111	Net Boiler Hp.
BTU's to Joules Value	1,054.3500			
Joules per Hour or Watt Seconds per Hr.	145,106,409			
Divide by 3,600 = Joules per Sec Result	40,307.3		1.433	Scale up Value
Divide by 1k = Kilowatt Hours Result	40.31			
Kw Hrs. to Hp. Hours	1.3419	1.35985	Kw Hrs. to Metric Hp. Hours	
Horsepower Hrs. (Mechanical & Electric)	54.09	54.8	Metric Horsepower Hours	
Find Lbs. per Hr. and Gal. per Hr.				
Proof of Mixture to Be Vaporized	20.00	10%	% Alcohol	
Lbs. per Hr. Vaporized	151.20	68.6	Kg per Hr.	
Gal. per Hr. Vaporized	18.40	69.7	Liters per Hr.	
Proof of Mixture Condensed	150.00	75.00%	Alcohol %	
Pounds Per Gallon of Condensate	7.30514			
Lbs. Vaped/Lbs. per Gal. = Gal Condensed	20.70	78.3	Liters per Hr.	

TABLE 183—Refer to Boiler Efficiency Worksheet

CHAPTER 8 Digital Stills

8.1 Boiler Still

Starting from boiler horsepower as the input value, this worksheet allows the user to determine how much alcohol of a given quality will be produced using a fermented mash of a given alcoholic content. It assumes that the mixture has already been raised to its vaporization temperature under standard atmospheric conditions (Table 184).

Boiler Horsepower Energy to Vaporize Alcohol and Water Mixtures		Gross Energy	
Boiler Horsepower Available	6.03	0.000293071	BTU's to kW.hr
BTU's per Hour per Boiler Hp.	33,475.00	59.16	Kw Hrs.
Total BTU's Available	201,854.3	$0.10	1 Kw. Cost
		$5.92	Total Cost per Hour
Heat Required to Vaporize water and alcohol mixtures at any Efficiency			
BTU's Per Hour Available Restated	201,854.25	33,475.00	BTU's per Boiler Hp.
Boiler Efficiency	72.50%	1.658	Boiler Hp. Loss
Available BTU's * Efficiency = Net Boiler BTU's	146,344.33	0.164	Transfer Hp. Loss
Heat Transfer Efficiency from Boiler to Still	96.25%	1.822	Total Hp. Loss
Actual BTU's Transferred to Contents of Vessel	140,856.42	4.21	Net Boiler Hp.
		1.433	Scale up Value
Find BTU's to Vaporize Alcohol & Water Mixtures		**Find Qualities of Alc. Vaporized**	
Alcohol % of Mixture @ 60° F	6.00%	0.947817	Kilojoules to BTU's
Proof Equivalent of Sample to Be Vaporized	12.00	2,060.47	BTU's per Kg.
Alcohol % of Mixture	6.00%	0.4535924	Kg to Lbs.
Water % of Mixture	94.00%	934.61	BTU's per Lb.
Energy Required to Vaporize Water	539.55	Cal per Gram	8.2576	Lbs. per Gal. @ Proof
Energy Required to Vaporize Alcohol	200.87	Cal per Gram	7,717.69	BTU's per Gal.
Find Latent Heat of Vaporization (LHV) of Mixture	519.23	Cal per Gram	3.7854118	Gallons to Liters
Calories per Kg	519,229	2,038.8	BTU's per Liter
Calories to Joules	4.18680	1,054.350	BTU's to Joules Converter
Kilojoules per Kg	2,173.91	2,149,607	Joules per Liter
Find Grams & Gallons per Hour Boil off Rate			
BTU's to Gram Calories	252.00		
BTU's * Converter = Gram Calories Available	35,495,818	68.36	Kilograms per Hr.
LHV of mixture restated	519.23	1,139.38	Grams Per Minute
Total Grams Vaporized = Gram Cal. /Cal. To Vaporize 1 Gram	68,362.52	2.51	Pounds per Minute
Grams to U.S. Pounds Converter	0.0022050		
Grams * Converter = Pounds per Hour	150.74	3.785413	Gal. to Liters
Pounds Per Gal. of Vaporized Mixture	8.25764	69.101	Liters per Hr.
Gallons Per Hour Vaporized	18.255	0.304	Gallons Per Minute
BTU's per Gallon	7,716.24	1.1517	Liters per Minute
BTU's per Gram	2.0604		

TABLE 184—Refer to Boiler Still Worksheet

Strip Run 3 Summary			
Run Hrs.	Lbs. per Hr.	Still Pres.	True Proof
1			
	34		102
1.0	124		115
	144		125
2.0	142		115
	144	1	115
3.0	147	1	102
4.0	154	2	93
	162	2	84
5.0	175	1	74
	144	1	65
6.0	147	1	54
	138	1	51
7.0	123	1	43
	131	1	36

TABLE 185. See also TABLE 148.

Table 185 is set up based upon the data I have collected with respect to the boilers in my shop, and the efficiency of transfer to the still that has been calculated previously.

The worksheet result of 150.74 lbs. per hr. (Table 184) is consistent with data I have collected from strip runs, to a reasonable degree. It is also consistent with the energy inputs we have calculated in the boiler test worksheets (Sections 4.3 through 4.7, *supra*), and my input and efficiency values are based on those conclusions.

We previously discussed the surge in lbs. per hour of distillate output when the batch reaches its optimum conditions. There is a sweet spot in the middle run where the output increases above the average. So far I can't explain it except with the fact that I'm running the boiler full on. The pressure does go up some.

8.2 Electric Still

Starting from kilowatt hours of energy available this worksheet allows the user to determine how much alcohol of a given quality will be produced using a fermented mash of a given alcoholic content. It assumes that the mixture has already been raised to its vaporization temperature under standard atmospheric conditions (Table 186, next page).

The results of 150.75 lbs. per hour match with those produced by the boiler still worksheet (Table 184) *supra*.

Electric Energy to Vaporize Alcohol and Water mixtures				
Kilowatts per Hr.	59.160			
Volts of Current	220.00		268.91	Amps per Hr.
Watts of Heating Element	59,160.00		220.00	Volts of Current
Volts/ Watts = Amps	268.91		59,160.00	Watts = Amps * Volts
Watts of Heating Capacity	59,160.00		**Check Converter**	
BTU's per Watt	3.41214160		0.00029307	BTU to KW Hours
BTU's per Hr.	201,862.30		59.160	Kw Hour OK
Heat Required to Vaporize water and alcohol mixtures at any Efficiency			6.03	Boiler Horsepower
BTU's Per Hour Available	201,862.30		1.658	Boiler Hp. Loss
Boiler Efficiency	72.50%		0.164	Transfer Hp. Loss
Available BTU's * Efficiency = Net Boiler BTU's	146,350.17		1.822	Total Hp. Loss
Heat Transfer Efficiency	96.25%		4.21	Net Boiler Hp.
Actual BTU's Transferred to Vessel	140,862.03		1.433	Scale up Value
Find BTU's to Vaporize Alcohol & Water Mixtures		**Proof**		
Alcohol % of Mixture @ 60° F	6.00%	12.00	0.947817	Kilojoules to BTU's
Proof Equivalent of Sample to Be Vaporized	12.00		2,060.47	BTU's per Kg
Alcohol % of Mixture	6.00%		0.4535924	Kg to Lbs.
Water % of Mixture	94.00%		934.61	BTU's per Lb.
Energy Required to Vaporize Water	539.55	Cal per Gram	8.2576	Lbs. per Gal. @ Proof
Energy Required to Vaporize Alcohol	200.87	Cal per Gram	7,717.69	BTU's per Gal.
Find Latent Heat of Vaporization (LHV)	519.23		3.7854118	Gallons to Liters
Calories per Kg	519,229		2,038.8	BTU's per Liter
Calories to Joules	4.18680		1,054.350	BTU's to Joules
Kilojoules per Kg	2,173.91		2,149,607	Joules per Liter
Find Grams & Gallons per Hour Boil off Rate				
BTU's to Gram Calories	252.000		1,139.42	Grams Per Minute
BTU's * Converter = Gram Calories Available	35,497,233		68.37	Kilograms per Hr.
LHV of mixture restated	519.23		2.51	Pounds per Minute
Total Grams Vaporized per Hour	68,365.25		3.785413	Gal. to Liters
Grams to U.S. Pounds Converter	0.0022050		69.104	Liters per Hr.
Grams * Converter = Pounds per Hour	150.75		0.304	Gallons Per Minute
			2.060	BTU's per Gram Vaporized

TABLE 186—Refer to Electric Still *Worksheet*

8.3 Digital Still Mass

Now we will turn the equation around and look at sizing a still based upon the output one wants from it in a given amount of time. Using the same basic framework we will take the mass we want to condense per hour and derive the energy required to do so (Table 187, next page).

Using the 150.75 lbs. per hour generated from the boiler still and electric still worksheets (Tables 184 and 186), we see that the BTU's required are essentially the same at 140,862.

Notice that the gallons produced per hour at the condensed proof are greater than the gallons vaporized from the prior worksheets. This is because the condensed gallons are each less dense because of their increased proof. If one sets the output value to 12 proof the values work out the same for vaporized and condensed alcohol (Table 188, next page).

We will have to deal with this problem in the next section when we look at Digital Still Volume.

Digital Still Mass			
Lbs. Condensed Per Hr.	150.74	68.4	Kg per Hr.
Proof of Mixture Vaporized	12.00	6.00%	% Alc.
Lbs. per Gal. @ 60° F	8.25764		
Total Gal. per Hr. Vaporized	18.25	69.1	Liters per Hr.
Proof of Alcohol Condensed	87.1	43.57%	% Alc.
Lbs. per Gal. @ 60° F	7.87836		
Gal. @ 60° F Condensed	19.13	72.4	Liters per Hr.
Find Energy Required			
Lbs. Condensed Per Hr.	150.74	12.00	Proof of Mixture Vaporized
Pounds Avdp to Kilograms	0.45359237	6.00%	Alcohol % of Mixture
Kilograms Condensed	68.4	0.991490	Specific Gravity in Air
Find Total Gram Cal. Required		6.00%	Alcohol % of Mixture
Grams Vaporized	68,375	94.00%	Water % of Mixture
LHV of Evaporite per gram	519.23	539.55	Energy Required to Vaporize Water
Total Gram Cal. Required to Vaporize	35,502,044	200.87	Energy Required to Vaporize Alcohol
Calories to BTU's Converter	0.0039683	519.23	Find LHV of Mixture
Vaporizing BTU's Required	140,883.5	519,229	Calories per Kg.
Lbs. per Gal. of Mixture	8.25764	4.1868	Calories to Joules
Gal Condensed = Lbs./Wt.per Gal.	18.25	2,173.9	Kilojoules per Kg.
BTU's per Gal. Condensed	7,717.7	8.2576	Lbs. per Gal @ Vaporized Proof
BTU's per Lb. Condensed	934.6	18.25	Gallons per Hr. of Vaporized Mixture
BTU's per Hour per Boiler Hp.	33,475	55.0	Drum size in Gal.
Boiler Horsepower Required	4.21	3.01	Hours per 55 Gal Drum

TABLE 187—Refer to Digital Still Mass *Worksheet*

The results in terms of boiler horsepower required, 4.21, and the number of hours required to collect one drum of alcohol, 3.01, are consistent with the values we have seen previously when calculating values from my stripping runs.

Digital Still Mass			
Lbs. Condensed Per Hr.	150.74	68.4	Kg per Hr.
Proof of Mixture Vaporized	12.00	6.00%	% Alc.
Lbs. per Gal. @ 60° F	8.25764		
Total Gal. per Hr. Vaporized	18.25	69.1	Liters per Hr.
Proof of Alcohol Condensed	12.0	6.00%	% Alc.
Lbs. per Gal. @ 60° F	8.25764		
Gal. @ 60° F. Condensed	18.25	69.1	Liters per Hr.

TABLE 188—Refer to Digital Still Mass *Worksheet*

8.4 Digital Still Volume

The digital still volume worksheet (Table 189, next page) allows one to gauge, from the volume per hour desired and the proof of the mixture vaporized, the energy required to accomplish the work.

The difficulty with this worksheet is that by starting from volume, one must use the volume at the proof of the mixture vaporized. This is different from the volume of the output after rectification by the still.

Digital Still by Volume			
Proof of Mixture Vaporized	12.00	6.00%	% Alc.
Gallons Per Hour Vaporized	17.00	64.4	Liters per Hr.
Proof of Gallons Condensed	87.1	43.55%	% Alc.
Gallons per Hr. Condensed	17.82	67.5	Liters per Hr.
Find Lbs. Condensed			
Lbs. per Gal. @ 60° F	8.25764		
Total Lbs. per Hour Condensed	140.38	63.7	Kg per Hr.
Find Gallons Condensed			
Lbs. per Gal. @ 60° F	7.87836		
Gallons per Hr. Condensed	17.818		
Solve for Energy required to Vaporize known Lbs. recovered			
Lbs. Vaporized Restated	140.38	12.00	Proof of Mixture Vaporized
Kilograms Vaporized	63.68	6.00%	Alcohol % of Mixture
Find Total Gram Cal. Required to condense weight		94.00%	Water % of Mixture
Grams Vaporized	63,675	539.55	Energy Required to Vaporize Water
LHV of Evaporite per gram	519.23	200.87	Energy Required to Vaporize Alcohol
Total Gram Cal. Required to Vaporize	33,062,038	519.23	Find LHV of Mixture
Calories to BTU's Converter	0.0039683207	519,229	Calories per Kg
Vaporizing BTU's Required	131,200.8	4.1868	Calories to Joules
Lbs. per Gal. of Mixture	8.25764	2,173.9	Kilojoules per Kg
Gal Condensed = Lbs./Wt.per Gal.	17.00		
BTU's per Gal. Vaporized	7,717.7	2.34	Lbs. per Minute
BTU's per Lb. Condensed	934.6	0.297	Gallons per Minute
BTU's per Hour per Boiler Hp.	33,475	3.79	Gallons to Liters
Boiler Horsepower Required	3.92	1.124	Liters per Minute
		1,061.25	Grams per Minute

TABLE 189—Refer to Digital Still Vol *Worksheet*

Comparison	
Boiler Still Lbs. per Hr.	150.74
Electric Still Lbs. per Hr.	150.75
Digital Still Volume Lbs. per Hr.	140.38
Net BTU's from Boiler Still	140,856
Net BTU's Digital Still Mass	140,883
Net BTU's from Digital Still Volume	131,201
Net BTU's from Strip Run 2	140,958
Gal. per Hr. Vaporized from Boiler Still	18.25
Gal. per Hr. Vaporized from Digital Still Mass.	18.25
Gal. per Hr. Vaporized from Digital Still Vol.	17.00
Gal. Per Hr. Condensed from Boiler Still	19.13
Gal. per Hr. @ from Digital Still Mass	18.25
Gal. per Hr. from Digital Still Vol.	17.82
Net Bhp. Boiler Still	4.21
Net Bhp. Digital Still Volume	3.92
Net Bhp. Digital Still Mass	4.21

TABLE 190—Refer to Digital Still Vol *Worksheet*

Accordingly, one has to look at the condensed volume, at the proof it is condensed, in order to accurately judge the volume output one will be dealing with. I have arranged the inputs and outputs so that one can keep an eye on the difference between them.

Other than that the still works well and is equivalent to the boiler still worksheet.

Looking at the volume still results compared to other worksheets shows that the energy and volume values have a close correspondence (Table 190).

Using these worksheets will assist the user to design equipment of the proper size and capacity at the scale at which they wish to operate.

CHAPTER 9 Condensing Energy and Systems

9.1 Find Condensing BTU's

Tables 191 and 192 show the initial conditions we will use to find the difference in energy required to vaporize and condense alcohol. We need to use the average values from our Strip Run 2 data to make a meaningful comparison. Starting with the average pounds per hour, average mash proof and distillate output proof we see that there is a gross difference of between 24.5% by mass and 28% by volume in the amount of energy required to condense the alcohol that is vaporized.

This comes with the caveat that the condensate will condense at a temperature near its boiling point and not at the temperature it exits the spout of the condenser output, which is generally around 80° F. Calculating that boiling point using Equation 1, we can calculate how much energy is required to reduce the distillate to the spout temperature at which it is discharged from the condenser (Table 193).

The energy required to reduce the condensate to the spout temperature is significant, amounting to 10.4% more energy required, and this decreases the total vaporization to condensation temperature energy difference to 14.1%.[45]

Digital Still Mass			
Lbs. Condensed Per Hr.	140.40	63.7	Kg per Hr.
Proof of Mixture Vaporized	12.00	6.00%	% Alc.
Lbs. per Gal. @ 60° F	8.25764		
Total Gal. per Hr. Vaporized	17.00	64.4	Liters per Hr.
Proof of Alcohol Condensed	87.14	43.57%	% Alc.
Lbs. per Gal. @ 60° F	7.87836		
Gal. @ 60° F Condensed	17.82	67.5	Liters per Hr.

TABLE 191—Refer to Digital Still Mass 2 Worksheet

Find Vaporizing to Condensing BTU difference			
BTU's per Lb. @ Vaporized Proof	934.6	7,717.7	BTU's per Gal. @ Vaporized Proof
BTU's per Lb. @ Condensed Proof	705.6	5,558.8	BTU's per Gal. @ Condensed Proof
BTU's per Lb. Dif.	229.0	2,158.9	BTU's per Gal Dif.
% Dif.	24.5%	28.0%	% Dif.

TABLE 192—Refer to Digital Still Mass 2 Worksheet

Reduce Condensed mass to spout temp.			
Proof of Liquid	87.14		
Boiling Point (Eq. 1)	182.55		
Spout Temperature	80.0		
Temperature Difference	102.5		
Mass	140.4		
Specific Gravity of Mass	0.94595		
BTU's per Hr. to reduce Mass to spout Temp	13,619	10.4%	% to change liquid temp
Total BTU's to Condense to Spout Temp	112,682.2	14.1%	% Difference Vape to Condense

TABLE 193—Refer to Digital Still Mass 2 Worksheet

45 Of course it would take a similar amount of energy to raise the 140 pounds to its boiling point, differing only by the difference in specific gravity between the condensate and the base stock. However this value only affects the input side from a boiler horsepower perspective and as long as we look at condensation energies will not affect our calculations appreciably.

Now we can compare these values to the known cooling energy applied to a strip run and note the difference (Table 194).

Find Tons of Cooling from Condensing BTU's				
Condensing BTU's Required	99,063.0			
Condense to spout Temp BTU's Required	13,619.2			
Total BTU's Needed per Hr.	112,682.2	From Strip Run 2 Cooling Calcs		
Water input Temperature	45.00	45.0	Water input Temp	
Water Output Temperature	103.60	103.6	Avg. Water Temp	
Temperature Change	58.60			
Wt. per Gal.as BTU's per ° of Change	8.32823			
BTU's per Gal.	488.03	483.6	Average BTU's per Gal.	99.1%
Total Gal. per Hr. Required	230.9	234.5	Avg. Gal per Hr.	101.6%
Gal. Per Minute	3.85	3.91	Average Gal. per Min.	101.6%
BTU's per Ton of Cooling	12,000.00			
BTU's / Net Tons = Tons per Hr. of Cooling	9.39	9.45	Tons of Cooling	100.7%
		113,430.4	BTU's of Cooling	

TABLE 194—Refer to Digital Still Mass 2 *Worksheet*

The result is a surprisingly close correspondence between my measured values for water use and the calculated values. Too close, really, given the assumptions and averages we are using and the precision of the instruments used. But it least in confirms that some degree of accounting for the additional BTU's required to reduce to the spout temperature must be included in the calculations.

Find Energy Required	
Lbs. Condensed Per Hr.	140.40
Pounds Avdp to Kilograms	0.45359237
Kilograms Condensed	63.7
Find Total Gram Cal. Required	
Grams Vaporized	63,684
LHV of Evaporite per gram	519.23
Total Gram Cal. Required to Vaporize	33,066,784
Calories to BTU's Converter	0.0039683
Vaporizing BTU's Required	131,219.6

TABLE 195—Refer to Digital Still Mass 2 *Worksheet*

As to the overall vaporizing to condensing difference, we know that the boiler input must be at least 131.2K BTU's in order to simply vaporize the known pounds condensed[46] (Table 195).

The question becomes what has happened to the remainder of the energy between the 112K required to condense it to the spout temperature and the 131.2K required to vaporize it.

The remaining BTU's are radiated BTU's from the system and amount to about 20% of the energy supplied to the system and include the 14.1% of energy required to cool the distillate from the spout temperature down to the input temperature (Table 196, next page).

Somehow 5.9% (6.9% in Table 196) of the energy delivered to the still is not being used to vaporize the known lbs. condensed.

128,810.0	Average BTU's per Hr.
31,092.1	Inferred Heat Exchange BTU Loss
19.4%	Avg. Inferred Radiated BTU's %

TABLE 197—Refer to Oil Boiler Test *Worksheet*

While not an exact comparison, we can refer to the inferred radiation we measured during our oil boiler test (Table 197).

---

46   We also know that the still on average generates 180K BTU's of which 140 can be delivered to the still contents.

	Total Condensing BTU's	Vaporizing BTU's	Total input BTU's
Total BTU's Needed per Hr.	112,682.2	131,219.6	140,958.1
Water input Temperature	45.00	45.00	45.00
Water Output Temperature	103.60	103.60	103.60
Temperature Change	58.60	58.60	58.60
Wt. per Gal.as BTU's per ° of Change	8.32823	8.32823	8.32823
BTU's per Gal.	488.03	488.03	488.03
Total Gal. Needed	230.9	268.9	288.8
Gal. Per Minute	3.85	4.48	4.81
Ton of Refrigeration in BTU's per Hr.	12,000.00	12,000.00	12,000.00
BTU's / Net Tons = Tot. Ton Hrs. of Cooling	9.39	10.93	11.75
BTU's Dif. Vaporize to Condense	18,537.4	9,738.5	BTU's Dif. Total to Vaporize
Condense Dif. From Vaporizing BTU's	14.1%	6.9%	% Dif
BTU's Dif. Total to Condense	28,275.9		
% Dif. From Total input BTU's	20.1%		

TABLE 196—Refer to Digital Still Mass 2 Worksheet

This indicates that during that test the still was radiating approximately the same total amount of energy 19.4% as we have calculated at 20%.

We can also refer to Cooling Calcs 2 which contains data from Strip Run 2 and find the same boiler input required 113K condensing BTU's applied by the system to condense to the spout temperature as well (Table 198).

Again, I have the feeling that the correspondence in numbers is a little too good to be true.

Finally, we can refer to the passive radiation measured when we let the batch stand for periods of time and measured the temperature decrease (Table 199).

Condensing Hrs.	7.0
Tot. Cooling BTU's	797,656
Avg. BTU's per Hr.	113,951
Average "Tons" of Cooling per Hr.	9.5
Avg. BTU's per Gal	483.4
Total Water Gallons used for Cooling	1,650.0
Avg. Gal. per Minute	3.93
Still Input Net BTU's per Hr.	140,958
Avg. Condensing BTU's per Hr.	113,951
Input to Output BTU Dif.	27,007
% Cooling BTU's	80.84%
% Radiated BTU's	19.16%

TABLE 198—Refer to Cooling Calcs 2 Worksheet

Starting Temperature	205.00	195.00	186.00	180.00	170.00
Time Elapsed (Minutes)	60.00	60.00	60.00	60.00	60.00
Ending Tank Temp	190.00	182.00	175.00	170.00	162.00
% of Radiated energy to total energy	13.04%	12.38%	11.46%	11.11%	10.00%

TABLE 199—Refer to BTU's Cool 2 Worksheet

The most relevant value is the second one between 195° F and 182° F indicating a passive radiation of 12.38%.

The only inference I can draw is that 6% of the energy supplied by the boiler to the still is required simply to maintain the temperature of the still against temperature loss, and the remainder of either 12.3% or 14.1% are the BTU's radiated by the entire still.

Keep in mind that these are the average values over the course of a run. During the middle of the run I regularly need to increase the gallon per minute flow through the condensers in order to accommodate the surge in pounds per hour generated by the still. Allowing for this it is prudent to be able to apply additional cooling capacity so that one does not have to back off the energy input of the still during these periods of peak flow.

What can also fluctuate is the spout temperature of the distillate and this can, within limits, carry excess heat out of the system into the collection reservoir where it can dissipate.

On occasion I've "gotten behind" on keeping an eye on the water flow to the condenser. I have let the condenser temperature get too high and had to frantically remove the hot water while simultaneously adding cold water in order to keep the coil covered. This can be a hectic time when you are trying to get energy out of the system and keep the spout temperature down since as the temperature in the condenser goes up so does the pressure in the still.

9.2 Find Water Flow to Condense

Find Gal. per Min. Flow to achieve same cooling at different water temps		
Water input Temperature	45.00	63.00
Water Output Temperature	104.00	104.00
Temperature Change	59.00	41.00
Wt. per Gallon used as BTU's per ° of Change	8.32823	8.32823
° of Change * Wt.per Gal. = BTU's per min.	491.37	341.46
Condensing BTU's Required	120,980.6	120,980.6
Gallons per Hour Required	246.2	354.3
Gallons per Min. Flow Result	4.10	5.91
Total BTU's per minute	2,016.34	2,016.34
Ton of Refrigeration Constant in BTU's	12,000.00	12,000.00
Tons of Refrigeration per hour Equivalent	10.08	10.08

TABLE 200—Refer to Digital Still Mass Worksheet

This worksheet (Table 200) allows the user to determine the gallons per minute of water flow required to achieve the same amount of cooling capacity using different water input temperatures.

Applying this portion of the worksheet will assist in determining the gallons per minute of flow required using different water temperatures to achieve the required amount of cooling to match the condensing BTU's.

The limiting factor is that the output temperature of the water cannot get too high and still maintain the spout temperature at a reasonable level. However, the output temperature does not need to be the same as the spout temperature. There is a temperature gradient in the condenser where it is very hot at the top and cold at the bottom as we discussed when we talked about the buffer of reserve cooling BTU capacity of the condenser.

9.3 Condenser Capacity

This worksheet demonstrates how much alcohol flow can be expected from a given diameter of the tubing used as a condenser coil.

In order to build a condenser system that matched the vapor emanating from my still I had to build several different coils and learn by trial and error.

With my first coil of 3/4-inch copper, I could tell that the coil was inadequate because the pressure in the still would rise but the outflow of alcohol from the condenser would not increase appreciably.

I first solved this problem by installing a second condenser in the system, which was my old 1/2-inch-diameter coil so that two condenser coils would accept the evaporated alcohol. This helped but I could still tell that the still needed to expel more vapor than the two coils could handle because the pressure in the still would increase during distilling runs.

So I decided to stop guessing and try to solve the problem and anticipate what the output flow would be based on the diameter of the copper coil I would use.

The first principal of condenser capacity is that by doubling the interior diameter one increases by a factor of four the area inside the condenser pipe. The following shows two methods of finding the area (Table 201).

	Interior Diameter	Radius	Radius Squared	Pi	Flow area of pipe In Sq. In.	Diameter Squared	Area Constant	Diameter Squared * Constant
Inches	0.50	0.25	0.06	3.14159	0.196	0.25	0.7850	0.1963
Inches	1.00	0.50	0.25	3.14159	0.785	1.00	0.7850	0.7850
Double the Diameter to Get 4 Times the Area.					4.00	Ratio	Ratio	4.00

TABLE 201—Refer to Condenser Capacity *Worksheet*

The first method is the traditional Pi x Radius Squared method and the second uses an area constant to multiply the diameter squared by the constant of 0.7850 to achieve the same result.

Applying the formulas to my system showed the following cross section areas for my two coils (Table 202).

My Current Still Setup Now W/ Two Condensers									
Nominal Size in Inches	Actual OD	Wall Thickness L type Pipe	Wall Thickness * 2	Outside Diameter minus Wall Thickness	Actual Diameter Squared	Area Constant	Inside area of pipe In Square Inches	Flow rate	
0.50	0.63	0.04	0.08	0.55	0.30	0.7850	0.23	5.40	Gal Per Hour
0.75	0.88	0.05	0.09	0.79	0.62	0.7850	0.48	9.38	Gal Per Hour
						My Area Now	0.72	14.78	Gal Per Hour

TABLE 202—Refer to Condenser Capacity *Worksheet*

Even though I had 3/4-inch and 1/2-inch pipe working in tandem, my total condensing cross section area was less than 3/4 of a square inch!

It should be noted that the gallon per hour rate sometimes exceeded the averages that are listed above. The maximum rate measured was 17.5 gallons of alcohol per hour.

Because the small condenser would only run at the pressure that the large coil was running, it actually produced less alcohol when it was running in tandem with the larger coil then when it was running alone.

I purchased a 60-foot roll of 1.250-inch copper pipe which was the largest diameter that was still flexible enough to bend on a large mandrel. Making some calculations I found that the new condenser coil, in conjunction with my 3/4-inch coil, would increase the area of my combined condensers by 239% (Table 203, next page).

Coil and barrel.

Replacing .5" pipe with 1.250" Pipe	Actual OD	Wall Thickness L type Pipe	Wall Thickness * 2	Outside Diameter minus Wall Thickness	Actual Diameter Squared	Area Constant	Inside area of pipe In Square Inches
1.25	1.38	0.06	0.13	1.25	1.56	0.785	1.23
0.75	0.88	0.05	0.09	0.79	0.62	0.785	0.48
	Avg. Flow Rate					Total Area	1.71
Actual Flow Rate	22.00					Both Condenser Increase	239%
Flow Rate of .75 in coil	9.38	No Change					
Flow Rate New Coil	12.62						
Flow Rate of old .5 in. Coil	5.40						
Increase in Flow Rate	7.22	Gal. per Hr. Increase		3.55	Ratio of Flow increase to Area increase		
% increase in flow	67.2%			28.2%	% increase as % of Area Increase		

TABLE 203—Refer to Condenser Capacity *Worksheet*

The actual results were a 67% increase in the gallons of alcohol condensed per hour, which is not a 239% increase in flow based on the area increase but roughly 1/4 of the area increase (28%). This makes sense since the flow increases arithmetically while the area increases by the square.

What I also noticed was that the pressure in my still dropped to the vapor pressure of just what was being vaporized and no more. I could open up the safety valve while the still was running 22 gallons per hour and barely any vapor would find its way out of the vent.

To me this indicated that there was actually excess capacity in the system and that the condensate flow was based on heat input and not on restrictions in the condenser system.

Since I was already running my boilers pretty much full on, there was no way to test this hypothesis by increasing the heat input into the still.

What I was able to do was to turn off the 3/4-inch coil with a ball valve and run the still with just the 1.250-inch coil.

This allows my 3/4-inch coil to serve as a reserve buffer of cold water to condense with in case it is needed.

For those trying to find out how many coils of a given diameter one can make out of a given length of tubing, the following worksheet will assist in making the calculation (Table 204).

Find Amount of pipe needed for condenser coil based on diameter and number of wraps in coil							
	Outside Diameter	Pi	Circumference	Feet of pipe	Inches	Total Inches	# of Wraps
Outside Diameter of Coil in Inches	17.00	3.14159	53.41	60.00	12.00	720.00	13.48

TABLE 204—Refer to Condenser Capacity *Worksheet*

I'm not sure if it matters if one specifies the inside or outside diameter but I specified the outside since the coil had to fit inside a 55 gallon drum with enough clearance for water to circulate freely and also to insert and remove the coil if necessary. I soldered copper pipe up the sides to keep the coils separated from one another.

9.4 Still Lid Pressure

While we are on the topic of still pressure, the following worksheet will demonstrate how many total pounds of pressure are being exerted by a given amount of vapor force inside a still.

Because my still has an actual lid that clamps down to make the seal, I can use the diameter of the lid itself as the surface area. Since the force exerted on this still is equal in all directions I can also assume that the total force is loaded to separate the lid from the rest of the still.

Before I made these calculations I used to pressure test my still to pressures above 4 PSI, not realizing just how much of a load I was placing on the still.

Now that I have a better condenser system that does not back up vapor pressure inside the still I do not run the still at pressures as high as I used to. I had seen 5 lbs. during a run at one point. This was dangerous and unnecessary. It was the condenser that couldn't process the vapor that was the problem, not the still or boiler system. If my calculations were correct I had loaded my lid with 12,000 lbs. of upwards force. No wonder I needed 15 C-clamps to hold it together around the lid (Table 205)!

Well, I learned my lesson without rupturing my still. Now I just test my still to 3 lbs. maximum. It only runs at 1 or 2 lbs. during a run and I can check the pressure with the pressure relief valve.

Still with lid secured with multiple C-clamps.

Lbs. Pressure	Total Lbs. of Pres.
1	2,463.01
2	4,926.02
3	7,389.03
4	9,852.03
5	12,315.04

TABLE 205—Refer to Still Lid Pressure *Worksheet*

Pressure-checking mechanism and dual safety valve system for still pressure. Note reinforcing ribs.

I also installed some brass and spring pressure vents but the spring tension changes when the still gets hot and both of them have been impossible to calibrate. They would get hot; the spring would lose its tension, and the valve would leak, just a little, and I wouldn't know about it. You don't want to just lose alcohol vapor out the still inadvertently, and having alcohol vapor around can be dangerous so I had to stop trying to use them.

At left is a picture of the pressure checking mechanism and dual safety valve system for still pressure.

You will notice reinforcing ribs on top of my still lid. This is because I once came back to the shop to find the entire lid caved into the still. Even though the coil output was open to the atmosphere and could drip overnight, there were enough low spots in the coil to form a liquid blockage that prevented air from entering the still.

As the still cooled the air inside, it contracted and created negative pressure. Eventually this pressure overcame the ability of the metal still lid to restrain it and it collapsed.

After hammering the still lid back into shape we installed the reinforcing ribs. But I don't trust them and I no longer trust the condenser coil to prevent negative pressure from building up when the still cools. Hence the safety valve which I leave open. One can also install an anti-collapse valve which is a one way valve that only allows air to enter the still when there is negative pressure inside it.

9.5 Counter to the Vapor Pressure

When designing a condenser unit it is important to direct the cold water in such a way that it runs counter to the vapor pressure coming from the still.

When the vapor pressure is rising out of the still and the condenser is on top of the column, the cold water input needs to be placed at the top of the coil and the hot water return exits from the lowest coil in the column (Figure 3, next page). As the vapor rises, it is in contact with a temperature gradient that will allow for the maximum exposure of the vapor to temperatures that are sufficient to condense it to a liquid.

If one placed the cold water inlet at the bottom of the coil, the vapor would meet the cold temperature in a collision and then pass on to hotter and hotter coils that would inhibit condensation.

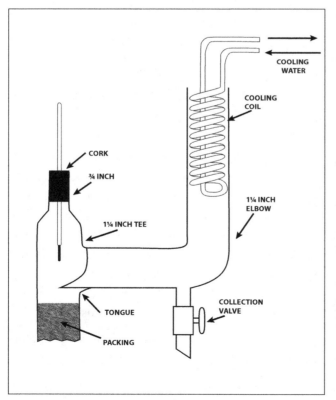

Figure 3: Condenser operation; vapor rises past coil.

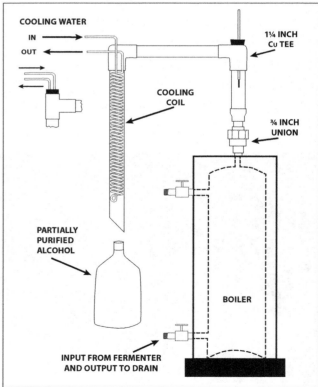

Figure 4: Condenser operation; vapor pressure directed downward past the coil.

Conversely, when the vapor pressure is directed downwards into a coil, as when it is immersed in a barrel below the top of the still, one should direct the cold water to the bottom of the condenser or the barrel it is immersed in so that it is farthest from the incoming vapor (Figure 4, next page). This means that the hot part of the coil and hottest water in the coil is at the top of the condenser or barrel and the colder water and coil are at the bottom. Again, this allows a gradient to develop where the maximum condensing effect can be obtained since the vapor is cooled incrementally from hot to cold rather than running into a wall of cold and then passing on to warmer and warmer coils.

Whiskey run in the wrong way will still condense by the time it exits the condenser, but it will run hotter than necessary.

CHAPTER 10 Double Run

10.1 Double Run Day 1 ———————————————

Now we can review my double run data and compare the energy expenditure to our digital still worksheets.

Loaded For Double Run	
Proof Gallons of Alcohol	494.57
Wine Gallons of Alcohol	510.00
Lbs. of Alcohol	4,098.60
(P.G./W.G.)*100=Avg. Proof	96.97

TABLE 206—Refer to Double Run Data Worksheet

Single-run spirits ready for double run.

Still loaded to the rim.

For this double run I took all the alcohol from four stripping runs which average around 100 gallons per run along with just under 100 gallons of heads and tails left over from prior double runs, and filled the still with as much alcohol as it would safely hold (Table 206).

I generally don't load alcohol above 100 proof into the still. 80 proof alcohol really won't catch fire in a spoon if you put a lighter to it, where 100 proof alcohol will. That is my rough and ready test for how volatile an alcohol to load into the still.

If the proof starts at under 100 then during the course of the run the contents are decreasing in proof and one is running the most risk for the least amount of time.

From a volume perspective, one has to be careful about how much alcohol one loads into the still, particularly on a double run. I have had runs where the alcohol has expanded and choked off the column. That can be a very dangerous situation as shown below. I've also had it happen in stripping runs where the cooker was too full with mash even though the expansion rate was not as great as with the higher proof alcohol used in double runs.

If you load the still to the rim and then heat it, it will expand and choke the still. Note in the picture at left the dirty color of the 95 proof alcohol loaded into the still and the oil and residue on the surface. Single run alcohol is not very pretty before you double run it.

10.2 Volume Correction

Volume Correction to any Table 7 Temp & Water @ 60° F	
US Gal. to be corrected = Present Vol. as Determined	510.00
What is the Present Temperature of the Alcohol	60.00
What is the True Proof of the Alcohol	100.00
Temperature at which it is desired to know Volume	100.00
Factor from Present Vol. to Desired Temp/Volume	1.0180
Gallons * Factor = Gallons at corrected Temp.	519.18
Desired Temp Wine Gallon Dif. from Present Vol.	9.18

TABLE 207—Refer to Vol Cor. any Temp Worksheet

Using a Table 7 volume correction (Table 207) we see that even raising the temperature to just 100 degrees, which is the maximum that Table 7 will accommodate, increases the volume of spirts in the still by about 9.2 gallons. Since the boiling point is going to be somewhere above 180° F this means that the spirits will increase substantially more between 100 degrees and 180° F. Since a 40-degree F increase resulted in 9.2 gallons of increase, a linear expansion would indicate 27.6 gallons (9.2 x 3 = 27.6) for 120° F of increase.

Using a Table 37b volume correction algorithm from ABS Software, and pushing it well past its design specifications of perhaps 35 or 40° C shows that the increase in volume is slightly greater than the linear increase shown above. The total increase would be 31.11 gallons (Table 208).

Volume Correction For Alcohol using Table 37b method.			
Sample Temp. of Alcohol or Water	60.00	0.0000	Thermometer Cor.
Apparent Proof	97.00	0.0000	Hydrometer Cor.
True Proof Result	97.00		
Present Gallons of Alcohol or Water	510.00	1,930.56	Present Liters
Present ° F Temp of Alc. Or Water	60.00	15.56	° C
FYI 60° Gal.	510.00	1,930.56	60° F Liters
Gallon Change from Present Gallons	0.00	0.00	Liters Change
Temp at which it is Desired to know vol.	180.00	82.22	° C
Gallons at Desired Temperature	541.11	2,048.32	Liters at Temp
Gallon Change from Present Gallons	31.11	117.76	Liters Change

TABLE 208—Refer to Vol Cor Alc T37b Worksheet

Head Space Calcs	
60° Gal.	510.0
t 37b to 180° F	541.1
Head Space	5.75%

TABLE 209—Refer to Vol Cor T7 Worksheet

In general it is necessary to leave sufficient head space above the alcohol in the still and the bottom of the column of more than 6%, and probably 10% just to be safe (Table 209).

Fortunately my still is slightly larger than the 510 gallons previously calculated because it has a dish bottom. Also my still lid has a dome shape, so even though the alcohol expands above the top of the rim, there is still head space. If I open up the safety valve in the lid and alcohol runs out then I know I'm choking the still.

For this double run I was trying to get absolutely the most alcohol into the still and use all the whiskey in the shop for one big run. I probably should not have cut it so close.

The double run data worksheet is just chock full of information (Table 210, next page).

Double Run Data												
Day 1	Hrs.	True Proof	Lbs. per 1/2 hr.	Lbs. Per Hour	Spout Temp	Boiler Return Temp	Tank Top Temp	Tank Bottom Temp	Tank Differential	Still Lid Pressure	Boiler Pressure	BTU's per Lb.
Start	0		0.0	0.0	52.0	53.0	49.0	49.0	0.0	0.0	15.0	
			0.0	0.0	52.0	97.0	70.0	75.0	5.0	0.0	15.0	
	1		0.0	0.0	52.0	128.0	100.0	104.0	4.0	0.0	15.0	
			0.0	0.0	52.0	151.0	126.0	129.0	3.0	0.0	25.0	
	2		0.0	0.0	52.0	171.0	146.0	148.0	2.0	0.0	34.0	
Shut Off Gas Boiler			0.0	0.0	52.0	185.0	166.0	167.0	1.0	1.0	40.0	
Running @ 3.0	3		0.0	0.0	52.0	187.0	179.0	178.0	1.0	1.0	45.0	
End Heads Begin Drum 2		161.6	93.0	186.0	70.0	189.0	177.0	177.0	0.0	1.5	45.0	
Cooling On	4	163.6	93.0	186.0	83.0	189.0	177.0	177.0	0.0	1.5	45.0	675.4
Run Cycle on			82.0	164.0	80.0	191.0	177.0	176.0	1.0	1.5	45.0	
17 & 1 min rest	5	163.0	81.0	162.0	78.0	190.0	180.0	175.0	5.0	2.0	44.0	689.4
17 & 2 min rest			88.0	176.0	78.0	190.0	180.0	175.0	5.0	1.0	43.0	
End Drum 2	6		84.0	168.0	78.0	191.0	180.0	179.0	1.0	1.0	42.0	664.8
		161.5	74.0	148.0	78.0	192.0	180.0	177.0	3.0	1.0	41.0	
More Heat	7		79.0	158.0	79.0	192.0	179.0	178.0	1.0	1.0	41.0	706.9
		159.4	79.0	158.0	80.0	193.0	179.0	179.0	0.0	1.0	41.0	
End Drum 3	8		79.0	158.0	79.0	192.0	178.0	177.0	1.0	1.0	41.0	795.1
Begin Drum 4		157.7	78.0	156.0	79.0	195.0	178.0	178.0	0.0	1.0	41.0	
	9		74.0	148.0	76.0	195.0	177.0	178.0	-1.0	1.0	41.0	848.9
		156.7	76.0	152.0	74.0	196.0	178.0	178.0	0.0	1.0	41.0	
Begin Drum 5	10		75.0	150.0	72.0	195.0	178.0	178.0	0.0	1.0	41.0	837.5
		154.6	73.0	146.0	70.0	196.0	179.0	179.0	0.0	1.0	41.0	
Middle Run Over Shut Down	11	154.0	73.0	146.0	74.0	196.0	179.0	179.0	0.0	1.0	41.0	860.5
Condensing Hours	8.0											
Loaded For Double Run												
Proof Gallons of Alcohol			494.57									
Wine Gallons of Alcohol			510.00									
Lbs. of Alcohol			4,098.60									
(P.G./W.G.)*100=Avg. Proof			96.97									

TABLE 210—Refer to Double Run Data Worksheet

We see that the boiler return temperature began the run at a return temperature of 187° F and rose smoothly to 196° F when the middle run was over.

The most reliable way to determine the cutoff point for the middle run is to look at the boiler return temperature. The still temperatures for the top and bottom of the tank suffer from contact problems, of the probe to the still, that make reliable measurements difficult. Installing a thermometer well into the body of the still at the top and bottom would assist in obtaining more reliable measurements. With these caveats in mind we can discuss the results.

From the data above we can see that the still did not start running until the temperature reached 177° F on the outside. Given that the vaporization temperature of 97 proof alcohol is 181.51° F this is not a bad concurrence.

I need to discuss some bumps in the data.

You will notice that the boiler pressure and still pressure rise to their highest point (45 lbs. and 2 lbs. of still lid pressure) when the still starts producing alcohol and then falls during the course of the first day's run. I'm not sure if this is the result of my running the boiler too hard or is an effect of distillation. I notice this often and I've mentioned it several times in this book; there is a surge of alcohol that flows when the middle run begins in earnest.

The problem is that one has to run the boilers hard to get the whole thermal mass to its boiling point. If one backs off the boiler too soon then the run will stop and it takes a long time to get it back up to running temperature. So the tendency is to overrun the boiler.

Still, I've done this enough to know that I need to back off the boiler after the run is well and truly started, and yet I see this pressure rise and flow increase shortly after the run starts.

10.3 Still Timer

During the double run the boiler cannot run continuously. It provides too much heat and the pressure builds up and even with the larger condensers there is just too much heat going into the system.

It is very tricky to try to back the boiler down by adjusting the flame and get just the right amount of heat into the system. One ends up spending all their time adjusting it up and down. Also, oil boilers are a little finicky. Once one gets them adjusted and operating properly it is best to let them run at the most efficient oil and air input settings and not try to play with the inputs too much.

Originally I had installed a temperature controller that was accurate to 1° F but this proved to be a disaster. One can't let the temperature of the still fall by 1° F. The boiling point of the contents is the temperature the still must operate at. If you let it fall, the still will stop running. The thermal mass of the still is so large with respect to the boiler reservoir that even after the boiler comes on, the temperature in the still will continue to fall so the difference can be 3° F by the time the boiler catches up and the temperature starts

rising again. It can take an hour for one to get the still back up and running, even from such a small temperature fall.

The solution was to build a timer that regulated the run time of the boiler with respect to a pause time.

The unit consists of two timers. Each timer has adjustable time scales that can be set by the user. The first timer's scale has been set to a 0- to 30-minute scale and it is used to set the run time for the boiler. The second timer is set to a scale of 0 to 5 minutes and is used to regulate the pause time of the boiler after each running cycle. It was a little tricky to get it wired up correctly because you want the pause scale to be first and the run scale to be second; that way, when you turn it on, you get the pause you are looking for. Once I got it working I simply had to wire in into the on and off switch of

Still timer.

my boiler in order to put it into operation. This unit was designed for me by Bill McLaughlin and I built it from the parts he told me to buy.

After I installed the boiler timer, the final step in the process was to find out what the run and pause cycle should be. It doesn't take much of a pause to keep the system in balance. I started this run with a 17-minute run cycle and a 1 minute rest but saw the pressure building up and increased the pause time to two minutes; this worked for the remainder of the run and means that the boiler ran 88% of the time and paused 12%.[47]

10.4 Double Run Day 1 Continued

Notice how gradually the boiler return and tank temperature rise during the course of the run and that the top and bottom temperatures are about equal. Also note the spout temperature; this is an indication of whether sufficient condenser water is being circulated to keep the whiskey from running too hot out of the end of the spout.

During this double run the greatest amount of alcohol weight per hour was collected at the beginning of the run before the surge in pressure that requires the application of the still timer to regulate the boiler was required. This is slightly different than what I've described in the stripping run sections where the greatest weight of alcohol is collected in the middle run pretty much concurrent with the surge in pressure.

I ran the still for 11 hours until the middle run was over and collected 5 drums of alcohol. Then I shut it down for the day. The total run time was 21 hours but there is no rush to take off the tails.

As long as one guards against negative pressure building up in the still by leaving a valve cracked just slightly, only minimal vapor will escape until the next day when we will finish this run.

The only other point I want to mention is that after I began using the still timer the boiler pressure fell to 41 lbs. At hour 7, which was 4 hours into the run, I did adjust the boiler to provide more heat because the stack temperature was not high enough to indicate the boiler was burning efficiently.

What we want to check is the lbs. per hour against our digital still using mass. We can only do this at the beginning of the run because that is the only point at which we know the proof of the contents of the still as loaded. Using that initial value of 97 proof and the known output of 186 lbs. during the first hour we find that 125K BTU's are required to vaporize the known pounds condensed (Tables 211–212, next page).

Comparing this energy to our scaling up worksheet (Section 4.8, Table 115), this energy shows that 5.38 boiler horsepower are required to vaporize this alcohol (Table 212).

---

47   My notes from the run show: "Back off early on heat once running. Start timer control early. This run was made with 17 minutes on with a 2-minute rest. Next time feed a little less heat by trying a 14-minute run with a 3-minute pause, then see if the still will even run with a 10-minute run and 2-minute off cycle or a 5 to 1 ratio."

Digital Still Mass

Lbs. Condensed Per Hr.	186.00	84.4	Kg per Hr.
Proof of Mixture Vaporized	97.00	48.50%	% Alc.
Lbs. per Gal. @ 60° F	7.80396		
Total Gal. per Hr. Vaporized	23.83	90.2	Liters per Hr.
Proof of Alcohol Condensed	161.6	80.80%	% Alc.
Lbs. per Gal. @ 60° F	7.17412		
Gal. @ 60° F Condensed	25.93	98.1	Liters per Hr.

Find Energy Required

Lbs. Condensed Per Hr.	186.00	97.00	Proof of Mixture Vaporized
Pounds Avdp to Kilograms	0.45359237	48.50%	Alcohol % of Mixture
Kilograms Condensed	84.4	0.937070	Specific Gravity in Air
Find Total Gram Cal. Required		48.50%	Alcohol % of Mixture
Grams Vaporized	84,368	51.50%	Water % of Mixture
LHV of Evaporite per gram	375.29	539.55	Energy Required to Vaporize Water
Total Gram Cal. Required to Vaporize	31,662,551	200.87	Energy Required to Vaporize Alcohol
Calories to BTU's Converter	0.0039683	375.29	Find LHV of Mixture
Vaporizing BTU's Required	125,647.2	375,290	Calories per Kg
Lbs. per Gal. of Mixture	7.80396	4.1868	Calories to Joules
Gal Condensed = Lbs./Wt.per Gal.	23.83	1,571.3	Kilojoules per Kg
BTU's per Gal. Condensed	5,271.8	7.8040	Lbs. per Gal @ Vaporized Proof
BTU's per Lb. Condensed	675.5	23.83	Gallons per Hr. of Vaporized Mixture
BTU's per Hour per Boiler Hp.	33,475	55.0	Drum size in Gal.
Boiler Horsepower Required	3.75	2.31	Hours per 55 Gal Drum

TABLE 211—Refer to Digital Still Mass *Worksheet*

Scale up to Energy Required to generate Lbs. Condensed

BTU's Per Hour Required Restated	125,647.2	3.75	Boiler Hp.		
Boiler Transfer Efficiency	96.25%		**BTU's lost in transfer from boiler to still.**		
Scale Up Value	1.039		4,895	0.1	Lost Boiler Hp.
Scaled up BTU's	130,542.5				
			BTU's lost in Generating Heat in Boiler		
Boiler Heat Generation Efficiency	72.5%		49,516	1.5	Lost Boiler Hp.
Scale Up Value	1.379		54,411	1.6	Total Hp. Lost
Scaled up BTU's	180,058.6	Total BTU's	180,059	5.38	Total Hp. Required
			125,647.2	Net BTU's After Loss	
BTU's per Hp.	33,475				
Boiler Hp Required	5.38				

TABLE 212—Refer to Digital Still Mass *Worksheet*

Comparing the gross and net values to our boiler tests for the oil boiler shows a result that is again very close to the value we have calculated and again must be considered serendipitous rather than precise given the uncertainties we are dealing with (Table 213, next page).

The remainder of the Day 1 calculations in the double run data worksheet consist of my first attempts to calculate the BTU's per gallon values and compare them to our formula-generated values. It was my inability to obtain any satisfactory results which led me to the conclusion that the BTU's must be compared to the volume per gallon of the vaporized alcohol and not that of the condensed alcohol.

Boiler Test Summary	Gross Hp.	Net	Delivered
Oil Boiler Oil use Calculations	5.38	3.9	3.75
Oil Boiler Test Results	5.51		3.85
Percentage Agreement	97.5%		97.5%

TABLE 213—Refer to Boiler Test Summary Worksheet

While unsuccessful in my attempt to calculate BTU's per gallon accurately what I could do was to calculate the BTU's per Lb. of material condensed and note that it increases during the course of the run. These values are shown in the last column of the Double Run, Day One table (Table 210, *supra*)

10.5 Double Run Day 2

Returning for another go at distilling the double run shows that it took three hours to get it back up to its vaporization temperature and to begin flowing alcohol and that I was able to distill out another 1,096 pounds of alcohol over a period of nine hours (Table 214).

At shutdown the still was continuing to operate at a 9 to 1 concentration. The remainder in still was 9 proof and yet I was still taking off 79 proof at shutdown. Using Equation 1 we can confirm this relationship between liquid proof and vapor proof (Table 215, next page).

Day Two	Hrs.	True Proof	Lbs. per 1/2 hr.	Lbs. Per Hour	Spout Temp	Boiler Return Temp	Tank Top Temp	Tank Bottom Temp	Tank Dif-ferential	BTU's per Lb.
Start	0.0		0.0	0.0	54.0	73.0	73.0			
Thump Keg On			0.0	0.0	54.0	77.0	74.0	77.0	3.0	
	1		0.0	0.0	54.0	109.0	82.0	110.0	28.0	
			0.0	0.0	54.0	157.0	107.0	135.0	28.0	
Noisy Keg	2		0.0	0.0	54.0	183.0	139.0	159.0	20.0	
Quiet Keg			0.0	0.0	54.0	202.0	164.0	179.0	15.0	
Running @ 3.0	3		0.0	0.0	54.0	204.0	185.0	187.0	2.0	
Backed off Heat		147.6	47.0	94.0	67.0	205.0	182.0	184.0	-2.0	
Quit Keg	4	48.2	96.4		66.0	204.0	183.0	184.0	-1.0	1,158.6
All coils			79.0	158.0	65.0	204.0	182.0	182.0	0.0	
17 & 2 min rest	5		75.0	150.0	64.0	204.0	182.0	182.0	0.0	744.6
17 & 2 min rest			65.0	130.0	63.0	205.0	183.0	184.0	-1.0	
Wide Open	6	148.3	57.8	115.6	62.0	207.0	183.0	186.0	-3.0	1,086.8
Start Drum 7			58.0	116.0	65.0	210.0	182.0	182.0	0.0	
	7		60.6	121.2	68.0	212.0	182.0	188.0	-6.0	1,036.6
Wide Open		140.7	60.0	120.0	72.0	214.0	184.0	186.0	-2.0	
More Heat	8		63.0	126.0	76.0	215.0	185.0	187.0	-2.0	997.1
Begin Drum 8			65.0	130.0	78.0	216.0	189.0	192.0	-3.0	
	9	124.8	61.0	122.0	79.0	216.0	189.0	192.0	-3.0	1,029.8
			61.0	122.0	77.0	217.0	190.0	194.0	-4.0	
	10	119.0	60.0	120.0	72.0	217.0	190.0	194.0	-4.0	1,046.9
			59.0	120.0	70.0	218.0	192.0	196.0	4.0	
Max Out Heat	11	98.6	58.0	116.0	76.0	218.0	192.0	196.0	4.0	1,083.0
			58.0	116.0	78.0	219.0	194.0	198.0	4.0	
Shut down	12.0	79.0	61.0	122.0	83.0	219.0	194.0	198.0	4.0	1,029.8
	Weight Condensed	1,096.6								

TABLE 214—Refer to Double Run Data Worksheet

As the run progresses higher boiling point compounds begin to perceptibly enter the distillate. Eventually the taste becomes unpalatable and the middle run is over. In this run, that occurred about one hour after the still began running. At that point I disconnected the thump keg and simply ran the vapor directly into the condensing coils to condense the remaining tails directly into collection drums.

Proof of Liquid	9.00
Temp Still will begin Running Alc. (Eq. 2)	105.67
Proof of Distillate (Eq. 4)	78.39

TABLE 215—*Refer to* Boiling Temp & Liquid Proof *Worksheet*

I continued to collect alcohol until the boiler return reached 219° F. The reason that I can do this is because a hot water boiler with a 50-lb. safety valve will contain water that hot because the pressure prevents it from turning to steam. I wish I had collected boiler pressure data so we could see the rise. You can be sure that the boiler pressure was maxed out at 50 when I shut it down. I did collect pressure data during strip run 2, and at 213° the pressure was 41 lbs.

One way to tell that your boiler is nearing its maximum operating pressure is to keep an eye on the over pressure valve outlet. The springs in over pressurization valves begin to lose their tension when heated. As the valve reaches its capacity, it will begin to weep boiler fluid out of it onto the ground. This is a good warning sign that one is reaching the pressure limit of the valve and it is time to back off. It is also very important to pipe the overflow valve outlet in such a way that if it does release pressure, it does so in a direction that will not scald anyone or damage other equipment. When it does let go, it does so with a great deal of force.

10.6 Double Run Recovery

Table 216 displays the results of this double run.

Double Run Recovery		Heads	Good	Good	Good	Good		
	Foreshots	Drum 1	Drum 2	Drum 3	Drum 4	Drum 5		
Drum Gross Weight	30.0	160.8	416.2	383.6	272.4	138.0		
Weight of Drum Empty	5.0	24.4	22.8	22.2	22.2	24.4		
Fluid Weight in Drum	25.0	136.4	393.4	361.4	250.2	113.6	1,280.0	
Temperature of Fluid	52.0	52.0	65.0	51.0	51.0	52.0		
Apparent proof of Fluid	159.0	159.0	163.0	156.0	154.0	152.0		
Table 1 -- True Proof of Fluid	161.2	161.2	161.4	159.0	157.0	154.7		
Table 4 -- W.G. Conv Factor	0.13928	0.13928	0.13935	0.13881	0.13837	0.13787		
Wine Gallons in Drum	3.5	19.0	54.8	50.2	34.6	15.7	177.7	
Table 4 -- P.G. Conv Factor	0.22438	0.22438	0.22491	0.22071	0.21724	0.21328		
Proof Gallons In Drum	5.6	30.6	88.5	79.8	54.4	24.2	283.0	

	Tails	Tails	Tails				Grand
	Drum 6	Drum 7	Drum 8		Totals	Thump Keg	Totals
Drum Gross Weight	390.0	273.4	433.6			175.0	
Weight of Drum Empty	22.2	24.4	24.4			25.0	
Fluid Weight in Drum	367.8	249.0	409.2	1,026.0	2,306.0	150.0	2,456.0
Temperature of Fluid	62.0	72.0	60.0			86.0	
Apparent proof of Fluid	149.0	145.0	107.0			65.0	
Table 1 -- True Proof of Fluid	148.3	140.7	107.0			53.4	
Table 4 -- W.G. Conv Factor	0.13655	0.13507	0.12950			0.12392	
Wine Gallons in Drum	50.2	33.6	53.0	136.8	314.6	18.6	333.2
Table 4 -- P.G. Conv Factor	0.20250	0.19004	0.13857			0.06617	
Proof Gallons In Drum	74.5	47.3	56.7	178.5	461.5	9.9	471.5

TABLE 216—*Refer to* Double Run Data *Worksheet*

In this run I was able to distill 246.8 Proof Gallons of middle run whiskey which amounted to 53.5% of the total Proof Gallons recovered and 49.4% of the volume (Table 217).

Recovery Totals	P.G	% By P.G.	Weight	% By Wt.	Volume	% by Vol
Foreshots & Heads	36.2	7.8%	161.4	6.6%	22.5	7.1%
Middle Run - Potable Spirits	246.8	53.5%	1,118.6	45.5%	155.3	49.4%
Tails but not Thump Keg	178.5	38.7%	1,176.0	47.9%	136.8	43.5%
Cross Check Totals	461.5	100%	2,456.0	100%	314.6	100%
Weight Loaded	4,098.6		Gal. Loaded	510.0		
Weight Recovered	2,456.0		Gal Recovered	333.2		
Weight Discarded	1,642.6		Gal. Discarded	176.8		
Proof Gallons Loaded	494.6		7.7	Gallons per P.G. Discarded		
Proof Gallons Recovered In Drums	461.5		13.06	Proof Gal. per Gal. = Proof of Discards		
Proof Gallons in Thump Keg	9.9		6.5	% By Volume of Discards		
Proof Gal. Accounted For	471.5					
Proof Gallons not Accounted For	23.1					
% not recovered	4.7%					

TABLE 217—*Refer to* Double Run Recovery *Worksheet*

Totals of Proof Gal. Employed	494.57	
	P.G	% By P.G.
Foreshots & Heads	36.2	7.3%
Middle Run - Potable Spirits	246.8	49.9%
Tails but not Thump Keg	178.5	36.1%
Cross Check Totals	461.5	93%
Unrecovered Proof Gallons	33.0	6.7%
		100%

TABLE 218—*Refer to* Double Run Recovery *Worksheet*

The above recovery data was calculated based upon the recovered Proof Gallons. It is also necessary to look at it with respect to the Proof Gallons actually employed in the run (Table 218).

Note the decrease in percentage of middle run to the total, down to 49.9% of the total Proof Gallons loaded into the still.

I was only able to take this run down to 148 proof or so before the middle run ended. I collected a lot of alcohol at 140 proof that was not useable in my products. In order to refine this alcohol further I would have to use my fractionating still to achieve a greater separation of the alcohol. We will discuss this procedure in the fractionating section *infra*.

10.7 Double Run Component Spirits

As a natural product of fermentation, various chemicals other than alcohol are produced. When one drinks wine or beer one is consuming all of these compounds in their naturally occurring proportions. Only distillation makes the separation required to remove most of these substances. In the distilling trade, all organic compounds, other than alcohol, are referred to as congeners. The strip run distillate is sometimes referred to as "low wines" and the double run or spirits run product is known as "high wines." Heads and tails are sometimes mixed together and called "feints." These are archaic terms but you will sometimes see them in older literature.

Some of these fermentation by-product chemicals have a boiling point lower than that of alcohol and others have a higher boiling point.

At the start of a distillation, whether a stripping run or a double run, the first compounds to come out of the still are the low boiling point compounds.

The very first distillate to emerge from the still are known as foreshots. They are comprised of principally alcohol, but this is contaminated with high levels of acetone, various esters, aldehydes and methanol.

The boiling point of these compounds are shown in Table 219.[48]

The foreshots are mostly alcohol but contain such a high concentration of the low boiling point compounds that they smell and taste like nail polish remover. Foreshots are to be considered poisonous and should be discarded.

	°C	°F
Acetone	56.50	133.70
Methanol	64.70	148.46
Ethyl acetate	77.10	170.78
Ethyl Alcohol	78.40	173.12
Propyl Alcohol	97.2	206.96
Water	100.0	212.00
Butyl Alcohol	117.5	243.50
Amyl Alcohol	137.8	280.04
Furfural	161.0	321.80

TABLE 219—*Refer to* Boiling Points *Worksheet*

Many distillers have a hard time discarding waste products because the TTB taxes "Alcohol" at the moment of creation. Therefore according to them any alcohol is taxable alcohol.

That creates a problem for distillers because they end up storing lots of "alcohol" on their books that they can't economically recover but is taxable whiskey once it appears on their books.

The position that I've always taken is that if it is not recoverable alcohol, with the equipment in my shop, then it is not taxable alcohol. I've met some resistance with this approach but generally my view has prevailed.

There is a line on the storage report where one can identify an unfinished spirits account and keep heads and tails there. These spirits are then withdrawn from storage for double runs and any heads and tails from that run are re-deposited into the unfinished spirits account. Losses in this account are tacitly recognized as appropriate given the nature of the spirits contained in them. I also discard immediately any demonstrably unrecoverable alcohol and do not put it on the books. I usually discard alcohol by dilution with water or use foreshots as fire starter for brush piles.

What is deceptive about foreshots is that they have a very low density and if proofed, show up as very high proof. It fools people into thinking that the still is running very high proof alcohol. It's not. It is running acetone. The alcohol will come later.

In the double run I collected about 3.5 gallons of foreshots before the distillate was sufficiently enriched with alcohol to call it "heads."

Heads are the next fraction of alcohol to emerge as distillate from the still.

They are not potable alcohol because they still contain a large fraction of the low boiling point compounds that contaminated the foreshots. Still, they are sufficiently enriched in alcohol such that they can be re-run in another double run to extract the alcohol from them.

In the double run summary I lumped the foreshots and heads together and we see that they comprised 7.1% of the total run and about 22.5 of the 315 gallons recovered (Table 220, next page).

Recovery Totals	P.G	% By P.G.	Weight	% By Wt.	Volume	% by Vol
Foreshots & Heads	36.2	7.8%	161.4	7.0%	22.5	7.1%
Middle Run - Potable Spirits	246.8	53.5%	1,118.6	48.5%	155.3	49.4%
Tails but not Thump Keg	178.5	38.7%	1,026.0	44.5%	136.8	43.5%
Cross Check Totals	461.5	100%	2,306.0	100%	314.6	100%

TABLE 220—Refer to Double Run Recovery Worksheet

The middle run comprises the potable alcohol that is produced by the run. In this double run they comprised 53.5% of the Proof Gallons recovered.

At some point late in the middle run a certain family of esters begins to bleed into the middle run. These esters are what give the whiskey most of its character and flavor. As these esters flow into the middle run they become increasingly intense and strong flavored.

Past a certain point they become so intense and strong that they are acrid and bitter and spoil the flavor of the whiskey. The distiller must make the call as to when to cut off the middle run before these acrid and bitter compounds contaminate the entire middle run.

Sometimes, to increase the middle run proportion I will collect separately a container of "late heads" and another of "early tails".

A portion of these two fractions can then be added back to the middle run to increase its proportion of the total run and to balance out the flavor of the whiskey I produce.

The goal in whiskey production is not to produce simply pure ethanol, unless one is producing vodka or grain neutral spirits. Some of these congener chemicals are required to give the alcohol its distinctive flavor.

Everything following the selected end of the middle run is called the tails.

My procedure is to keep the heads and tails in separate drums, since that is the way they have been collected and there is no reason, other than space in the shop, to combine them.

This also allows me to adjust the proof of my double run to be near 100 proof at the start. If I want to raise the proof, I will add heads and if it is too high, I add tails.

Even though the high boiling point compounds listed above are substantially above the temperature that the still is running, some molecules of each compound acquire enough energy to leave the still vessel and become a part of the condensate.

After collecting all of the middle run I have 3 1/2 drums of good whiskey but they don't all taste the same. The first drum still tastes faintly of heads and the last drum tastes slightly of tails. So, all the middle run drums have to be pumped into the blending tank and mixed together. Only then will I know the character of this run. At that point I can add some late heads or early tails to achieve the flavor I want.

The tails, at least in my judgment, comprised a high proportion of this run. My feeling is that this was caused by using a large proportion of heads and tails while loading the still with fluid.

You can't get something from nothing. Heads, and particularly tails, are already depleted in alcohol and enriched in other compounds. One can achieve some improvement with one run of heads and tails but accumulating ever more concentrated heads and tails reaches a point of diminishing returns.

10.8 Yield

Following is a summary of the yield achieved through two production years at the distillery. First we will look at the 2008 production (Table 221).

First distillation (Stripping Runs) Yield 2008			
2008	**Lbs.**	**Kg.**	
Total Corn	6,800.00	3,085.30	
Total Bushels	121.43		
Proof Gallon yield	437.40		
PG Per Bushel	3.60	0.142	PG per Kg.
% of Max Yield Coarse Grind	68.0%		
Loaded For Double Run 2008			
Proof Gallons of Alcohol	437.40		
Wine Gallons of Alcohol	510.00		
Lbs. of Alcohol	4,098.60		
(P.G./W.G.)*100=Avg. Proof	85.76		
Second Distillation (Double Run) Yield 2008			
Proof Gallons Loaded in Still	437.40		
Proof Gallons Distilled	**Proof Gal.**	**Of total**	**Of Recovered**
Heads	54.40	12.4%	12.6%
Middle Run - Good whiskey	279.00	63.8%	64.9%
Tails	96.80	22.1%	22.5%
Total Proof Gal. Distilled	430.20	98.4%	100.0%
Proof Gallons Lost	7.20	1.6%	
% accounted for		100%	Of Proof Gal.
Total Heads & Tails	151.20	34.6%	35.15%

TABLE 221—Refer to Yield 2yr Worksheet

In this production year I conducted five fermentations and stripping runs in order to obtain enough alcohol to fill my still for a double run. The production of middle run alcohol amounted to 64% of the total recovered during the double run.

In 2009 I only performed four fermentations rather than five as in the year before. This is because I knew that I had the heads and tails to make up the difference and assist me in loading the still to its capacity.

My supposition that re-running heads and tails is an exercise in diminishing returns is borne out by the results showing my middle run to be 64% of the 2008 production where I had no heads and tails to contribute to the run compared to the 2009 double run where I had augmented the strip run production with heads and tails left over from the last year and the middle run declined to 50% of the total (Table 222, next page).

The results also show that the total of heads and tails rose to 45% of the total alcohol recovered, up from 35% in 2008.

The total heads and tails went up from 151 Proof Gallons to 215, and this difference of 64 Proof Gallons is essentially 1/2 of the 125 Proof Gallons of heads and tails that were added to the 2009 run in order to fill the still. From this one could make the argument that I did increase the middle run by 64 Proof Gallons by using heads and tails left over from prior years. However, this conclusion is diminished somewhat by the fact that I loaded a total of 57 more Proof Gallons into the 2009 double run so I am unable to make any definite

First distillation (Stripping Runs) Yield 2009			
2009	**Lbs.**	**Kg.**	
Total Corn	6,000.00	2,727.27	
Total Bushels	107.14		
Total Proof Gallons	369.82		
P.G. per bushel	3.45	0.136	PG per Kg.
% of Max Yield Coarse Grind	65.1%		
Loaded For Double Run			
Strip Run Proof Gallons	369.8		
Heads & Tails Proof Gallons	124.75		
Proof Gallons of Alcohol	494.57		
Wine Gallons of Alcohol	510.00		
Lbs. of Alcohol	4,098.60		
(P.G./W.G.)*100=Avg. Proof	96.97		
Proof Gallons Distilled	**Proof Gal.**	**Of total**	**Of Recovered**
Foreshots & Heads	36.21	7.3%	7.8%
Middle Run - Potable Spirits	246.83	49.9%	53.5%
Tails but not Thump Keg	178.50	36.1%	38.7%
Total PG Distilled	461.54	93.3%	100.0%
Proof Gallons in Thump Keg	9.93		
Total PG Accounted for	471.47		
Proof Gallons Lost	23.10	4.7%	Of Proof Gal.
Total Heads and Tails	214.72	43.4%	46.52%

TABLE 222—Refer to Yield 2yr Worksheet

conclusions except to say that a pot still is not the most efficient tool to use when dealing with re-running heads and tails.

If you are going to re-run heads and tails you need more than just a pot still in order to achieve a better fractionation in order to adequately separate the alcohol from the congeners. This involves reflux and that costs energy as we will see below.

10.9 Double Run Costs

Table 223 is a pretty straightforward worksheet that totals the energy required to conduct a double run.

The worksheet in Table 224 also allows one to calculate the cost per Proof Gallon and the cost per bottle based on the percentage of the alcohol one is using.

Double Run Costs	
Find Gross Boiler BTU Burn Rate	
Number of Runs	1.00
Hours Boilers Operated	23.00
Total Boiler Hours	23.00
BTU's per Hour for Boiler 1	180,000
BTU's per Hour for Boiler 2	60,000
Gross BTU's consumed per Hr.	240,000
Total BTU's	5,520,000
Cost Per 1,000 Cubic Feet (MCF)	$15.00
BTU's per cubic foot	1,000
BTU's per 1,000 cubic feet	1,000,000
Total BTU's applied	5,520,000
Total MCF Used	5.52
MCF * Cost per = Cost of Energy	$82.80
Cost per Hour	$3.60
Double Run Cooling Costs	
Gallon per Minute Flow	3.00
Runs	1.00
Cooling Hrs. per Run	17.00
Hours of Cooling	17.0
Minutes of Cooling	1,020.00
Total Gallons	3,060.00
Cost per Gallon	$0.01
Total Cooling Cost	$30.60
Total Double Run Costs	$113.40

TABLE 223—Refer to Double Run Costs *Worksheet*

Find Cost per Proof Gallon and per Bottle	
Proof Gallons produced	246.83
Cost per Proof Gallon	$0.46
Proof Gal. per Case of 80 Proof	1.902
Cost Per 80 Proof Case	0.87
Bottles per Case	12.00
Cost per 80 Proof Bottle	$0.07
% that this alcohol makes to your blend	
% This Alcohol in Blend	50%
Cost per Bottle for this Alcohol	$0.04
100 Proof P.G. per Case	2.3775
Cost Per 100 Proof Case	$1.09
Cost per 100 Proof Bottle	$0.09
% that this alcohol makes to your blend	
% This Alcohol in Blend	50%
Cost per Bottle for this Alcohol	$0.05

TABLE 224—Refer to Double Run Costs *Worksheet*

10.10 Rerunning Heads and Tails

Some distillers report that if they accumulate their heads and tails over and over again, the concentration of congeners is beneficial and that if these heads and tails are diluted with water and run separately they will produce excellent alcohol. I don't find this to be true.

If one uses only heads and tails in a double run one may extract some useable alcohol but unless a fractionating still is used, rather than a pot still, the majority of the run will be the same heads and tails as were the source material.

The only thing that will change is the boiling point and since the still is loaded with about 100 proof alcohol each time it is loaded, the boiling point throughout each run is similar and thus the proof of the vapor is similar at each stage in each run.

For the record, the following is a summary of this procedure and the anticipated results.

"Some distillers mix the heads and tails together and call them Feints. As the feints are repeatedly recycled through spirit run after spirit run, they become more and more richly embued with the desirable whiskey congeners, so each batch of whiskey is incrementally improved over the previous. After numerous spirit runs, more and more feints will accumulate. At some point, the distiller can dilute the feints with water and do a special spirit run on the accumulated feints alone. Many distillers contend that the whiskey produced by this special run is the smoothest, richest, most flavorful whiskey of all, and it is often escalated to the status of the distiller's "Special Reserve" or "The Queen's own cask."[49]

I have never run a batch this way so I can't say for sure how it would turn out. I'm not sure it would be worth the time and energy use to engage in this procedure. See the fractionator still data for how much can be recovered using that type of still.

---

49 Source: Ian Smiley

CHAPTER 11 Other Still Components and Types

11.1 Thump Keg Description

Between the 2008 and 2009 seasons I built a thump keg because I was told it would improve the quality of the alcohol my still produced. I was looking for ways to extend the middle run and recover a higher proportion of potable alcohol from each run.

Thump keg (side view, tilted) with insulation.

The original reason that thump kegs were invented was that moonshiners would ferment more mash than their still could run and hold. This was particularly true of the people who made sugar liquor and who did not need to cook their mash in order to break starch down into sugar. In order to get all the mash run off as soon as possible they would hook up one or two thump barrels to their boiler and in effect increase the size of their still and not have to change the charge in the still so often. If you have enough heating capacity you could hook ten 55-gallon barrels together in a series and drive the alcohol out of all of them in one run. Just heat up the first barrel and the steam/alcohol vapor will heat all the barrels to a temperature sufficient to drive off the alcohol. In the process the alcohol from the first barrel will be condensed and re-vaporized ten times.

I was going to use my thump keg for a different purpose. My idea was to use it to wash the spirits through a condensation and re-vaporization through clean water.

Thump keg interior.

At first I ran the entire runs through the thump keg. This really had no effect on the total output of middle run. The keg did concentrate some less desirable rather unpleasant things into the water. The water became oily and the smell was very distinct. It smelled like dirty socks and the contents were about 30 proof or so.

I had to learn to fill the keg with only about 1/3 clean water because the keg would fill up during the run and end up 2/3 full by the end of it. What I was doing was wasting the Proof Gallons that accumulated in the thump keg because there was no way to recover them from the contents because they were just too dirty and foul to deal with.

Thump keg exterior.

To try to avoid soiling the thump keg with heads and since the goal was to extend the middle run by scrubbing the end of the middle run of high boiling point compounds, during subsequent double runs I decided to bypass the thump keg until the end of the middle run. This would keep the water clean until it was needed to wash out compounds in the late middle run and hopefully extend it. So I ran the heads and the middle run directly through the condenser coils and into drums. Then, at the end of the middle run, when I detected the oily taste of tails, I redirected the vapor stream into the thump keg before it reached the condenser coils. This involved some time lost because it then took about 45 minutes for the vapor stream to heat the contents of the thump keg to its boiling point where alcohol would re-vaporize and leave the keg. During this warm-up time the keg would really burble and thump until it reached operating temperature at which time the thumping would subside to a muted vibration of the keg itself.

The short story is that it didn't work. The distillate at the spout still tasted like late middle run and early tails. Even though I was "washing" the alcohol in water and accumulating alcohol and other compounds in the thump keg, it did not really change the character of the whiskey coming out of the spout. The tails were still tails. Also, there was no noticeable effect on the proof of the output towards increasing it. There had been some allegations that the re-vaporization would increase the proof of the spirits but this also did not turn out to be the case.

11.2 Fractionator (Reflux) Still

In order to deal with the heads and tails from my double run I would need to use my reflux still.

It has a vertical column that can be packed with stainless-steel wool or copper scrub pads so that the alcohol has a surface to condense and re-evaporate on as it ascends the column. It will also work without packing, but not as well.

When I say packed, I don't really mean it in the common sense of jamming in a lot of material. The vapor has to have a relatively free passage up and down the column. The desired effect is that of a lattice or stairway. Using four or five copper pads, spaced about 6 inches apart will act as still plates, and will allow the passage of vapor. You can achieve this separation of the pads by tying them together with stainless-steel wire so that they are separated by the right amount and then pulling the chain of pads up through the column. When using stainless-steel wool it is easy to simply double up a four-foot length of the material and push it gently through the column with a broom handle.

The following picture shows the interior of my still room with my original stills. In the foreground are two stripping stills and the fractionating still is in the background. These stills are converted 40-gallon hot water heaters and they work remarkably well. The interiors are porcelain and do not affect the taste of the alcohol. It is even possible to clean the interior by making a length of copper that is blocked at one end and that has holes drilled in the sides to let the water spray out horizontally.

Original still room showing fractionator column.

A few modifications were necessary to put one of these units into service. The zinc anode needed to be removed and the unit needed to be wired in order to deliver 110 volts to the heating elements rather than the 220 that are ordinarily supplied to it.

However, in order to speed things up one can use the full 220 volts to warm up the still and then switch to 110 when the still begins to run. The still is turned on and off from a breaker box, you can see the box on the wall near the foreground still. Before the power gets to the box, one leg or lead of the two hot wires needed for 220 volt power is run through a simple light switch. To make the change from 220 to 110 volts one simply throws the breaker switch off, flips the light switch and then turns the unit back on. It is very important to turn the unit off before making the change. It cannot be done on the fly.

One can also adjust the power by using different-sized heating elements. I use the largest elements I can find which are 4,500 watt elements.

The coils themselves are made with 1/4-inch copper tubing that is wrapped carefully around a broom handle with compression fittings on each end. When one does this, it helps if the copper is warm and care must be taken to wrap it so that it does not kink. Also, the return line should go up the center of the coil and so must be laid straight up the center alongside of the broom handle used as a mandrel. The hardest bend to make is the bend at the bottom where this takes place, which of course is the first bend one has to make. One can use a little teardrop shape at the bottom to make this an easier bend.

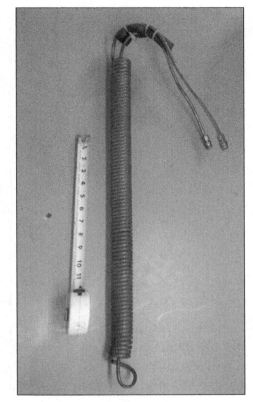

Wound copper condenser coil.

The only thing that can go mechanically wrong with this still is if an element burns out during a run. Then one has to wait for the alcohol to cool down, drain it out, replace the element and start over.

These two still designs were created by John Stone and described in his book *Making Gin & Vodka*.

Figures 5 and 6 (next page) show how the coils work.

In order for the condenser water to run counter to the vapor pressure, in this case, the cold water must enter at the top of the condensing coil and then flow out from the bottom of the coil at the hottest part of the condenser in contact with the vapor.

I know this seems a little weird and that one would want to put the cold water to work as far down the column as possible in order to meet the hot vapor rising up as soon as possible. It will work this way as well, but you will get a better separation if one runs the water counter to the vapor pressure with cold water meeting hot water gradually rather than all of a sudden. Just keep the water output temperature around 100° F to 105° F and it will run fine.

Figure 5 is an open-top unit so you can over-fire the still and drive vapor out the top. If one sees vapor coming out of the top you are wasting alcohol and filling your shop with an inflammable mixture, so keep an eye on this. But if the still is being operated properly the cold water will keep the vapor contained in the fractionating column and will condense it in the condensing portion. The collection valve can be calibrated by running it full open to obtain a flow rate and then decreasing that flow rate by a factor to slow down the alcohol take by the number of refluxes desired as a fraction of the total possible take.

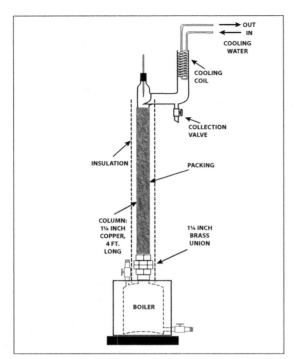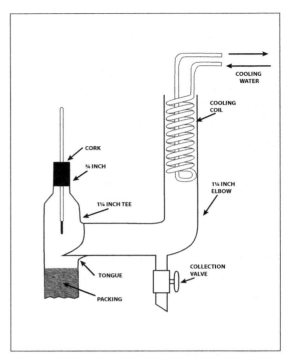

Left: Figure 5: Fractionator column. Right: Figure 6: Close-up view of the still head. (Figures from Making Gin & Vodka, *John Stone, privately published.)*

I find that running this still without any reflux at all allows me to take off alcohol at just under one gallon per hour and using reflux would just reduce that amount. I can recover about 1/2 of the Proof Gallons in my heads and tails which is sufficient, just barely, to make it worthwhile.

Figure 6 shows a close up of the still head. Note the tongue that directs the condensed alcohol down the center of the packed column.

Table 225 is a summary of a run I made with heads and tails to extract the recoverable alcohol.

The still was loaded with 24 gal. of 140 proof heads and tails diluted with 10 gal. of water to reduce initial volatility. The run lasted almost 12 hours from the time the still began flowing. At 110 volts, the 4,500 watt element is producing 1/4 of those watts or 1,125 watts per hour.

Using Tables 226-1 and 226-2 (next two pages) with an input of 1.125 kilowatts per hour, we can confirm the gallons per hour produced using reasonable variables for the proof of the mixture to be vaporized and the starting and ending output proof of the run. The output is less than one gallon per hour which makes it time-consuming for the amount produced.

	Beginning	Middle	End
Column Top Temp	165	168	170
Column Bottom Temp	155	160	165
Tank Temp	181	182	184
Proof Collected	178	168	164
Proof Gallons Loaded			
Gallons	24.0		
Proof	140.00		
Proof Gallons	33.60		
Proof Gallons Collected			
Gallons	10.4		
Avg. Proof	167.6		
Proof Gallons	17.43		
Proof Gal Remaining	16.17		

TABLE 225—Refer to Fractionator Data *Worksheet*

This type of a run will also produce heads, middle run and tails; so not all of the output will be usable alcohol. Increasing the reflux rate by regulating the amount of alcohol that is allowed to leave the still can increase the concentration of heads into a smaller volume of the total take. The same holds true of the tails. The middle run really doesn't need a lot of reflux applied and the still can be run wide open during that portion of the run (Tables 226-1, below, and 226-2, next page).

Electric Energy to Vaporize Alcohol and Water mixtures				
Kilowatts per Hr.	1.125			
Volts of Current	110.00		10.23	Amps per Hr.
Watts of Heating Element	1,125.30		220.00	Volts of Current
Volts/ Watts = Amps	10.23		2,250.60	Watts = Amps * Volts
Watts of Heating Capacity	1,125.30		**Check Converter**	
BTU's per Watt	3.41214160		0.00029307	BTU's to KW Hours
BTU's per Hr.	3,839.68		1.125	Kw Hour OK
Heat Required to Vaporize water and alcohol mixtures at any Efficiency			0.11	Boiler Horsepower
BTU's Per Hour Available	3,839.68		0.000	Boiler Hp. Loss
Boiler Efficiency	100.00%		0.000	Transfer Hp. Loss
Available BTU's * Efficiency = Net Boiler BTU's	3,839.68		0.000	Total Hp. Loss
Heat Transfer Efficiency	100.00%		0.11	Net Boiler Hp.
Actual BTU's Transferred to Vessel	3,839.68		1.000	Scale up Value
Find BTU's to Vaporize Alcohol & Water Mixtures		**Proof**		
Alcohol % of Mixture @ 60° F	50.00%	100.00	0.947817	Kilojoules to BTU's
Proof Equivalent of Sample to Be Vaporized	100.00		1,469.11	BTU's per Kg
Alcohol % of Mixture	50.00%		0.4535924	Kg to Lbs.
Water % of Mixture	50.00%		666.38	BTU's per Lb.
Energy Required to Vaporize Water	539.55	Cal per Gram	7.7803	Lbs. per Gal. @ Proof
Energy Required to Vaporize Alcohol	200.87	Cal per Gram	5,184.61	BTU's per Gal.
Find Latent Heat of Vaporization (LHV)	370.21		3.7854118	Gallons to Liters
Calories per Kg	370,210		1,369.6	BTU's per Liter
Calories to Joules	4.18680		1,054.350	BTU's to Joules
Kilojoules per Kg	1,550.00		1,444,069	Joules per Liter
Find Grams & Gallons per Hour Boil off Rate				
BTU's to Gram Calories	252.000		43.56	Grams Per Minute
BTU's * Converter = Gram Calories Available	967,600		2.61	Kilograms per Hr.
LHV of mixture restated	370.21		0.10	Pounds per Minute
Total Grams Vaporized per Hour	2,613.65		3.785413	Gal. to Liters
Grams to U.S. Pounds Converter	0.0022050		2.804	Liters per Hr.
Grams * Converter = Pounds per Hour	5.763		0.012	Gallons Per Minute
			1.469	BTU's per Gram Vaporized

TABLE 226-1—Refer to Electric Still *Worksheet*

Pounds Per Gallon of Vaporized Mixture	7.78028				
Gallons Per Hour	0.74				
BTU's per Gram (Derived)	1.469087				
BTU's per Gallon (Derived)	5,183.64				
Find Liter Volume per hour With No Rectification					
Specific Gravity of Vaporized Grams	0.934180				
Milliliters Per Hour = Grams per Hour/ Specific Gravity of Vapor	2,797.80				
Liters Per Hour	2.80				
Milliliters Per Minute	46.63				
Liters to Gallons	0.26				
Gallons Per Hour	0.739				
Find BTU's to Condense Alcohol & Water Mixtures					
Proof of Mixture Condensed	168.00	84.00%	Alcohol % of Mixture	7.09774	Pounds Per Gallon of Condensate
Alcohol % of Mixture	84.00%			0.812	Gallons Per Hour
Water % of Mixture	16.00%			0.947817	Kilojoules to BTU's
Energy Required to Vaporize Water	539.55	Calories Per Gram		1,012.16	BTU's per Kg
Energy Required to Vaporize Alcohol	200.87	Calories Per Gram		0.4535924	Kg to Lbs.
Find Latent Heat of Vaporization (LHV) of Mixture Expressed as Calories per Gram to Vaporize Mixture	255.06	LHV per Gram		459.11	BTU's per Lb.
Calories per Kg	255,059			7.0977	Lbs. per Gal. @ Proof
Calories to Joules	4.1868			3,258.6	BTU's per Gal.
Kilojoules per Kg	1,067.88			1,926.0	BTU's per Gal. Dif. = Condensing Advantage

TABLE 226-2—Refer to Electric Still *Worksheet*

Even with reflux applied, eventually the tails become such a large proportion of the base alcohol that it is not possible to remove their taste from the alcohol distilled and the run must end. For my time and money there is no sense running more tails out of the run just to simply put them back into the tails tank. Even if they are higher proof tails, with the existing equipment in my shop there is no way to separate them or recover the alcohol. Since there is no longer any recoverable alcohol remaining in the tank, the remainder can be discarded.

11.3 Reflux Energy

Still Output Based on Reflux Ratio	Refluxes		Take
Reflux Ratio	4.00	To	1.00
Total ml per Hour Possible to Vaporize	90,034.02		
Milliliters Per Hour/Reflux Ratio	22,508.51		
Liters Per Hour	22.51		
Liters to Gallons	0.26		
Gallons Per Hour	5.95		
BTU's Input Restated	125,647.16		
BTU's per Gallon at Reflux Ratio	21,131.12		

TABLE 227—Refer to Digital Still Mass *Worksheet*

People talk about reflux as refining the alcohol and achieving a better separation. While this can be desirable it increases the energy required for a run to the point that it becomes uneconomical for a distiller to engage in it (Table 227).

If one wants four refluxes it essentially drives up the energy costs by a factor of four and the cooling costs by the same amount.

11.4 Strip Run Still

My original stripping run stills were simply three hot water heaters with simple coils where the vapor was directed down towards the collection jugs. With this setup I could distill 120 gallons of mash at a time using 60 amps of electricity. On a stripping run one can power the element with a full 220 volts of power until it starts boiling but then one has to cut back to 110 just like when using the fractionating column. The condensers will simply not accommodate the amount of vapor that is driven off when applying 220 volts to the heating element and the mash. Of course, in order to use these stills the mash must be filtered before it is loaded into the still since there are no openings in the vessels that are large enough to get any appreciable volume of mass in or out of the still.

Figure 7 is a diagram of how the still is constructed. In this case the vapor pressure is flowing downwards. Therefore the cold water must go to the lower part of the coil and the cold water ascending will meet the vapor as it descends down towards the collection jug.

Three original stripping run stills.

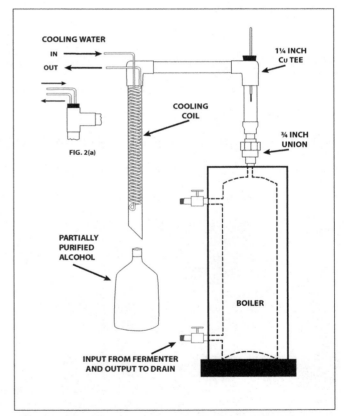

Figure 7: Construction of lower-facing condenser coil. (From Making Gin & Vodka, *John Stone, privately published.)*

11.5 Still Specifications ———————————————

These are the characteristics of my large pot still:

- Capacity 512 gal.

- Still timer in order to cycle still on and off during run. Generally 15-minute run to 2-minute rest during run.

- Dual condenser system to prevent pressure buildup and for taking heads and tails through separate condenser.

- Closed circuit condenser system with water meters measuring in gallons per unit of time.

- External pressure gauge and two safety pressure relief valves.

- Anti-collapse ribs on the lid.

- A large 5" effective diameter drain that uses a 6" ball valve.

- Cooling jacket surrounds column. Column can be packed.

- Hydraulic mixer with variable speed and reverse.

- Winch and trolley for lifting still lid on and off.

- Dual hot water boilers: 300K BTU natural gas 25 lb. and 300K BTU waste oil 50 lb. pressure boiler.

- Production of 15–20 fluid gallons of 160° proof corn whiskey per hour.

- Produces 110 Proof Gallons per fermentation. Can ferment up to 1,500 lbs. of corn per batch.

- 55-gallon stainless-steel thump keg.

- Heating coils double as cooling coils to speed cooling and setting batches.

- Insulated for heat retention during operation. Removable for cooling fermentations.

- Stainless tank with copper condensers for ease of cleaning.

Still setup.

Ideally one would want a vessel with a water jacket rather than internal coils. As you can see from the pictures my still does have internal coils but I did not have the luxury of affording a jacketed still vessel. They work fine for heat transfer but can be hard to clean of all the baked-on corn.

I later added external coils on the bottom because it was difficult to heat the bottom of the tank with only the internal coils.

11.6 Costs Summary

Following is the "Cost Summary" worksheet that I use in order to calculate the costs associated with making my products (Tables 228-1–228-3).

Cooking, Striping and Double Run Cost of Energy	
Find Gross Boiler BTU Burn Rate	
Number of Cook Runs	4.00
Hours Boilers Run Time per Run	3.50
Total Boiler Hours	14.00
BTU's per Hour for Boiler 1	120,000
BTU's per Hour for Boiler 2	154,286
Gross BTU's consumed per Hr.	274,286
Total BTU's	3,840,004
Average BTU's per Run	960,001
Cost Per 1,000 Cubic Feet (MCF)	$15.00
BTU's per cubic foot	1,000
BTU's per 1,000 cubic feet	1,000,000
Total BTU's applied Restated	3,840,004
Total MCF Used	3.84
MCF * Cost per = Cost of Energy	$57.60
Cost per Hour	$4.11
Second Method to determine Cost	
Assumes always 1,000 BTU per cubic foot	
Total BTU's	8,777,142.72
Constant of 1,000,000	1,000,000
BTU's /1,000,000 = MCF	8.78
Cost Per MCF	$15.00
Total Run(s) Heating Costs	$131.66
Hours of Boiler Run Time	32.00
Costs per Hour	$4.11
Cooling Costs	
Gallon per Minute Flow	6.00
Hours of Cooling	25.0
Minutes of Cooling	1,500.00
Total Gallons	9,000.00
Cost per Gallon	$0.01
Total Cooling Cost	$90.00
Heating and Cooling Costs Tot.	$221.66

TABLE 228-1—Refer to Costs Summary Worksheet

Stripping Run Costs	
Find Gross Boiler BTU Burn Rate	
Number of Runs	4.00
Hours Boilers Ran per Run	10.00
Total Boiler Hours	40.00
BTU's per Hour for Boiler 1	60,000
BTU's per Hour for Boiler 2	154,286
Gross BTU's consumed per Hr.	214,286
Total BTU's	8,571,428
Average BTU's per Run	2,142,857
Cost Per 1,000 Cubic Feet (MCF)	$15.00
BTU's per cubic foot	1,000
BTU's per 1,000 cubic feet	1,000,000
Total BTU's applied	8,571,428
Total MCF Used	8.57
MCF * Cost per = Cost of Energy	$128.57
Cost per Hour	$3.21
Cooling Costs	
Gallon per Minute Flow	3.00
Runs	4.00
Cooling Hrs. per Run	7.00
Hours of Cooling	28.0
Minutes of Cooling	1,680.00
Total Gallons	5,040.00
Cost per Gallon	$0.01
Total Cooling Cost	$50.40
Heating and Cooling Costs Tot.	$178.97

TABLE 228-2—Refer to Costs Summary Worksheet

Double Run Costs	
Find Gross Boiler BTU Burn Rate	
Number of Runs	1.00
Hours Boilers Ran per Run	23.00
Total Boiler Hours	23.00
BTU's per Hour for Boiler 1	60,000
BTU's per Hour for Boiler 2	154,286
Gross BTU's consumed per Hr.	214,286
Total BTU's	4,928,571
Cost Per 1,000 Cubic Feet (MCF)	$15.00
BTU's per cubic foot	1,000
BTU's per 1,000 cubic feet	1,000,000
Total BTU's applied	4,928,571
Total MCF Used	4.93
MCF * Cost per = Cost of Energy	$73.93
Cost per Hour	$3.21
Double Run Cooling Costs	
Gallon per Minute Flow	3.00
Runs	1.00
Cooling Hrs. per Run	23.00
Hours of Cooling	23.00
Minutes of Cooling	1,380.00
Total Gallons	4,140.00
Cost per Gallon	$0.01
Total Cooling Cost	$41.40
Heating and Cooling Costs Tot.	$115.33
Production Costs Summary	
Cook Run Costs	$221.66
Strip Run Costs	$178.97
Double Run Costs	$115.33
Total Energy Costs	$515.96
Proof Gallons produced	221.20
Cost per Proof Gallon	$2.33
Proof Gal. per Case of 80 Proof	1.902
Cost Per 80 Proof Case	4.44
Bottles per Case	12.00
Cost per 80 Proof Bottle	$0.37
% that this alcohol makes to your blend	
% This Alcohol in Blend	50%
Cost per Bottle for this Alcohol	$0.18
100 Proof P.G. per Case	2.3775
Cost Per 100 Proof Case	$5.55
Cost per 100 Proof Bottle	$0.46
% that this alcohol makes to your blend	
% This Alcohol in Blend	50%
Cost per Bottle for this Alcohol	$0.23

TABLE 228-3—Refer to Costs Summary *Worksheet*

CHAPTER 12 Blending, Formulas and Administration

12.1 Standard Moonshine Blend

I would be remiss if I did not include a blending sheet showing how my batches of moonshine are put together and blended. The first thing I learned when I started my distillery was that there was no way to make sufficient amounts of good tasting middle run moonshine to make a profit.

There is a point near the middle of the middle run where the alcohol is devoid of heads and tails and has a flavor that is very palatable. This was the moonshine that legend referred to as being clear, clean and crisp and that I wanted to produce. Unfortunately, this comprises only about 20% of the total output from the still in any given run. The remainder of the middle run, even though still good potable alcohol, is slightly colored by tastes that are not as appealing. In my hubris I thought I could make the whole middle run and all my output taste like that portion of the middle run. I was wrong. That realization and the fact that even if I could make all my corn whiskey taste as good as the middle of the middle run I still would not be able to ferment and distill enough alcohol to make a profit required me to begin blending the corn whiskey I produced with grain neutral spirits (GNS) of 190 proof to achieve the taste profile I was looking for.

I decided to take the entire middle run each year and then blend back some heads and tails to change the taste to where, when blended with grain neutral spirits, the entire batch tasted like the middle run. This proved to be possible and each year the proportion of heads and tails added back changes slightly based on the corn whiskey made that year.

To do this properly it is necessary to collect late heads and early tails separately and in separate containers. One cannot simply take all the heads and all the tails and try to blend them back in. I've never tried this but my guess is that the results would be disastrous. What I am trying to achieve is to extend the edges of the middle run on each side, both heads and tails, so that when the alcohol is blended with the grain neutral spirits the overall effect of the larger batch is that it tastes like the heart of the middle run that we started with. If I just took the middle run and diluted it with GNS I would not achieve the effect I wanted, I would just have diluted middle run.

Because my formula is based on the percentage of alcohol on a Proof Gallon basis and we store our alcohol on a Proof Gallon basis and we inventory our cases on a Proof Gallon basis, that is the basis on which the blend is designed. For the most recent year the percentage of corn whiskey was 16% of the total Proof Gallons included in each batch. The proof of the entire blend in that year was 151.7 which is under the 160 proof required by my standard of identity for corn whiskey.

Batch Planning	
Planned Cases	**P.G. Per Case**
90.000	2.3775300
Tot P.G.	213.9777
A1 P.G. %	16.00%
A1 P.G.	34.236
Weight of A1	164.444
Weight of A2	640.785

TABLE 229—Refer to Blend 2A Wt. Worksheet

Planning a batch required finding the total Proof Gallons required and then allocating 16% of those Proof Gallons to the corn whiskey component. In this blend I was making 90 cases of 100 proof alcohol and each case of 12 bottles would require 2.37753 Proof Gallons of alcohol (Table 229).

Knowing the total Proof Gallons required I simply multiplied by 16% to find the number of Proof Gallons of my alcohol that was required. Since I know the weight of each Proof Gallon of my whiskey I can multiply that value by the number of Proof Gallons and find the weight of my corn whiskey to use. Similarly, I can perform the same procedure, using the weight per Proof Gallon of GNS to find the total weight of GNS required.

Taking those two values and applying them to my worksheet that blends two alcohols by weight results in finding the amount of water required to blend the batch to the target proof of 100 proof (Table 230).

Blend Two Alcohols by Weight then using Table 4 add components by weight or volume				
What is the Target Proof of the Batch	100.00			
What is the Temperature of Alcohol 1	60.00	**True Proof**	0.000	Thermometer Correction
What is the Apparent Proof of Alcohol 1	151.70	151.7	0.000	Hydrometer Correction
Weight Alcohol 1 at Present Temp to be used	164.4440		0.0015	Tolerance
Proof Gallons of Alcohol 1	34.239		0.300	Tolerance as ° of Proof
What is the Temperature of Alcohol 2	60.00	**True Proof**	0.000	Thermometer Correction
What is the Apparent Proof of Alcohol 2	190.40	190.4	0.000	Hydrometer Correction
Weight of Alcohol 2 to use	640.785			

		Vol. as %	P.G. As %.	Wt. as %
Proof Gallons of Alcohol 1	34.24	19.30%	16.00%	20.42%
Proof Gallons of Alcohol 2	179.74	80.70%	84.00%	79.58%
Total Proof Gallons	213.98	**Water Ratios**	5.250	3.897
60° F. Wine Gallons of Water to add to Alcohol 1	12.24	0.542	3.897	Weight Ratio of A1 to A2
60° F. Wine Gallons of Water to add to Alcohol 2	90.97	1.038	4.183	Present Vol Ratio of A1 to A2
Total Gallons of water to add	103.21		4.183	Vol Ratio of Al 1 to Alc 2
Gross Volume of Batch	220.18		5.250	Proof Gallon Ratio
Total Volume Change due to Blending	6.21			
Actual "net" Volume Available for Bottling	213.98		23.49	Volume Difference in Liters
Weight Both Alcohols	805.23		31.32	# of 750 ML bottles "Short"
Weight of Water to add to Alcohol 1	101.94		2.82%	Vol Difference/Gross Gallons
Weight of Water to add to Alcohol 2	757.64		2.90%	(Gross Gal/Net Gal)-1
Total Weight of Water to Add	859.59		106.99	Absolute Alcohol Gallons
Total Weight of Batch	1,664.82		50.000%	% Alcohol By Volume
Alcohol Weight Tolerance A1	0.25		0.05	Proof Gallon Tolerance A1
Alcohol Weight Tolerance A2	0.96		0.27	Proof Gallon Tolerance A2
Total Alcohol Weight Tolerance	1.21		0.32	Total Proof Gallon Tolerance
Water Weight Tolerance A1	0.15		0.03	Water Gallon Tolerance A1
Water Weight Tolerance A2	1.14		0.14	Water Gallon Tolerance A2
Total Water Weight Tolerance	1.29		0.18	Total Water Gallon Tolerance

TABLE 230—Refer to Blend 2A Wt. *Worksheet*

The blending tolerance for alcohol in the US is 15 parts out of 10,000 (15/10,000). This amounts to 0.3 proof. Therefore my 100 proof batch must fall within the limits of 99.7 proof and 100.3 proof. In order to accomplish this precision I have calculated the mass and volume of 15/10,000 of each component. For this batch using a total of 805.23 pounds of alcohol the total weight tolerance of that alcohol is 1.21 lbs. Similarly, the water component weighs 859.59 pounds and the tolerance is 1.29 lbs.

It is actually easier to blend larger batches than smaller ones because the tolerance values go up with the total mass. For example, dividing the batch size by 10 down to 9 cases shows the following tolerance values of 1/10th the former ones (Table 231, next page).

Blend Two Alcohols by Weight then using Table 4 add components by weight or volume				
What is the Target Proof of the Batch	100.00			
What is the Temperature of Alcohol 1	60.00	**True Proof**	0.000	Thermometer Correction
What is the Apparent Proof of Alcohol 1	151.70	151.7	0.000	Hydrometer Correction
Weight Alcohol 1 at Present Temp to be used	16.4444		0.0015	Tolerance
Proof Gallons of Alcohol 1	3.424		0.300	Tolerance as ° of Proof
What is the Temperature of Alcohol 2	60.00	**True Proof**	0.000	Thermometer Correction
What is the Apparent Proof of Alcohol 2	190.40	190.4	0.000	Hydrometer Correction
Weight of Alcohol 2 to use	64.078			
		Vol. as %	P.G. As %.	Wt. as %
Proof Gallons of Alcohol 1	3.42	19.30%	16.00%	20.42%
Proof Gallons of Alcohol 2	17.97	80.70%	84.00%	79.58%
Total Proof Gallons	21.40	**Water Ratios**	5.250	3.897
60° F. Wine Gallons of Water to add to Alcohol 1	1.22	0.542	3.897	Weight Ratio of A1 to A2
60° F. Wine Gallons of Water to add to Alcohol 2	9.10	1.038	4.183	Present Vol Ratio of A1 to A2
Total Gallons of water to add	10.32		4.183	Vol Ratio of Al 1 to Alc 2
Gross Volume of Batch	22.02		5.250	Proof Gallon Ratio
Total Volume Change due to Blending	0.62			
Actual "net" Volume Available for Bottling	21.40		2.35	Volume Difference in Liters
Weight Both Alcohols	80.52		3.13	# of 750 ML bottles "Short"
Weight of Water to add to Alcohol 1	10.19		2.82%	Vol Difference/Gross Gallons
Weight of Water to add to Alcohol 2	75.76		2.90%	(Gross Gal/Net Gal)-1
Total Weight of Water to Add	85.96		10.70	Absolute Alcohol Gallons
Total Weight of Batch	166.48		50.000%	% Alcohol By Volume
Alcohol Weight Tolerance A1	0.02		0.01	Proof Gallon Tolerance A1
Alcohol Weight Tolerance A2	0.10		0.03	Proof Gallon Tolerance A2
Total Alcohol Weight Tolerance	0.12		0.03	Total Proof Gallon Tolerance
Water Weight Tolerance A1	0.02		0.00	Water Gallon Tolerance A1
Water Weight Tolerance A2	0.11		0.01	Water Gallon Tolerance A2
Total Water Weight Tolerance	0.13		0.02	Total Water Gallon Tolerance

TABLE 231—Refer to Blend 2A Wt. (2) *Worksheet*

I will simply say that from experience it is very hard to measure to an accuracy of 0.12 lbs. out of a total weight of 82.5 lbs. One tenth of a pound is 1.6 ounces. About what you can hold as a liquid in the palm of your hand.

When blending alcohol, knowing the weight of each component and the weight of each drum empty and dry allows one to subtract the weight of the drum and only add the weight of the alcohol contained in it. Same goes for the water component. In this way it is possible to blend to within the tolerance required.

If one were to use volume as the means of adding alcohol and water to the batch, one must perform a volume correction to find the 60° F volume of each component of the batch and then contribute the present volume equal to the 60° F volume. Performing this correction on the blend water required shows that if the blend water was 75° F,

Volume Correction to any Table 7 Temp & Water @ 60° F.	
US Gal. to be corrected = Present Vol. as Determined	103.21
What is the Present Temperature of the Alcohol	75.00
What is the True Proof of the Alcohol	0.00
Temperature at which it is desired to know Volume	60.00
Factor from Present Vol. to Desired Temp/Volume	0.9980
Gallons * Factor = Gallons at corrected Temp.	103.00
Desired Temp Wine Gallon Dif. from Present Vol.	-0.21

TABLE 232—Refer to Vol Cor. any Temp *Worksheet*

the volume required would be 0.21 gallons less than required. This seems insignificant until one looks at the tolerance for water which is only 0.18 gallons. The volume difference has used up all the tolerance and there is none left over for the vagaries of actually adding the volume to the batch let alone measuring the volume accurately (Table 232, previous page.)

A great deal of additional information on blending is contained in the user's manual for ABS software. One point that is worth noting here is the change in volume due to the blending of alcohol and water. In a blend for ninety cases the reduction in volume amounts to over 6 gallons of volume out of 220 gallons contributed to the batch. This amounts to over 2.5% of the components contributed.

The explanation for change in volume due to blending is that when alcohol molecules are combined with water molecules they tend to arrange themselves in a more compact arrangement than when they are separate. They also form chemical bonds, or if not actual bonds, affinities for locating themselves around certain parts of the other molecules. As a result of this, the molecules of each substance act like sand filling in the spaces between gravel. The net result is usually a slight reduction in volume from the original volume of each separate component. When blending low proof spirits with water a slight increase in volume actually does occur. Again, this is based on how the molecules of each component chemically arrange themselves.

The fact that alcohol and water do not blend to a volume equal to 100% of components contributed makes it difficult to plan a batch based upon how much volume of each component to add because one cannot predict the volume reduction with different proofs for the input alcohol. What one can do is to work backwards from the total Proof Gallons required to the total weight of the batch and then subtract out the weight of the alcohol to find the weight of the water required. Only then, from the weight of the water and the weight of the alcohol, can one find the 60° F volume of the alcohol and water. Of course if the alcohol and water themselves are not 60° F at the time they are blended together then a volume correction will have to be performed to find the volume of alcohol and water at their present temperatures to be accounted for so that the correct 60° F volume is added.

12.2 Moonshine Formula 1 ─────────────────────

Every alcohol brand or product in the US is required to have an approved formula before it can be produced. When I first started applying for formulas for my products I tried to make them as specific as possible so that the recipe was repeatable from the formula itself. This was the wrong approach. The best way is to design the formula from the regulatory requirements down towards the final formula by setting the outside limits of what is possible and still stay within the formula boundaries. For instance, my first formula was filed and approved for just 80 proof mountain moonshine. Then, when I wanted to bring out a 100 proof version of the same product, I had to file for a new formula just to change the proof at which it could be bottled. Subsequently I began filing my formulas for a range of proofs so that I did not have to have a different formula to produce and sell a different proof of the same product.

I then applied this lesson to all the components of the formula and worded them as broadly as possible while maintaining compliance with the standard of identity that I had chosen. I essentially defined the formula to stay within certain parameters rather than by listing the specific components in precise ratios.

The government has promulgated certain "standards of identity" that govern the types of alcohol that are permitted and their components.[50] Many of these are very restrictive and precise. Some of the requirements are for

─────────────────────

50 http://www.ecfr.gov/cgi-bin/text-idx?SID=f67b4ba78400beb8b43ac1be3d98db61&mc=true&tpl=/ecfrbrowse/Title27 /27cfr5_main_02.tpl, accessed September 15, 2015, "Labeling and Advertising of Distilled Spirits," 27 CFR Part 5. "Standards of Identity" are found in Subpart C.

health reasons and the rest can be interpreted as either legislating a business model or as protecting the consumer so they know that when they buy Bourbon it actually comes from the US or that Scotch comes from Scotland. Following are the regulatory definitions for Scotch and Bourbon.

"The words "Scotch," "Scots," "Highland" or "Highlands" and similar words connoting, indicating, or commonly associated with Scotland, shall not be used to designate any product not wholly produced in Scotland."

"Provided, That the word "bourbon" shall not be used to describe any whisky or whisky-based distilled spirits not produced in the United States. If whisky of any of these types is composed in part of whisky or whiskies produced in a foreign country there shall be stated, on the brand label, the percentage of such whisky and the country of origin thereof."

As my standard of identity I chose a simple catch-all called "spirit whiskey":

" 'Spirit whisky' is a mixture of neutral spirits and not less than 5 percent on a Proof Gallon basis of whisky, or straight whisky, or straight whisky and whisky, if the straight whisky component is less than 20 percent on a Proof Gallon basis."

This sounds confusing but in fact it is simple. Any blend under this standard of identity can contain up to 95% grain neutral spirits. The remainder of the blend must be one of the different types of whiskys listed (note the alternative spelling of whiskey in all the regulations).

Since I was making "whisky" under the above definition, that component of my blend could vary between 5% and 20% of the blend and still fall within the formula boundaries. This gave me the flexibility to vary the blend within those parameters based on the quality and taste of the corn based whiskey that I had produced each year.

At left is a copy of my formula for 100 proof to 150 proof moonshine.

I never became a big fan of my moonshine. It tasted like good moonshine but that taste was not something that I wanted to drink. That was a good thing. Even not liking my product very much I still ended up with a low dose of alcohol poisoning from breathing fumes, getting alcohol on my skin or starting siphons to move whiskey around. Exposure to alcohol is simply an occupational hazard of being a distiller. Eventually I did

DEPARTMENT OF THE TREASURY
BUREAU OF ALCOHOL, TOBACCO AND FIREARMS
FORMULA FOR DISTILLED SPIRITS UNDER THE FEDERAL ALCOHOL ADMINISTRATION ACT
(See Instructions and Conditions on reverse)

31/96)
00070-004-000001

Proprietor's Copy

1. CLASS AND TYPE OF PRODUCT

Spirit Whisky

3. PROOF *(Range may be shown)*

100-150

4. FORMULAS SUPERSEDED:

PLANT NUMBER	FORMULA NUMBER
DSP- WV-181	
WV- DRB- 1	2000 - 1

2. NAME, ADDRESS, AND PLANT NUMBER(S) OF MANUFACTURER *(See Instructions)*

Business Office

West Virginia Distilling Co., LLC
1425 Saratoga Ave. Suite C.
Morgantown, WV 26505

Sole Plant Facility Where Manufactured

239 Hess Street
Granville, WV 26534

5. FORMULA *(Use reverse if more space is needed)*

Mountain Moonshine Spirit Whiskey Formula for 100 to 150 Proof
A blend of ethyl alcohol bottled at 100 to 150 Proof (50% to 75% Alcohol by Volume). Such blend exceeding 5% of Corn Whisky, and containing the following ingredients:

1. Not less than 5% on a proof gallon basis of Corn Whisky produced at not exceeding 160 degrees of proof from a fermented mash of not less than 80% corn grain. Such Whisky not stored or aged in oak containers per 27 CFR Part 5 Section 5.22 (b).

   a. Not blended with any "Straight Whisky" under 27 CFR Part 5 Section 5.22 (b)(iii)

2. Not more than 95% on a proof gallon basis grain neutral spirits distilled from corn grain per 27CFR Part 5 section 5.39 (a)(1).

3. Water

6. DATE	7. MANUFACTURER	8. BY *(Signature and Title)*
02/23/00	West Virginia Distilling Co., LLC	Manager

FOR ATF Use ONLY (Items 9, 10 and 11)

9. ☐ Harmless coloring, flavoring or blending materials must not total more than 2.5% by volume of the finished product.

☐ Sugar, dextrose or levulose or a combination thereof must be used in an amount not less than 2.5% by weight of the cordial or liqueur.

☐ The use of refining agents must not alter the basic characteristics or composition of the spirits.

☐ The blended whiskey must contain not less than 20% straight whiskey on a proof gallon basis.

LABELING *(finished product only)*

☐ The designation of the product must include a truthful and adequate statement of composition.

☐ The label must indicate the use of:

☐ caramel ☐ certified color

☐ artificial flavor ☐ wine

☐

10. DATE	11. APPROVED - ATF SPECIALIST FOR THE DIRECTOR, BUREAU OF ALCOHOL, TOBACCO AND FIREARMS	12. FORMULA NUMBER
MAR 15 2000	Pamela Jamison	2000 1

ATF F 5110.36 (5-87)

PROPRIETOR'S COPY   011337 Form Ap
02028-004-000013

DEPARTMENT OF THE TREASURY
BUREAU OF ALCOHOL, TOBACCO AND FIREARMS
FORMULA FOR DISTILLED SPIRITS UNDER THE FEDERAL ALCOHOL ADMINISTRATION ACT
(See Instructions and Conditions on reverse)

1. CLASS AND TYPE OF PRODUCT

Spirit Whisky

3. PROOF (Range may be shown)

80-160

4. FORMULAS SUPERSEDED:

PLANT NUMBER	FORMULA NUMBER
DSP- WV-181	
WV- DRB- 1	2001 - 3

2. NAME, ADDRESS, AND PLANT NUMBER(S) OF MANUFACTURER (See Instructions)

Business Office

West Virginia Distilling Co., LLC
1425 Saratoga Ave. Suite C.
Morgantown, WV 26505

Plant Facility Where Manufactured

239 Hess Street
Granville, WV 26534

5. FORMULA (Use reverse if more space is needed)

Spirit Whisky Formula for: Mountain Moonshine, Old Oak Recipe.

A blend of ethyl alcohol bottled at 80 to 160 Proof (40% to 80% Alcohol by Volume). Such blend exceeding 5% of Whisky, and containing the following ingredients:

1. Not less than 5% on a proof gallon basis of Whisky distilled and produced at under 190 degrees of proof from a fermented mash of grain, Per 27 CFR Part 5 Section 5.22 (b). Corn whiskey used shall be so designated.

2. Not more than 95% on a proof gallon basis grain neutral spirits distilled from grain per 27CFR Part 5 section 5.39 (a)(1).

3. Water is added to recitify to 10 degrees of proof above bottling proof.

4. Infusion of oak chips and caramel not to exceed 2 1/2 % by volume, such blend to steep for three (3) to sixty (60) days prior to filtering, final rectification, and bottling, Per Part 5 Section 5.23 (a)(2) per trade useage for production of spirit whisky in general and Old Oak Recipe specifically.

6. DATE	7. MANUFACTURER	8. BY (Signature and Title)
12/06/2001	West Virginia Distilling Co., LLC	Manager

FOR ATF USE ONLY (Items 9, 10 and 11)

9. [X] Harmless coloring, flavoring or blending materials must not total more than 2.5% by volume of the finished product.

[ ] Sugar, dextrose or levulose or a combination thereof must be used in an amount not less than 2.5% by weight of the cordial or liqueur.

[ ] The use of refining agents must not alter the basic characteristics or composition of the spirits.

[ ] The blended whiskey must contain not less than 20% straight whiskey on a proof gallon basis.

LABELING (finished product only)

[ ] The designation of the product must include a truthful and adequate statement of composition.

[X] The label must indicate the use of:

[X] caramel   [ ] certified color

[ ] artificial flavor   [ ] wine

[ ] Spirit Whiskey Colored and Flavored With Oak Chips

10. DATE	11. APPROVED - ATF SPECIALIST FOR THE DIRECTOR, BUREAU OF ALCOHOL, TOBACCO AND FIREARMS	12. FORMULA NUMBER
JAN 3 1 2002		02-01

ATF F 5110.38 (5-87)

Old Oak Recipe W-Caramel.max

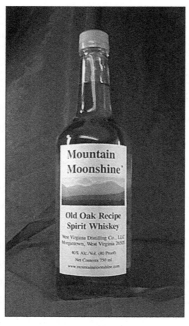

Specimen bottle of Old Oak Formula Spirit Whiskey.

Mountain Moonshine®

Old Oak Recipe
Spirit Whiskey

West Virginia Distilling Co., LLC
Morgantown, West Virginia 26505

40% Alc/Vol. (80 Proof)
Net Contents 750 ml
www.mountainmoonshine.com

learn to avoid as much contact with alcohol and alcohol vapors as possible around the shop.

But I did want to make a better tasting moonshine. I tried treating my moonshine with oak chips and found that in a few days I could change the character of the whiskey entirely to something resembling a light Canadian whiskey and with a few more days it would take on a much richer and fuller flavor. So I decided to make this experiment into a product and filed a formula for it.

This formula (left) is essentially my moonshine formula treated with oak chips. I can't say "aged" on the label, only "treated."

This allows the same formula to be used, with slight variation, in this case wood chip treatment, or the addition of caramel. Note that the formula is valid for a range of proofs from 80–160. Therefore one can produce and bring to market different proofs of the same product without having to obtain a separate approval for each. All of this is subject to the limitation that no more than 2 1/2% by volume can be added to the batch.

In my case the oak chips are added while contained in muslin bags and hung inside the tank at different heights. They act like tea bags and one simply tugs them up and down once a day to circulate the alcohol through them. If one keeps the lid closed on the tank it is surprising how little alcohol escapes. I was expecting the proof to drop dramatically even with a plastic sheet covering the tank and the lid on top of it but that was not the case.

The reason I blended to 10 proof above the bottling proof was to allow for this anticipated loss of proof during the treatment process. Still it is a good insurance policy to do it this way because when the treatment is concluded one can simply add water to the batch to bring it down to bottling proof.[51] However, by diluting the batch one will dilute the taste so the original batch has to be denser in flavor than you want the final product to be so that when it is diluted it will taste the way you want it to. This is a judgment call on the part of the distiller. I generally wait two days after I have achieved the taste I want to let the batch become even more saturated with flavor and then blend it down to bottling proof.

As I mentioned above, the corn whiskey component of my moonshine is about 16%, on a Proof Gallon basis, of the total product. It varies from year to year by one or two percent based on the taste of the whiskey that year. The flexibility of this formula allows me that latitude.

FORMULA FOR DISTILLED SPIRITS UNDER THE FEDERAL ALCOHOL ADMINISTRATION ACT.

FORMULA: Mountain Moonshine Spirit Whisky

A blend of ethyl alcohol bottled at between 70 and 160 proof (35 to 80% Alcohol by Volume). Such Blend exceeding 5% of Corn Whisky, and containing the following ingredients:

1. Not less than 5% on a Proof Gallon basis of Whisky distilled and produced at under 190 degrees of proof. 27 CFR Part 5 Section 5.22 (b). Corn Whisky used shall be so designated.

2. Not more than 95% on a Proof Gallon basis grain neutral spirits distilled from corn grain per 27 CFR Part 5 Section 5.39 (a)(1).

   a. Not blended with any "Straight Whisky" under 27 CFR Part 5 Section 5.22 (b)(iii).

3. Water

Attachment to form ATF F5110.36 (formula text only).

12.3 Transfer in Bond Application

For a small distillery, the only way to produce enough bottled alcohol to make a profit is to purchase some of your whiskey from other suppliers. The market is now filled with grain neutral spirits available from many different distributors. These distributors are now making available corn whiskey, rye, and rum to their customers in artisan sized 55-gallon drums. With an approved transfer in bond form one can move whiskey from distillery to distillery without paying the excise tax because it is moving from one bonded warehouse to another.

---

51 Increasing the proof of a batch can be calculated using my ABS software but it is so much simpler to simply take higher proof alcohol and blend it down with water.

With grain neutral spirits I found that the cost was much less than what I was paying to produce my corn whiskey. From Strip Run 2 I determined that it was costing me $2.34 per Proof Gallon to make my whiskey (Table 233).

This was for recovering strip run alcohol. The finished alcohol is only 50% of the fermented alcohol. Therefore, the cost per finished Proof Gallon is double that of the cost of strip run Proof Gallons: $4.67. When one adds in the energy costs per Proof Gallon the price soars to $6.26 per finished Proof Gallon. Now, my costs are slightly less because I use waste oil as the fuel source of my oil boiler, which is not that easy and takes a lot of time and that has a cost too.

Looking at my GNS costs we see that they are much less than what I can produce my alcohol for (Table 234).

Lbs. per Bag of Corn	50.0
Corn Cost per Bag	$8.50
Lbs. Per Bushel	56.0
Bags per Bushel	1.12
Cost per Bushel	$9.52
Bushels used	26.79
Total Corn Cost	$255.00
Proof Gallons Produced	109.10
Cost per Proof Gallon	$2.34
Double Run Middle Run %	50.0%
Corn Cost per Finished Proof Gallon	$4.67
Energy Costs per Finished P.G.	$1.59
Total Costs per finished P.G.	$6.26

TABLE 233—Refer to Strip Run 2 *Worksheet*

GNS Costs	2013
Per Dum $	$445.00
Number of Drums	7.00
Total Drum Cost	$3,115.00
Freight & Delivery	$315.00
Freight Per Drum	$45.00
Proof Gallons Per Drum	103.86
Total Proof Gallons	727.02
Total Cost	$3,430.00
Cost per Proof Gallon	$4.72

TABLE 234—Refer to Costs per Bottle *Worksheet*

The cost savings are almost 25%. This comparison is just strictly on a costs basis with no accounting for the overhead of labor and utilities and the months of my work, day and night, to produce those few precious Proof Gallons of corn whiskey.

Given these economic facts my business model had to change and I became a rectifier and blender of my alcohol with grain neutral spirits to achieve a good balance of taste that was similar to very good middle run whiskey. I did this by using more heads and tails to augment my middle run so that the overall flavor of the diluted GNS would match the taste profile I was looking for.

In essence I bring in pure alcohol and modify its taste with corn whiskey.

Transfer in bond forms are easy to come by. On the next page is a sample of what I used with one company. I have seven or eight different transfer in bond relationships. Prices vary.

Sample "Transfer in Bond" form.

12.4 Approved Labels

Label approval is another regulatory hurdle that must be cleared before a product can be brought to market. That topic is beyond the scope of this work. One could spend an entire semester learning about their requirements and intricacies. For a detailed look at the regulations and the requirements for label approval see the *Beverage Alcohol Manual* tutorials available at my business websites.

I do want to provide a sample of what an approved label looks like so following is my approved label for 100 proof mountain moonshine (next page).

12.5 Blending Water Time

I use a small commercial reverse osmosis system to process the water I use in my blending and bottling operations. It is rated at 200 gallons per day. When the filters are brand new and the temperature is 65° F the unit does process that amount of finished water. The problem is that the filters are only new once and they are very expensive. The output degrades quickly but given that limitation, they still retain their efficacy to process the blending water. Also, the water temperature has a significant effect on the efficiency of the unit. Since I do most of my blending and bottling in the winter I am sometimes using water from my utility board that is 45° F, sometimes 42° F at the coldest. I've even gone to the trouble of trying to heat the water pipes with heat tape and even electric heating pads with no apparent effect on the output water temperature. There is too much thermal mass in the pipes and in the ground to safely apply the amount of heat needed.

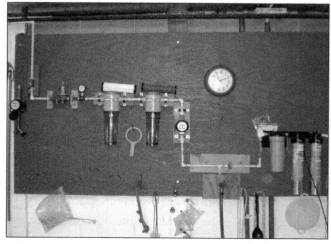

Mountain Moonshine "Label/Bottle Approval" form.

The water input comes directly off of the street pressure which runs 115 psi. Therefore I have a separate water pressure regulator and gauge on the input feed into the unit. The unit is designed to operate at 65 psi but the filter age or the temperature changes can increase the pressure on the filters to 80 or 85 psi in order to increase the flow through the molecular sieve of the filter.

I stopped using carbon filters to treat my city water. They do remove chlorine, but only for a short time, and they are expensive. If they are left too long in the filter housing they contaminate the water in the housing and also the water flowing through the system with a distinct rubbery taste from the rubber in the filter.

Reverse osmosis setup.

As to chlorine, since my water is processed over several days it has a chance for the chlorine to evaporate before it is used. I've never used straight city water in my blending operations, except a couple of gallons here or there when the proof was too high and I had no time to wait on the system to process more.

The reason I process my water is because the reverse osmosis system does change the character of the water in a favorable way. My city water tastes fine, but you can tell a difference after it is processed. This doesn't sound like a compliment, but the processed water tastes "flat," not devoid of taste but very neutral.

The processed water is depleted in calcium carbonate and other minerals that are in my water supply. This is a good thing since one of the factors that can make whiskey go cloudy is that these minerals can interact with congeners and specifically residual oils that are in the alcohol to produce colloidal particles that add a haze to the alcohol.

You don't think of alcohol as having oils in it but the corn I used had, in addition to 73% starch, 23% corn oil, germ, and other seed components. During the process of fermentation the yeast produced oils and other metabolic by-products. Some of these elements were inevitably transferred to the "alcohol" that was distilled.

These oils and other by-products are a varied bunch and can bind to compounds in the water with very deleterious effects. Since my moonshine is clear, any obscuration is fatal to the product. I've had more than one whole blended batch of 90 cases go cloudy in the blending tank when I mixed it together. The only solution was to put all 200 gallons back in the still and try to recover as much of the alcohol as possible.

The worst experience I had was the one time I decided to put the water in the tank first and then add the alcohol to it, the whole batch went cloudy and so it was back into the still again to try and recover the alcohol. I learned the hard way that one should never add alcohol to water. Always add water to alcohol. Just think of the way you make a drink. One pours the shot of alcohol into the glass and then adds water to taste.[52]

Blending Water - Time to Process	
Minutes Measured	100.00
Pounds output from RO System	15.00
Water Weight Per Gallon Value =	8.328230
60° F. Gallons processed.	1.80
Lbs. Needed	871.32
60° F. Gallons needed	104.62
Minutes per Day	1,440.0
Measurement Periods per Day	14.40
Pounds per Day	216.00
Days Required	4.03

TABLE 235—Refer to Blending H$_2$O Time *Worksheet*

In order to quantify how much time I will need to process my blending water I've had to time the output over an interval and determine the total time required. Since I blend by weight and also because volume will vary with temperature, I use the weight of water processed to make my calculations (Table 235).

A reverse osmosis system works by forcing water through a molecular sieve. The water molecules can wiggle through the membrane but larger molecules are blocked. There is also another component to the process; the membrane is not just a trap it is to some degree a barrier. The water pressure is exerted against the membrane; some water flows through but most of the water does not, it leaves the system before it can all be processed. This "waste water" is enriched with the molecules that were rejected by the barrier/sieve.

To give an idea of the ratio to processed water and waste water I measured the waste water output and compared that volume to the finished water output. (Table 236, next page).

The ratio is about 2:1 of waste water to finished water.

---

52   For additional information on blending, see the ABS user's guide (included in the software package).

Measure Waste Water Volume	
Minutes Measured	100.00
Pounds output from RO System	31.00
Gallons of Waste Water.	3.72
Waste Water to Good Water Ratio	2.07
Gallons of Waste Water Total	216.22
Total Gallons Used to process water	320.84
Cost Per Gallon	$0.010
Cost to Make Blending Water	$3.21

TABLE 236—Refer to Blending H₂O Time *Worksheet*

This militates against simply turning up the pressure on the input feed to obtain more output per unit of time since the filter can only process so much water given its surface area. If one turns up the pressure they may be wasting more water than the increase in output might suggest. Only by comparing waste water to the finished water values can one make the best use of the system and contain the costs.

12.6 Exothermic Reactions Due to Blending Alcohol and Water

As a practical matter, the process of blending alcohol and water together results in an exothermic reaction that liberates substantial amounts of heat. Following are the results of a blending operation conducted at my distillery that shows just how much energy is released.

All the components of the batch were the same temperature to begin with because they were all in the same shop and been there long enough to acquire the same temperature as the ground temperature of the shop.

While the temperature change was only 5.3° F the large thermal mass of the batch itself means that this small difference amounted to enough energy released to power a 100-watt bulb for a full day (Table 237).

As components are mixed together, the initial blended temperature of a batch will always be above temperature of each component part used. However, if you let the batch sit for a while it will assume the ambient temperature of the distillery, which may be above or below 60° F. Above 60° F, volume expansion of the

Exothermic Reaction Resulting From Blending Alcohol and Water			
Target Proof	100.00		
Temp. in ° F of Components	58.20		
Blended Temperature of Components	63.50		
Temp change	5.30		
BTU's per ° of temp rise per pound	1.00		
Total BTU's per Lb.	5.30		
Weight of Alcohol in Blend	805.23		
Weight of Water in Blend	859.59		
Total Weight of Components in Pounds	1,664.82		
Temp Change times Total Pounds	8,823.55		
Specific Gravity of Blend @ Target Proof	0.934180		
BTU's Times Specific Gravity = Net BTU's	8,242.78		
		Constants	
Kilowatt Hours	2.41	0.0002929	1 BTU to KW Hours
Horse Power Hours	3.24	0.0003930	1 BTU to HP hours
Calories	2,077,181	252.00	1 BTU to Calories
Foot Pounds	6,409,990	777.65	1 BTU to Foot Pounds
Joules	8,690,775	1,054.35	1 BTU to Joules
Watt Seconds	8,690,775	1,054.35	1 BTU to Watt Seconds

TABLE 237—Refer to Exothermic Reactions *Worksheet*

batch will cause more bottles to come off the line than the 60° F blended volume would indicate. This results in a gain in the processing account. This gain will offset any losses in processing during bottling. Below 60°, volume contraction of the batch will cause fewer bottles to come off the line than the 60° F blended volume would indicate. Below 60° F, the loss in the processing account is in addition to other losses that inevitably occur during bottling operations.

Once the batch is blended and in the processing account, the only way out of the processing account is by bottling it with the resulting loss usually associated with that operation. The temperature of the batch at the time of bottling will either offset (above 60° F) or amplify (below 60° F) those losses.

The regulations allow for this discrepancy in bottling temperature from the 60° F standard in a catch-all section that requires sound practices and also recognizes that evaporation does occur:

> § 5.47a (1) Discrepancies due to errors in measuring which occur in filling conducted in compliance with good commercial practice. (Author note: i.e. At a comfortable working temperatures.) . . . And (3) Discrepancies in measure due to differences in atmospheric conditions in various places and which unavoidably result from the ordinary and customary exposure of alcoholic beverages in bottles to evaporation.[53]

I always want my alcohol and water as cold as possible when I blend. This is in part to account for the exothermic effect, but also in part because the components just seem to work better together the cooler they are.

Hot alcohol has a real tendency to develop colloidal opacity because of the corn oil, calcium carbonate, or other congeners that are in the alcohol. The same is true of water, in particular the dissolved minerals in water can combine with oils in the alcohol to form colloidal substances. The danger is that the batch can become cloudy. This is a real problem when trying to blend clear spirits, as you can imagine. See the blending water time discussion above for more about cloudy alcohol.

12.7 Bottling Volume Correction

The volume of the blended batch varies with temperature. It is important to note just how much difference there is between the actual volume of the batch at the time of bottling and the 60° F volume that is required. Some leeway is permitted as quoted above and in the footnote below.

---

53 Title 27: Alcohol, Tobacco and Firearms PART 5—LABELING AND ADVERTISING OF DISTILLED SPIRITS Subpart E—Standards of Fill for Bottled Distilled Spirits§ 5.47a Metric standards of fill (distilled spirits bottled after December 31, 1979). (a) Authorized standards of fill. The standards of fill for distilled spirits are the following: (1) For containers other than cans described in paragraph (a)(2), of this section— 1.75 liters 1.00 liter 750 milliliters 500 milliliters (Authorized for bottling until June 30, 1989) 375 milliliters 200 milliliters 100 milliliters 50 milliliters. (2) For metal containers which have the general shape and design of a can, which have a closure which is an integral part of the container, and which cannot be readily reclosed after opening— 355 milliliters 200 milliliters 100 milliliters 50 milliliters
(b) Tolerances. The following tolerances shall be allowed: (1) Discrepancies due to errors in measuring which occur in filling conducted in compliance with good commercial practice. (2) Discrepancies due to differences in the capacity of bottles, resulting solely from unavoidable difficulties in manufacturing such bottles to a uniform capacity: Provided, That no greater tolerance shall be allowed in case of bottles which, because of their design, cannot be made of approximately uniform capacity than is allowed in case of bottles which can be manufactured so as to be of approximately uniform capacity. (3) Discrepancies in measure due to differences in atmospheric conditions in various places and which unavoidably result from the ordinary and customary exposure of alcoholic beverages in bottles to evaporation. The reasonableness of discrepancies under this paragraph shall be determined on the facts in each case. (c) Unreasonable shortages. Unreasonable shortages in certain of the bottles in any shipment shall not be compensated by overages in other bottles in the same shipment.

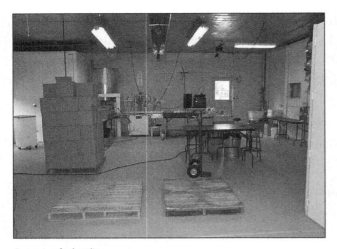

Preparing for bottling.

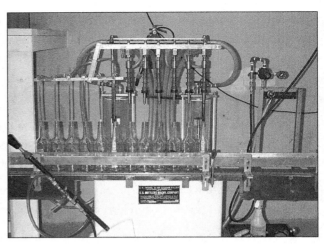

Close-up view of bottling machine.

Volume Correction to any Table 7 Temp & Water @ 60° F	
US Gal. to be corrected = Present Vol. as Determined	213.98
What is the Present Temperature of the Alcohol	60.00
What is the True Proof of the Alcohol	100.00
Temperature at which it is desired to know Volume	70.00
Factor from Present Vol. to Desired Temp/Volume	1.0040
Gallons * Factor = Gallons at corrected Temp.	214.84
Desired Temp Wine Gallon Dif. from Present Vol.	0.86

TABLE 238—Refer to Vol. Cor. any Temp Worksheet

Using the true proof based volume correction worksheet we see that there is a discrepancy in the volume in the tank and the volume we are required to fill (Table 238).

In this case we have entered the known 60° F volume for the present volume and temperature. This provides the result as a positive value indicating the increase in volume of the batch at its present temperature.

Usually the temperature of the alcohol is higher than 60° F at the time of bottling because working conditions in and around the shop are generally between 65° and 75°.

This results in a volume increase that masks to some degree the amount of processing losses. What this also means is that some effort must be made to increase the amount of fill in each bottle to compensate for the volume difference from 60° F gallons.

Usually this is done by eye. If I'm blending a hot batch of 75° F or so I will increase the fill by adding washers to the spouts to raise the fill level in the neck of the bottle. Putting a bottle in the refrigerator for three minutes will reduce the temperature and you can look at the fill height to see if it meets your personal standard.

As a practical matter most liquor stores are kept around 60–70° F so your bottle, sitting on the shelf, will be somewhat increased in volume from its standard fill temperature volume.

12.8 Recall Procedures

Recently the Food and Drug Administration has begun inspecting distilleries. Alcohol is now a food. Part of the requirements for compliance with the FDA rules are that a distillery have written recall procedures. This is really a pretty good idea, so here are the ones I wrote up in case they were ever needed.

West Virginia Distilling Company Recall Procedures:

Identify defective product and quarantine it. Make note of cases affected. Wrap separately and put signage on the affected batch.

Contact:

WV ABC Administration
Attn: Ms. Marilyn Smith
900 Pennsylvania Ave. 4th, Floor
Charleston, WV 25302

Phone: 304-356-5500

Inform them of code # of product to be recalled. Have them quarantine all inventory of that product in warehouse. Fax or email them signage to indicate that product is recalled.

Go to the West Virginia ABCA portal: Username: xxxxxxx Password: xxxxxxxx

Search sales by store for product in question. Identify all stores that have purchased product since batch was sent to Charleston.

Call all affected stores and have them pull product from shelves and quarantine it. Find out if there is a way to identify any purchasers of the product.

Make up driving directions to these stores and either pick up inventory directly or have it returned to ABC Warehouse in Charleston to be included in quarantined inventory to be returned to premises.

Report the recall to the Food and Drug Administration.[54]

Notify the public particularly in the areas towns closest to the stores where product was on the shelves.

Distilleries are also required to register with the FDA for purposes of identifying their location for inspection and also because it is required by the department of Homeland Security to identify businesses with volatile and dangerous chemicals on their premises.

12.9 Costs per Bottle

This worksheet (Tables 239-1 and 239-2, next two pages) is also included in ABS Software but is duplicated here as well. It shows one method of calculating how much it costs to produce a product, and how to calculate your markups to find the consumer price.

It is necessary to infer the retailer markup from comparisons to shelf costs as seen in stores. The ABCA markup is fixed and can be calculated.

---

54 The FDA's *Reportable Food Registry for Industry* page now contains the following notice:
   "The Reportable Food Registry (RFR) is now part of the FDA-NIH Safety Reporting Portal. New, user-friendly software offers conveniences to reporters to the RFR. Reports can be pre-populated with contact information and saved as drafts or partially completed reports. Users can now view any previous submissions they have made to the Safety Reporting Portal."
The Safety Reporting Portal is located at https://www.safetyreporting.hhs.gov/fpsr/WorkflowLoginIO.aspx?metinstance =AA521087FB7227C0166341F530B28A6861955E13. You can also navigate to the *Reportable Food Registry* at http://www.fda.gov /food/complianceenforcement/rfr/default.htm and click the button labeled *For Industry/Regulators: Submit a Report.*

Cost per Bottle	100 Proof	Difference	80 Proof	375 80 Proof
Federal Tax	$2.67	0.53	$2.14	$1.07
City Privilege Tax	$0.01	0.00	$0.01	$0.01
Bottle	$0.79	0.00	$0.79	$0.67
Cap	$0.06	0.00	$0.06	$0.02
Bottle Labels	$0.14	0.00	$0.14	$0.11
Case Label Cost Per Bottle	$0.01	0.00	$0.01	$0.01
Grain Neutral Spirits	$0.79	0.15	$0.64	$0.32
WV DR Corn Spirits Energy Costs	$0.32	0.00	$0.32	$0.16
Corn for WV Spirits	$0.11	0.00	$0.11	$0.06
Shipping to ABC	$0.23	0.00	$0.23	$0.23
Bailment Plan Receiving	$0.07	0.00	$0.07	$0.07
Labor	$0.30	0.00	$0.30	$0.60
Overhead	$1.50	0.00	$1.50	$1.50
Sub Total - Bottle Costs	$7.00	0.68	$6.32	$4.830
Number of Bottles Per Case	12.00		12.00	12.00
Sub Total Case Cost	$84.00	$8.16	$75.84	$57.96
	Current		**Current**	**Current**
Case Sales Price to ABC	$105.00		$95.00	$63.00
Working Case Profit Margin	$21.00		$19.16	$5.04
Working Profit Per Bottle	$1.75		$1.60	$0.42
Wholesale Markup Charges	**Present ABCA Price**			
Present Retail Price	$136.70		$123.90	$82.94
Present Bottle Price Calculated	$11.39		$10.33	$6.91
Present Catalog Bottle Price	$11.39		$10.33	$6.91
ABC Wholesale Gross Markup $	$28.90		$28.90	$28.90
ABC Markup Percentage	30.2%		30.4%	31.7%
If Available find Store Price				
Actual On Shelf Price	$14.99		$0.00	$9.29
Actual Retail Markup	31.61%		-100.00%	34.44%
Retailers' Cost Restated	$11.39		$10.33	$6.91
Retail Mark-up %	31.61%		31.61%	34.44%
$ Amount of Retail Markup	$3.60		$3.27	$2.38
Bottle Cost Sitting on Shelf	$14.99		$13.60	$9.29

TABLE 239-1—Refer to Cost per Bottle *Worksheet*

Some people have criticized this worksheet for calculating the tax paid by the consumer and feel this is not a factor that need be considered. My feeling is that people remember the amount of money that they actually paid and when over a certain amount it is the total amount paid that affects their purchasing decisions.

My strategy has always been to price my products as low as possible and be a "middle shelf" product rather than a "top shelf" product. I wanted people to be able to afford my products and not be dissuaded by price from trying them. I felt that moonshine in general should be affordable. Even doing everything I could to meet this goal it was difficult to compete with large distilleries and their economies of scale.

Many other distillers have adopted the strategy of selling fewer bottles at a higher price. I call this the "You think you get what you pay for theory," where regardless of the intrinsic quality of the product the consumer exults in the costliness of the product as somehow making it tasteful.

Cost per Bottle	100 Proof	Difference	80 Proof	375 80 Proof
Sales Tax %	11.0%		11.0%	11.0%
Sales Tax Amount	$1.65		$1.50	$1.02
Consumer Bottle Price In Hand	$16.64	$1.55	$15.09	$10.31
Case Price In Hand	$199.67		$181.09	$123.74
Proposed Case Cost	$109.00		$99.00	$67.00
Working Profit per Case	$25.00		$23.16	$9.04
Working Profit per Bottle	$2.08		$1.93	$0.75
Increase in Profit per Bottle	$0.33		$0.33	$0.33
Percentage Markup	3.67%		4.04%	5.97%
ABCA Wholesale Markup	30.2%		30.4%	31.7%
Anticipated Case Cost	$141.91		$129.12	$88.21
Anticipated Bottle Cost	$11.83		$10.76	$7.35
Retailers' Cost Restated	$11.83		$10.76	$7.35
Retail Mark-up %	31.61%		31.61%	34.44%
$ Amount of Retail Markup	$3.74		$3.40	$2.53
Bottle Cost Sitting on Shelf	$15.56		$14.16	$9.88
Consumer Shelf Cost	$15.56		$14.16	$9.88
Sales Tax %	11.0%		11.0%	11.0%
Sales Tax Amount	$1.71		$1.56	$1.09
Consumer Bottle Price In Hand	$17.28		$15.72	$10.97
Case Price In Hand	$207.31		$188.62	$131.63
Starting Shelf Price	$14.99	$1.40	$13.60	$9.29
Ending Shelf Price	$15.56		$14.16	$9.88
Total Consumer Price Change	$0.57		$0.57	$0.59
Ratio of Costs	1.0382		1.0416	1.0637
Total Consumer Price Change %	3.82%		4.16%	6.37%
Starting Consumer Price In hand Price	$16.64	$1.55	$15.09	$10.31
Ending Consumer Price In Hand	$17.28		$15.72	$10.97
Total Consumer Price Change	$0.64		$0.63	$0.66
Ratio of Costs	1.0382		1.0416	1.0637
Total Consumer Price Change %	3.82%		4.16%	6.37%

TABLE 239-2—Refer to Cost per Bottle *Worksheet*

12.10 Cost of Goods or Cash Basis

I see a lot of distilleries tie themselves to "cost of goods" accounting methods when they do not need to use this method of accounting. If you are a new distillery grossing under $500K per year then you do not have to use cost of goods as your accounting method.

If you are already using cost of goods accounting and you want to change and use a simpler Schedule C, you will have to do what I did, and that is to file IRS form 3115. The form is long and complicated but the change is automatic if you meet the requirements and sign the form. The benefits of being able to use a Schedule C rather than keeping track of all the intricacies of cost of goods accounting make the change worthwhile.

12.11 Alcohol Properties

Included in the workbook is a true proof algorithm, for the use of Table 1, described in §186.23 and §30.23 (http://www.ttb.gov/foia/gauging_manual_toc.shtml#27:1.0.1.1.25.3.504.3), to find true proof at 60° F and the qualities of alcohol at that true proof (Table 240).

Find True Proof @ 60° F Using §186.23 & §30.23 Method of Apparent Proof and Temperature Correction			
Temperature of Alcohol	78.40	0.000	Thermometer Correction Factor
Apparent Proof of Alcohol	104.20	0.000	Hydrometer Correction Factor
True Proof Rounded to Nearest 1/100 proof		96.60	
True Proof Rounded to 1/10 Proof		96.60	

Table Values Expanded so all tables read to 1/10 proof accuracy						
Properties of Alcohol Corrected to 60° F. True Proof Rounded to 1/10 Proof	Proof Gallons per Lb. Table 4	Wine Gallons per Lb. Table 4	Pounds Per Wine Gal	Pounds Per Proof Gal.	Specific Gravity in Air	Specific Gravity Vac
96.6	0.12373	0.12809	7.80701	8.08211	0.93745	0.93752

TABLE 240—Refer to Alc Properties *Worksheet*

12.12 Chemical Resistance

I have never found any material that is completely impervious to alcohol. The only thing that comes close is high grade Tygon tubing. What I have found is that by exposing quality tubing to alcohol one can work harden it so that it can be used in your operations. First, the tubing should be rated for alcohol. However, I have been able to get braided PVC line to work harden sufficiently to be useful. The way I do this is to use high proof heads to soak the tubing in it for as long as possible. Sometimes I hang the tubing in a bow shape and simply fill it from end to end, then let it sit. I repeat this operation a couple of times and eventually the tubing will stop imparting flavor to the alcohol. Also, time is a factor; if the alcohol passes quickly through the tubing it is less likely to pick up any taste from it.

12.13 Methanol

Every distiller should be able to explain the difference between ethanol and methanol or wood alcohol. Many people ask me if they will go blind drinking my products because they are aware that methanol can cause blindness and death.

Methanol (also known as methyl alcohol, wood alcohol, wood naphtha or wood spirits) is a chemical with the formula CH_3OH (often abbreviated MeOH). Methanol is the simplest alcohol, and is a light, volatile, colorless, flammable liquid with a distinctive odor very similar to that of ethanol. Methanol acquired the name "wood alcohol" because it was once produced chiefly as a by-product of the destructive distillation of wood. This process is similar to that used for making coke out of coal. The wood is essentially cooked in an oven, and the liquid turpentine and other oils are taken off as a fluid, just like coal oil is during the coking process. Then the organic compounds are distilled and various fractions are removed. One of the fractions is methanol. This process is no longer extensively used. Most modern day methanol production occurs in a catalytic industrial process directly from carbon monoxide, carbon dioxide, and hydrogen. When methanol is ingested in large quantities it is metabolized to form formic acid, or formate salts, which are poisonous to the central nervous system, and may cause blindness, coma, and death.

Methanol is produced naturally in the anaerobic metabolism of many varieties of bacteria, and is commonly present in small amounts in the environment. As a result, there is a small fraction of methanol vapor in the atmosphere. Over the course of several days, atmospheric methanol is oxidized with the help of sunlight to carbon dioxide and water. Methanol is also a natural by-product of fermentation to a very small degree. All the beer and wine one drinks contains some small trace amounts of methanol in it.

Because methanol boils at a different temperature than ethanol the process of distillation removes the methanol during the foreshots or heads part of the distillation and the final product is depleted in methanol compared to the mash, or wine or beer for that matter.

Methanol	148.46
Ethyl Alcohol	173.12

12.14 Shut Down List

This is my general shutdown list for the distillery. Not all the machinery is in use every day but enough of it is so that it is good to look at the list at the end of the day as a reminder of what needs to be attended to before leaving the shop.

1. Compressor
2. Water heater
3. 240 volt breaker
4. Office lights
5. Gas furnace
6. Oil boiler
7. Electric heaters
8. Coffee pot
9. Water heater
10. Main water line
11. Osmosis water line
12. South garage door
13. South garage lights
14. North garage door
15. Front door

I can't tell you how many times I have left the distillery, driven a short way towards home and gone back to make sure that the doors were shut or the furnace was really off. You could call it OCD but occasionally I've returned to the shop to find that I actually did not close or shut down the thing that I remembered on the way home.

12.15 Constants and Converters

Getting the program to work consistently has required considerable effort devoted to finding converter values that produce reciprocal results based on different inputs of mass, volume, volatility, atomic weight, energy source and metric vs. English units. This effort has been complicated by the fact that I must also generate relatively reciprocal results whether working from energy inputs to volume and mass outputs or from mass or volume inputs to the energy required.

For unit conversion I have found that the computer program titled "Uconeer," published by Harvey Wilson and Katmar Software, contains the best and most consistent set of interrelated conversions. The conversions are available to eight decimal places if the particular converter requires them. They are also very closely reciprocal with one another. I use Version 2.4 and the software can be found at http://www.katmarsoftware .com?referrer=Uconeer24A.

I also have used converters and physical constants from the *Handbook of Chemistry and Physics* 72nd Ed. 1991 ISBN 0-8493-0565-9. Converters labeled "HCP" refer to this work. Also, some values have been gleaned from a book titled: *Machinery's Hand Book* 22nd Edition ISBN 0-8311-1155-0.

My original source for converters and values come from a book titled *Pocket Ref*, compiled and written by Thomas J. Glover, 2nd Ed. Values for this work are abbreviated "Pocket Ref."

Energy Required to Vaporize Water		**Check Reciprocality**		539.55	Gram Calories to Vaporize 1 Gram of H_2O Pocket Ref. P. 108
Gram Calories to Vaporize 1 Gram of H_2O	539.55	2,258.99	Joules per Gram	539.00	Traditional Calories per Gram to Vaporize Water
Calories to Joules (Uconeer Value)	4.18680	0.2388459	Joules to Cal. (Uconeer)	540.00	Traditional Value Gram Calories to Vaporize 1 Gram of H_2O
Gram Cal to Vaporize * Joules per Gram = Joules per Gram Vaporized	2,258.99	539.55	Gram Calories		
				4.18680	Calories to Joules (Uconeer Value)
Kilojoules per Kg to Vaporize Water	2,258.99			4.18680	Intl. Steam Table Gram Calorie= 4.1868 Joules
Kilojoules to Calories (Uconeer)	238.84590			4.1900	Second Source One Mean Gram Calorie = 4.190 Joules
Calories per Kg	539,550				
Calories per Gram	539.550				
Grams per Lb.	453.59237			2,260.0	Joules per Gram Engineering Toolbox Source
Gram Calories per Lb.	244,736			2,257.0	Traditional Joules per Gram
Calories to Kilojoules	0.00418680			2,258.99	Derived Value from 539.55 G. Cal.
Kilojoules per Lb.	1,024.66				
Kilojoules to BTU's	0.947817120			539.55	Gram Calories to Vaporize 1 Gram of H_2O Pocket Ref. P. 108
BTU's per Lb.	971.19			539.55	Derived Value
Find BTU's per Lb. and Gal.				539.00	Traditional Calories per Gram to Vaporize Water
Kg to Lbs.	2.2046226			540.00	Traditional Value Gram Calories to Vaporize 1 Gram of H_2O
Cal per Kg/Kg to Lb. = Calories per Lb.	244,736				
Calories to BTU's (Uconeer)	0.0039683207			970.00	Traditional Value BTU's per lb.
BTU's per Lb.	971.19			1.19	BTU's per Lb. Dif.
Lbs. per Gal. (Air)	8.328198				
BTU's per Gal.	8,088.26			8,088.26	Compare to Vap Alc 2 when set to water
				0.00	BTU's per Gal Dif.
Find Kilojoules per Mole		**Compare Value**			
Kilojoules per Kg to Vaporize Water	2,258.99	2,258.99			
Kilojoules per Gram to Vaporize Water	2.25899	2.25899			
Atomic Wt. of Water Grams per Mole	18.0153	18.0000		40.650	Machinery's Handbook Value
Kilojoules per Mole	40.70	40.66		40.680	Wikipedia kJ/mol

TABLE 241—Refer to Vaporize H_2O 1 *Worksheet*

The engineering toolbox website also has some values that I have used or compared to: http://www .engineeringtoolbox.com/

Occasionally I will use a value labeled "traditional value." This is the common value listed in dictionaries, encyclopedias and other reference works. Usually these values are used for comparison only. In some cases I have had to derive my own value for a constant to apply. These derived values are noted as such and also have comparisons to more authoritative values to demonstrate their close correspondence thereto.

In particular a good deal of work was put into getting the kilojoules per mole to vaporize alcohol and water to harmonize with the published values for calories per gram and joules per gram values that are extant (Table 241, previous page).

Constants and Converters

Numerous constants and converters are listed in the constants worksheet. A few of the important ones I have used are listed in Table 242).

Gallons per Liter §19.722 To 6 Digits	0.2641720
Liters per Gal.	3.7854118
Pounds Avdp to Kilograms	0.45359237
Kilograms to Pounds Avdp	2.2046226
Wt. Oz. Avoirdupois To Grams	28.3495230
Grams to Ounces	0.0352740
Gallon = U.S. Gal. of 231 Cubic Inches	231.0000

TABLE 242—Refer to Constants Worksheet

It is also interesting to note the various values that have been reported for the weight of a gallon of water (Table 243).

Compare All water Values In Air	Lbs. per Gal.	Gal. per Lb.
HCP 89th Value based	8.328342	0.120072
HCP 72nd Lbs. per Gal. Air 15.556	8.328264	0.120073
Pounds Per Gallon @ 60° (15.56° C) Sec. 5.47a	8.328230	0.120074
Lbs. per Gal. Water in Air @ 60° F §30.41	8.328198	0.120074

TABLE 243—Refer to Constants Worksheet

These small variations give some idea of the difficulty in finding and adopting an authoritative value for use in operations.

12.16 Newtons, Joules, BTU's and Calories

The following definitions describe how we quantify energy and its expenditure.

The newton is the unit of force as defined in the SI system; it is equal to the amount of net force required to accelerate a mass of one kilogram at a rate of one meter per second per second (i.e., 1 meter/second^2).

Therefore, F=ma, by multiplying m (kg) by one (m/s^2), the result equals 1 newton.

One joule is defined as the amount of work done by a force of one newton moving an object through a distance of one meter. Other relationships are:

The work required to move an electric charge of one coulomb through an electrical potential difference of one volt, or one coulomb volt (C•V). This relationship can be used to define the volt.

The work required to continuously produce one watt of power for one second, or one watt second (W•s) This relationship is used to define the watt.

A second method of defining energy for the centimeters, grams seconds (CGS) version of the metric system is the gram calorie. This unit is similar to the BTU in that it defines the energy required to raise one gram of water by 1 degree centigrade. Because of the size difference between the pound and the gram the conversion factor between them is a very large ratio of 251.99576 gram calories to 1 BTU.

This unit is also expressed as a kilocalorie, equivalent to the energy required to raise a kilogram of water by 1 degree centigrade. In this case the converter is reduced by 1,000 and refers to a mass of water larger than the pound. The ratio is reversed and now a BTU is 1/4 the size of a kilocalorie using the ratio 0.25199576 BTU's, so 1 BTU is equal to 25% of a kilocalorie.

Applying this on a rule of thumb basis when converting energy from BTU's to kilocalorie one can use 4 BTU's per kilocalorie or four times the BTU's one would need, expressed by the converter as 3.9683207 BTU's per kilocalorie.

Finally, if one wants to think of the energy required in terms of the mass of water only, the ratio can be expressed as the same as between one degree Fahrenheit and one degree centigrade. That ratio is 1.8. Accordingly, an equivalent mass of water will require 180% more energy to raise it 1 degree centigrade than it takes to raise it 1 degree Fahrenheit. So, if you are looking at energy change in a mass of water and the change is expressed in degrees centigrade one can roughly multiply by 2 to find the amount of energy expressed in BTU's. Conversely, if one wants work in change by degrees Fahrenheit one can divide by 2 to find the energy required on the centigrade scale.

12.17 Angel's Share

Aging whiskey in barrels is a traditional method of changing its character and for some types of whiskey is required in order for the final product to meet a specific standard of identity.

Personally, I think it is a very wasteful and expensive exercise. The evaporation of alcohol from the millions of barrels in the US at any given time is one of the largest unregulated sources of volatile chemicals in the country. It is a legislated business model that is archaic. For some reason consumers have been convinced that the longer alcohol sits around in a barrel the better their alcohol will taste. When I made my old oak recipe product I found that the same job could be done just as well by immersion of toasted oak chips in a couple of weeks. For those who do age whiskey in barrels it is difficult to predict just how much alcohol will be lost in a given amount of time.

Barrels need to be turned every so often because the wood on the top dries out and alcohol will escape or leak. The wood on the bottom swells and then is turned so that it is on top. When the turn is made the dried wood from the top side leaks alcohol until it swells, while the top side dries and allows more alcohol to escape.

Factors like heat and humidity have a direct effect on what will happen to the alcohol as well. Alcohol and water evaporate at different rates when stored in barrels.

One description of this process was written up in the Winter 2009 issue of *Malt Advocate*: "And the World in Our Whiskey" by Gavin D. Smith. It was about many factors but I want to quote his comments on warehouse ecology.

> "In a warehouse with a high level of humidity, a greater amount of ethanol is lost than water and consequently the strength decreases. Conversely, low levels of humidity lead to a greater loss of water; and a consequent increase in strength."

There are several possible reasons as to why alcohol and water will escape from barrels at different rates. One explanation of why more water than alcohol escapes from the barrels (thus increasing the proof) is that water molecules are much smaller than alcohol molecules and so water molecules may diffuse through the wood more easily. It is like a reverse osmosis water system that lets the pure water through and holds the "impurities" back.

The molar mass of water being 18 grams per mole: $O = 16 + 2H = 18$ grams per mole.

The molar mass of alcohol is 46. Alcohol $C2 = 24 + H6 + O = 16 = 46$ grams per mole.

Another explanation is that alcohol has a strong affinity to water; yet, it is possible that water has a stronger affinity to cellulose. It is possible that water is binding to cellulose and then evaporating. The carbon in the wood is probably inert in this process.[55]

What we can say is that the concentration gradient is probably determinative. Nature does not like different concentrations in different places and this causes the water and ethanol to move from the area of high concentration inside the barrel to the low concentration in atmosphere outside it.

In very humid cellars the losses of ethanol are actually greater than those of water and the proof can go down with storage; because there is more water in the air outside the barrel the water concentration gradient is less and there is less driving force to make the water go through the wood. On the other hand, there is still very little ethanol in the air outside the barrel, so the diffusion of ethanol is unaffected by the outside humidity, making the relative diffusion of ethanol now greater than water.

In terms of the amount of loss, I can cite a History Channel program on Jameson's whiskey in which it was related that the loss per year was 2.3%; but it was not specified whether this was on a volume basis or an alcohol basis.

I was able to find some calculations regarding the "angel's share" from *The Art of Blending and Compounding Liquors* by Joseph Fleishman, 1885.[56] This work has some interesting information in it, including the only reference I've seen, on page 21, to the constituents of beading oil, which is quite toxic.

The author begins by stating that in his experience the warehouses are "heated so as to keep a uniform temperature of about 90° Fahrenheit all year round [so] there is a natural shrinkage in the contents of every barrel. This shrinkage is mainly due to the absorption and evaporation of the water and the consequence is an increase in the proof-strength of what remains in the barrel"

The only thing one can say about that is that energy must have been really cheap to keep a warehouse that hot all the time.

In large barrel houses in Kentucky, where it is very hot in the summer, the distilleries do move their barrels from the top of the warehouse, where it is hot and dry, to the bottom where it is cool and moist, because

---

55   This is the hypothesis proposed by David Yelton.

56   This book is in the public domain. A digitzed version is available at https://books.google.com/books?id=zbdBAQAAMAAJ, accessed September 15, 2015.

they recognize the differences in aging characteristics that occur in different parts of the barrel house and want to even out the character of their products with stints in each location.

Given that Mr. Fleishman (above) is describing a high temperature, low humidity environment, his conclusion that water will escape the barrels is consistent with the descriptions related earlier.

Unfortunately, the numbers provided in the book do not allow me to reproduce the results claimed by the author. They simply don't add up. Taking the general outlines of his method I have created the following worksheet for a high temperature, low humidity environment where the total volume loss is greater than the alcohol loss (Table 244).

Aging Whiskey in Bond						
Wine Gal. in Barrel	45.0		5.00%	Volume % Loss per Year		
True Proof	125.0					
Fluid Weight in Barrel	340.16					
Proof Gallons	56.25		2.30%	Alcohol % Loss per Year		
Months	**Proof Gal**	**P.G. Loss**	**PG. Remaining**	**W.G. Loss**	**W.G. Remaining**	**Proof of Remaining**
0	56.2					
12	54.96	1.29	54.96	2.25	42.75	128.55
24	53.69	1.26	53.69	2.14	40.61	132.20
36	52.46	1.23	52.46	2.03	38.58	135.96
Total PG Lost	3.79			Total W.G. Lost	6.42	
Total P.G. % Lost	6.7%			Total W.G. % Loss	14.3%	
% Remaining	93.3%			% Remaining	85.7%	
Find Proof of Remaining						
Proof Gal. per WG * 100	135.96	Proof of Remaining				
Degrees of Proof Change	10.96					
% change in Proof	8.06%		**Mass H₂O**	**Mass 200 Proof**		
			8.3282	6.6098	Per Gal.	
Find Wt. of Remaining & Wt. Lost			Lbs.H₂O	1.90	P.G./2 = Gal. AA	
Lbs. per WG	7.452		40.13	12.53	Gal. AA/Wt. Per = Mass	
Fluid Weight in Barrel	287.50	Gal. H2O	4.82	1.90	Gal. AA	
Fluid Wt. Lost	52.67			6.72	Total Gal. Lost	
				0.30	Gal. Dif. From above	

TABLE 244—Refer to Angel's Share Worksheet

I have included a rough comparison to the mass of each component lost. It is not exact but it gives an idea of the relative mass involved in the process.

Reversing the loss rates allows one to predict the effects of a high humidity environment (Table 245, next page).

In this case we see that the proof has gone down because the high humidity has inhibited the loss of water relative to the alcohol loss.

Because I am using two different methods to calculate the fluid weight lost, there is some discrepancy and a negative value is showing up in the pounds of water lost in this instance.

I wish I had data to back this up but with the percentage method I've outlined one can determine their own loss rates empirically and then use the worksheet to predict future losses.

Aging Whiskey in Bond

Wine Gal. in Barrel	45.0		2.30%	Volume % Loss per Year
True Proof	125.0			
Fluid Weight in Barrel	340.16			
Proof Gallons	56.25		5.00%	Alcohol % Loss per Year

Months	Proof Gal	P.G. Loss	PG. Remaining	W.G. Loss	W.G. Remaining	Proof of Remaining
0	56.2					
12	53.44	2.81	53.44	1.04	43.97	121.54
24	50.76	2.67	50.76	1.01	42.95	118.18
36	48.23	2.54	48.23	0.99	41.97	114.92
Total PG Lost	8.02			Total W.G. Lost	3.03	
Total P.G. % Lost	14.3%			Total W.G. % Loss	6.7%	
% Remaining	85.7%			% Remaining	93.3%	

Find Proof of Remaining

Proof Gal. per WG * 100	114.92	Proof of Remaining			
Degrees of Proof Change	-10.08				
% change in Proof	-8.77%		**Mass H$_2$O**	**Mass 200 Proof**	
			8.3282	6.6098	Per Gal.
Find Wt. of Remaining & Wt. Lost			Lbs.H$_2$O	4.01	P.G./2 = Gal. AA
Lbs. per WG	7.653		-7.51	26.51	Gal. AA/Wt. Per = Mass
Fluid Weight in Barrel	321.16	Gal. H20	-0.90	4.01	Gal. AA
Fluid Wt. Lost	19.00			3.11	Total Gal. Lost
				0.08	Gal. Dif. From above

TABLE 245—Refer to Angel's Share *Worksheet*

CHAPTER 13 History and Anecdotes

13.1 The Early Years

How a Practicing Attorney Was Inspired to Make Moonshine

I've told this story so many times, and I'm sure I've written it down somewhere, but for the life of me I can't find it, so I'll have to start again.

In 1999 I was the first distiller licensed in West Virginia since the end of Prohibition.

I had the idea to start the distillery for several reasons. I'd always wanted to make a product or do something economic other than just practice law. I'd tried inventing golf gadgets and explored the possibility of retrofitting cars to run on natural gas. I'd written a very bad book on golf and tried to start a coal mining operation. Nothing that I'd tried had worked out. In addition to my law work I spent a lot of time fixing cars and making gadgets at my buddy Bo McDaniel's shop. He was my mechanical mentor and let me hang around. I wasn't a very good mechanic but I'd gotten to the point where I could at least change parts. Well perhaps that is an understatement; by 1998 I had gotten to the point where I could rebuild engines and restore an entire car, my mother's old roadster, but I was no professional. I was the Mr. Magoo of mechanics, somehow it seemed to work out.

The Daimler, twenty-five percent complete.

After the "rebuild."

During the summer of 1998 I was invited to a wedding by some friends who lived in New York City. I'd grown up there and used to live in Manhattan as a child. I love going to the city; it is one of my favorite journeys. While I was there, my friends asked me why I was living in West Virginia and invited me to come establish myself up there with them. It was a very generous invitation and I said I'd think it over. During the drive back to West Virginia I thought about the twenty years I'd spent living and working there and whether I really wanted to continue to make it my home. I felt that my life there was lacking something and resolved to think of reasons to stay there or else find someplace else to make my way in the world. I started thinking of all the things that West Virginia was known for exporting or that made money—coal, gas, timber—and I tried to think of something else that hadn't been discovered yet. I wanted something that was value added and not a raw product. Somewhere just north of Harrisburg the idea of moonshine occurred to me. Moonshine was a value-added product that was known far and wide, and also known to come from West Virginia. Bo McDaniel had occasionally made some and kept a mason jar of it in the refrigerator at the shop. It was terrible tasting, but I occasionally took a swig and it was for real so I knew we could make something. Nothing was beyond Bo, and I could certainly handle the regulatory side. At the moment Bo was into drag racing and we were tearing up the race car every weekend and spending all week fixing it up so we could break something else the next weekend. Surely it would make more sense to build some equipment that we didn't have to fix all the time and might make a little money for us.

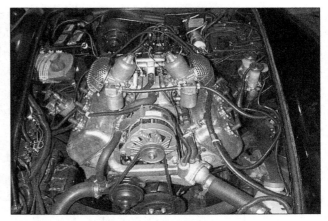

A front view of the Daimler engine.

Jumping Regulatory Hurdles

Bo was reluctant but agreed to help me and be a part of the business so I started the process of getting a license. I have a possibly false memory of looking up the distillery sections of the West Virginia code and reading them in the law library while I was in law school. The reason I'm pretty sure I really did do this is that I remembered that the annual license fee was $1,500 a year and back then that was a lot of money just for an annual license. When I looked at the code again in 1998 all the provisions were still there and hadn't changed. My initial thought was there probably were distilleries in the state already and I just didn't know about them.

I called the West Virginia State Alcohol Control Commission and found out that there were no licensed distilleries in the state and got the impression that they didn't want any. They didn't even have an application form. Even though I was an attorney they didn't want to talk to me at all about the prospect of obtaining a license.

The big hurdle was to get a federal license to operate a distillery, and they did have an application form that was very complicated, including requirements for a background check and even an environmental impact statement. There were also hundreds of pages of regulations about how distilleries were licensed and operated. This was my bread and butter so I started studying the regulations and eventually got my application completed and submitted.

Bo agreed to provide space in his shop for me to operate the distillery. We had to build a wall in the shop to separate it from the remainder of the operation. Mind you, this was a transmission shop and general car repair business. It was generally filthy with oil on the floor, and lots of dirty cars sitting around inside. How I was going to get the place cleaned up so that it looked presentable for the inspectors was going to be a big challenge.

Apart from those problems I still had to find a way to apply for a state license. Since they would not provide me an application I decided to make up my own. I read the code sections about licensing a distillery and found that it could not be within one thousand feet of a church, that I had to advertise in the paper on two occasions and post a sign on the door announcing my intention and wait 60 days. So I made sure the shop was not within a thousand feet of a church, published my legal notice in the paper and posted a notice on the door. After that I made up an application and attached the publication notices and also included my full forty-page federal application. I wrote out a check to the state for $1,500 and sent the whole package certified mail to the alcohol commission figuring that it would force their hand. It didn't. They sent it back to me. They even sent back the check! That is the only time that I've ever seen the State of West Virginia not accept money.

After a polite interval I sent the application and check back to them with a cover letter that said I was proceeding with my federal application and they should keep the material submitted on file. This time they did not send it back, but neither would they do anything about it or cash the check. The person in charge of keeping me at bay was a very senior bureaucrat, Ms. Lola Walters. She was a pro from the old school of post-Prohibition alcohol regulation and I'm sure that the idea of a moonshine distillery was anathema to her. Her position evolved to telling me that the state would not even consider my application until after I was issued my federal license.

Meanwhile my federal application was being reviewed by Ms. Yolanda Whitehead from the Cincinnati office. She kept asking me how my state application was proceeding and told me in no uncertain terms that the federal government would not issue a license to me until I had obtained my state license.

I was involved in an exercise in Federalism in which two separate agencies were required to authorize my activities and neither one wanted to go first.

This conflict played out over an eight month period from September of 1998 until April of 1999 while I built the facility and obtained all the supporting documentation for my application. I had to obtain a bond for the tax I was obligated to pay, I had to have explosion-proof lights. I had to have, by the regulations, a nine-foot fence around my building. There were so many ways that I could be out of compliance and it seems that there was no way that I could actually meet all the requirements. Because my facility was inside another business was another sticking point. At one point I was directed to paint lines on the floor to indicate where the bonded premises were located and no alcohol was to be allowed outside those lines until the tax was paid. I learned that I would have to file tax returns every two weeks or 26 times a year because the government wanted the alcohol excise tax that often. That tax is $13.50 per Proof Gallon of whiskey. A Proof Gallon being one gallon of 100 prof alcohol. This is a stiff tax and represents about 1/3 of my cash flow through the distillery. At one point it was ten times my cost of production. When corn was cheap I could make a Proof Gallon for $1.35.

The other uncertainty was that the government would not approve any plans before my facility was built. They would only come and inspect the facility after it was complete down to the last detail and if they didn't like it in any way it was my tough luck.

Meanwhile I had to learn how to build a facility and make it as safe as possible. If I couldn't afford explosion-proof lights I could at least have the safest lights and be aware of the danger.

My response was to make the distillery look as much like a laboratory as possible. I put fire extinguishers everywhere and large Exit signs and No Smoking signs up. I had eye wash stations installed and white lab coats hanging on pegs. Everything was painted white, and spic-and-span.

I also went about forming the company in West Virginia and getting a business license from the City of Granville. I can't tell you how much Bo's reputation in the community helped me with getting my local regulators to approve my plans.

Bo had a reputation in the community as one of the best mechanics around and a sole proprietor who ran a good shop. He was admired for his good sense and acumen. The attitude around town was that if Bo was willing to let me start a distillery in his shop then it must be alright. Accordingly when I had the fire chief and the city building inspector come over and look around they pretty much shrugged and said that it all looked OK to them. Fortunately, I did not need a food handler's license for Bo and myself. The health department said we didn't need them.

After covering as many of these bases as possible I was able to persuade the inspectors from the Bureau of Alcohol Tobacco and Firearms to schedule an inspection of the distillery. It went pretty well overall, except for telling me to paint lines on the floor. They were pretty uptight about licensing a facility inside another business.

Still no word from the State of West Virginia; Lola Walters would not process my application or send an inspector. Ms. Whitehead would not issue a license without the state issuing one first.

I kept trying to get the two agencies to communicate to one another, at any level. They wouldn't talk to each other. There was absolutely no cross communication at all between them and I got the impression that it was beneath them to actually coordinate their actions with another regulatory body. By April of 1999 I was really becoming anxious. Ms. Whitehead really thought she had a winning hand by stonewalling me, and she was right.

One day Yolanda Whitehead called me and said she was ready to issue my license and asked about my progress with the state. I explained all the efforts I had made to push my application with the state forward and my lack of success. She didn't say anything explicitly but I got the impression that she might call the state and talk to them.

Fifteen minutes later I received a call from Keith Roberts the second-in-command at the state Alcohol Beverage Control Commission. He wanted to know if it would be OK if he sent an inspector to my facility the next day and that based on that inspection the state would decide whether to issue my license. I was dumbfounded. The inspector came the next day and he didn't know what to look for. He'd never inspected a distillery and had no idea what was going on except that he was to look over my plant.

Later that week, on April 19, 1999, the state and federal governments simultaneously issued my permits to operate a distillery. The West Virginia Commission actually held a press conference to announce this exciting new development in the economic progress of West Virginia and the state chamber of commerce issued me an award for a First of Its Kind business in the state. I was a good sport about the whole thing and kept quiet about the run up to the State's change of heart as to my application.

I never heard from Lola Walters again. Somehow Yolanda Whitehead had taken down Lola in a bureaucratic celebrity death match that was over in less than 15 minutes. I have no idea what was said or done to facilitate the change in attitude by the state and I was sure that Ms. Whitehead would never tell me so I was polite enough not to ask.

Time to Start Making Moonshine

So now it's April of 1999 and now I actually have to make some whiskey. I have absolutely no idea how to do this. I've never fermented anything and no concept whatsoever of how to convert the starch in corn to sugar. We start by spouting corn to extract the enzymes that way but it is time consuming and inefficient. I go to the local brew pub and borrow some malted barley and then begin ordering bags of it from a supply company. Bo and I are having minor conflicts about the processes we are going to use and I am overwhelmed by the regulatory requirements for keeping track of the alcohol that we are going to produce.

I should also note that during this time I was also practicing law full time and handling a number of cases that involved actual litigation. Also, my father passed away in October of 1998 and in terms of grief and overall ennui it was the worst year of my life; far more difficult than my divorce had been and that was no picnic. I'd cashed in my life insurance policy to raise the forty thousand dollars to finance the distillery and I learned that I'd wasted about half of that amount on services or equipment I didn't need or that didn't work. The only consolation was that I didn't have eighty thousand to spend because I'm sure I would have wasted half of that amount as well.

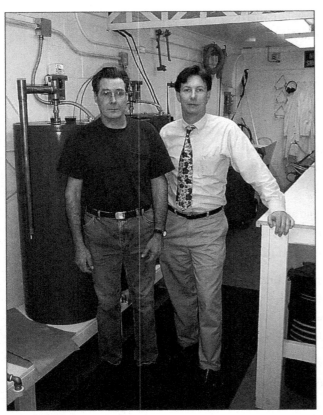

Bo and Payton.

Going it Alone

About six weeks after we obtained a license for the distillery Bo calls me aside for a talk and tells me that he does not want to continue to participate in the business. His heart is not in it and he doesn't want to continue working on it in part because of the differences in outlook between us and in part because he is too accustomed to being his own boss to take on a partner. There is one other reason he cites: his mother is opposed to the venture. There had been a good deal of publicity and many national and regional newspaper articles about our venture and our picture was included in the articles. Bo's mother found out about it and must have said something to her son. Even though Bo was 55 years old and his own man in all respects, his mother's opinion still carried weight. I've only seen Bo cry on two occasions, during this conversation was one of them and the other was at a funeral for a friend of ours killed in a senseless car accident.

Well, I wanted to cry too and probably did tear up some. I really admired Bo and his approval or disapproval was very important in my decisionmaking overall. If he didn't want to work with me it felt like a huge personal rejection. It was his shop and I was just a guest. Bo made it clear that I could continue to work in the shop but it was my baby and I would be responsible for all of it.

So, we became two independent businessmen. Bo continued to help me build equipment and to offer advice but I had to do all the work. In fact Bo incubated my business for five years for essentially my contributions of keeping the place stocked with coffee and paper towels as well as sweeping the floors. Eventually Bo decided to retire and I bought the building from him. He gave me a deed for the entire building and I only had to pay him half. He carried my debt to him for another six years with no deed of trust or lien on the building, and not even so much as a promissory note as evidence of the debt. The only thing I did was to re-write my will so that if I died, my executor would know that I owed him thirty-eight thousand dollars. Now, that's friendship on Bo's part.

None of this heartwarming personal friendship did anything to actually get whiskey made and into bottles. I'd lost my partner and now my job would be twice as hard.

First Batches: "Learning by Doing"

In order to cook corn I found an old torpedo heater that had a copper coil in the exhaust flow and we used it as our hot water generator. I couldn't have a fixed cooking tank because there was no room in the shop so we used six 50-gallon heavy-duty plastic trash cans to cook the corn in. The only problem was that when we added hot water to the drums they would get so hot that they would start to get soft and begin to melt. We couldn't really cook the corn fully because all we could do was add hot water once and that was not enough heat to do the job properly, but we did get it hot enough to break down some of the starch to sugar using the malted barley.

Then the problem became how to cool the batches down to under 95° F so we could safely add the yeast and start the fermentation. If it was cold outside we would wheel the containers of hot corn mash out into the street and stir them with canoe paddles to get the heat to dissipate. I never took pictures of this operation because I was afraid that I'd get my license revoked if anyone found out I was doing it this way.

There was one additional level of crazy that we went through to cool these batches down. I borrowed an old chest-sized freezer and filled it full of plastic milk jugs filled with water. It would take a full week for the entire mass to turn to ice but then we had 30- or 40-gallon-sized ice cubes that we could throw into the barrels.

In addition to this jury-rigged cooking operation, I didn't have a filler, I didn't have a bottling line, I didn't have approved formulas or labels. All of this had to be taken care of. I had to get a bar code assigned to my business and then learn how to put the bar code onto the labels so it would scan.

My "Yuppie Moonshine" Gets Some Press.

Eventually I got it all worked out. I achieved some degree of notice for my accomplishment. In 2002 I caught the attention of the *New York Times* and made the front page on a Monday, which is the slowest day in the newspaper business because everything goes into the Sunday paper. The headline read, "Yuppie Moonshine With the Old Kick, and It's Legal Too."[57] From there the *Sunday Telegraph* in London picked up the story and I was pretty much the only story not about the Queen on the day of her 50th-Year Jubilee celebration.[58]

13.2 Lessons Learned

One-hundred Gallons of Moonshine in the Back of My SUV Meet a West Virginia Speed Trap.

Using my three converted hot water heater stills I tried making enough corn whiskey to meet the demand but it was just not possible to do it. The real limitation was that I didn't have a way to cook and ferment enough corn mash using the trash can methods I'd improvised. I had to build a larger cooker and still and that would take time.

I had made a friend in the distilling business, Chuck Miller who ran the Belmont Farms distillery. He was really ahead of his time and had begun making a product called Virginia Lightning in the early '80s. He had a huge 1,100-gallon still at his facility in Culpepper, Virginia. Initially he was reluctant to help me out because I was a competitor of his but I assured him that I would not sell my products in Virginia and my word was good enough for him. This was probably an agreement in restraint of trade and hence illegal but between us it did not matter.

Chuck agreed to sell me corn whiskey so that I could have enough to meet demand and would be able to concentrate on building my new cooker and still. We obtained the required Transfer in Bond authority so that we could transport whiskey between our facilities but the problem was shipping. Chuck didn't have a loading dock and I really could not afford the extra time and expense of trying to arrange shipping. I only needed about 100 fluid gallons of 160 proof whiskey at a time, so, I decided that I would simply run the whiskey over the Allegheny Mountains from Culpepper to Morgantown in the back of my Dodge Raider. It was about a 4-hour trip and most of it was in West Virginia so if I got stopped and arrested at least I would be in a West Virginia jail and could call a friend to come bail me out.

---

57 The *New York Times*, Monday May 13, 2002, No. 52,117

58 The *Sunday Telegraph*, June 2nd 2002, No. 2,138

While the approval to transfer the whiskey was legal, and I had a license to be a distiller, I had no commercial driver's license and no authority at all to haul that much hazardous material in what was essentially an SUV. Now, people haul 55-gallon drums of gasoline in their trucks all the time and because I was doing the "shipping" for myself I didn't really need a commercial driver's license, at least in my view. Still, I was pretty sure that if I got caught or had an accident, I'd end up in the pokey for at least one night.

To try to dress things up a little I had all the documentation with me—licenses, permits, transfer in bond authority, material data safety sheets, tie down straps, fire extinguishers, everything but the kitchen sink. Maybe enough to talk myself out of going to jail. And so it proceeded. I'd put two empty drums into the truck, drive over to Chuck's and we would park my car next to the holding tank and drain whiskey into them till they were full. Chuck only charged me about $10 per Proof Gallon and I'd write him a check and be off. We did this a bunch and I'd bite my fingernails as I drove back to Morgantown with 100 gallons of whiskey in the back of my car. I almost got caught once and that was the end of it. There is a town in West Virginia called Paw Paw, and they have a nasty police force that raises revenue by stopping anyone who is speeding and ticketing them. Everyone knows not to speed through Paw Paw and I never did. But they also have random, hassle the public days, where they stop everyone on the road and look them over. Because they stop everyone it is an approved method of law enforcement and you have probably seen these set up around your town once in a while when the police are looking for drunk drivers. Well, I drove right into one of these checkpoints. As I was waiting in line I was thinking, at least I'm in West Virginia and my buddy Greg can come get me out of jail. I did have the drums covered with a tarp and some golf clubs and the like in the car but there is no way that a nosy cop was not going to want to look at what I had in the car and I was probably just the kind of John Q. Public they would love to bust for something to justify their road block.

They took a long time with the cars in front of me and traffic was backing up behind us, when it came my turn to run the gauntlet they just waved the cars in front and behind me through to clear out the line. I smiled and waved to them as I went by and after I got back to Morgantown decided that I wouldn't make that run again.

Right Bottles, No Labels

I've been very lucky with my products in that very few have been defective. I've sent out a few cases with only 11 bottles in them by mistake and been charged with a shortage. You wouldn't think it would be possible to short a case by a bottle but when you are making several hundred it is possible to lose count as you put on the labels and end up sealing a case that is a bottle short.

I found that trying to fill bottles and label them at the same time was not possible. Bottling is too hectic an operation to combine with labeling, which requires patience and attention to detail. The hand cranked labeling machines I used required my constant attention in order to feed labels properly and I was also the only person who could run the bottling machine so it just wouldn't work to try to do both at the same time.

Consequently we had to actually fill the bottles and put them into cases since there was no room to keep 1,000 bottles of uncased whiskey around the shop. This was the most inefficient part of what was already a very inefficient operation and led to the possibility that someone could mistake a case of unlabeled bottles for labeled ones. Of course much hilarity ensued, including my getting a call from the Greenbrier resort down in White Sulphur Springs about a case they had received. The Greenbrier actually had its own liquor store on the premises and actually included a bottle of my whiskey in gift baskets that they made up for important guests. That was quite a nice honor, so you can imagine how mortified I was when they called me at my office to tell me that they had ordered a case and it came with all the bottles and no labels on ten of the twelve in the case.

Usually that would be sent back to the distribution warehouse in Charleston but since they knew me they had decided to call. I ended up sending them a bunch of labels and they were kind enough to actually apply them to the bottles they had purchased so they could be sold. After that we tightened up our procedures for segregating cases considerably.

Right Bottles, Wrong Labels!

That did not prevent the next small disaster from besetting me. We were having a labeling session and I had four or five people working. Some were labeling by hand and some helped by moving unfinished cases onto the table and others helped by sealing and stacking cases after they were labeled. I was turning the crank on the labeling machine one bottle at a time. My friend Steve Sutton ran out of labels and I told him where the labels were kept and sent him to get another roll of them. He dutifully came back and started labeling and also passed labels around to others that needed them. Meanwhile I kept labeling with my roll. About an hour later I ran out of labels and went to get another roll and I happened to look at Steve's labels along the way. He was putting the wrong labels on the bottles. My 80 proof labels look similar to my 100 proof labels and he was putting 80 proof labels on 100 proof bottles. Steve knew we were bottling 100 proof but did not look to see that he chose the right labels from the bin. The bottles that Steve and others had labeled with the wrong labels were mixed in with the bottles that I had labeled with the right ones and there were 30 or so cases of them that had been labeled in the last couple of hours. We had to take all the cases off the pallet and open them up and inspect each bottle. Then we had to try and peel the labels off, which they are very reluctant to do, and soak off the ones that were really stubborn. I had all the sinks in the shop and some five-gallon buckets filled with water in which bottles were bobbing around while the labels got loose enough to come off. Finally we got down far enough into the pallet of cases where no more incorrectly labeled bottles showed up. It took hours and hours to sort out this mess and eventually I had to do it myself since I couldn't keep the help around into the night to finish up. After this experience I took all the labels out of the shop and kept them at my house. I would only bring over the labels that were actually being used for any given bottling run so that this particular error could not happen again.

That brings up another point. I have to take responsibility for everything. Stated another way, everything is my fault. Everything. It was a lesson I learned early on. I was not going to get anywhere by blaming anyone else, ever. I had to take responsibility for everything.

Driving down the Interstate—with an Unhitched Trailer

One last near miss deserves mention. After I fermented my corn mash and distilled out the alcohol I still had to get rid of the spent corn. I found several farmers that would gladly take it to mix in with their cattle feed. One has to be careful about this and I learned that if I did not fully distill as much of the alcohol out of it as possible that enough was left in the corn to get cattle really drunk. While this may seem funny it is also possible to kill cattle with very small amounts of alcohol and you can imagine how a good friendship could go bad in a hurry if my corn had done that to their herd.

When I pumped the spent mash of corn and water out of the still and into the trailer I actually had to put jack stands under each corner of it to keep it from breaking. Then I would let it stand for a couple of days while the water drained off of it and reduced the weight to probably three thousand pounds or so. That was way more than my little Dodge Raider was rated to tow and generally the trailer had almost as much mass as the SUV so it was driving me rather than I towing it. Also braking was a big issue. I had to be very careful because it took a long time to stop.

One wet, cold, rainy day in February I had to move a load of spent corn mash across town. I went and hooked up the trailer and drove over bumpy pothole strewn roads to the interstate and then two exits down the interstate to my friend's farm. I backed up to where I had to unload the trailer and began shoveling off the corn mash into a pile starting at the back of the trailer and moving towards the front. When I shoveled the last corn out of the trailer and walked to the end farthest from the trailer hitch the tongue of the trailer rose up off the hitch ball and only the safety chains held it from tipping over. Somehow I had failed to engage the trailer hitch onto the ball and it was only the tongue weight that had kept it from coming off. If that had happened on the interstate or anywhere else for that matter the tongue would have hit the ground and probably whipped my truck around sending me and tons of corn flying everywhere. Even if the safety chains had held, it would have caused a huge accident.

I Miss a Trademark Renewal Deadline—and Battle a Major Distiller in Court

My final major screw up, to date, was when I malpracticed on myself by failing to renew my trademark for Mountain Moonshine.[59] That trademark was central to my business plan and my initial application for it was rejected on the ground that it was a generic term that could not be trademarked. I scratched my head about that and filed an appeal that argued that since Mountain Moonshine was not in legal commerce and no one could actually find any legal and above board product called Mountain Moonshine that it was incorrect to call it a generic product. That somewhat flimsy argument prevailed and I was awarded a registration for the trademark in the category of distilled spirits. All well and good, I receive the official document and it says that the trademark is good for ten years, so I frame and hang it on my wall. About eight years later I say to myself, "I should start thinking about renewing my trademark." I start looking around to see how to do this and find out that my trademark has been canceled after six years because I failed to file a form that was due after five years saying that I was still using the trademark. That information had been written on the back of the document that I had framed and put on my wall. So, back to the drawing board. The trademark was thankfully still available and I filed a new application asking to have the mark re-issued. This time I don't have to fight the generic fight because in the meantime dozens of trademarks have been issued with moonshine as part of their wording. The application was published for opposition and I expected it to be re-issued as soon as the comment period was up.

Well, was I in for a surprise. In the meantime, while my mark was in limbo, a company called Diageo had taken a wine trademark called Moon Mountain and reapplied to make it applicable to distilled spirits and were bringing out a brand of vodka called Moon Mountain. Anyone who knows the distilling industry is aware that Diageo is a huge company promoting some of the world's biggest brands and that it takes its trademarks very seriously.[60] They filed an objection to the issuance of my mark on the basis that my proposed mark was confusingly similar to theirs. They hired the sharpest and most expensive lawyers to prosecute their case, they earned their pay and had me tied up in knots pretty quickly. It took 18 months of litigation in the Trademark Trial and Appeal Board to get this matter sorted out. At one time I had five lawyers in three states working on it. It consumed a third of my work life during that time in addition to about $40,000 of my money. I wouldn't knuckle under but it was a close run thing. Eventually a settlement was reached whereby Diageo dropped its objections if I agreed to never make vodka with my trademark and they agreed never to make moonshine with theirs. I don't think that Moon Mountain vodka succeeded as a brand and therefore it was not generating the revenue to justify continuing to litigate against me. Had the brand taken off I would probably still be litigating the case. When I got my new trademark, I again hung it on the wall. I'll be sure to file my renewal form after five years.

---

59   Registration #4374346 http://tmsearch.uspto.gov/bin/showfield?f=doc&state=4804:kh48gq.2.12 Serial #85260693 http://tmsearch.uspto.gov/bin/showfield?f=doc&state=4804:kh48gq.2.12 The TTAB proceeding with Diageo was: 91202864 http://ttabvue.uspto.gov/ttabvue/v?pno=91202864&pty=OPP

60   Diageo's brands include Smirnoff Vodka, Johnny Walker Scotch, Tanquery Gin, Gordons Gin, Crown Royal, J&B Scotch, Captain Morgan Rum, and Baileys Irish Cream.

13.3 Some Personal Notes in Closing ——————————

Several years after becoming a distiller and particularly after the Diageo litigation I came to the conclusion that alcohol is essentially poison. It tastes like poison, acts like poison and despite its ameliorative effects on blood pressure and mood, was essentially a hazardous substance.

So far as I'm concerned there is no way to make alcohol taste like anything but poison and the acquired taste is simply us making a bargain that we will drink one type of poison taste rather than another.

This tied into my notion, that I now realized was delusional, that somehow I could make alcohol taste not like poison. Despite my best efforts, that proved impossible. Since I was unable to produce alcohol that did not taste like poison, it was only a short intellectual step to the conclusion that I was essentially a poison merchant and that any thinking person would have known this going into the business; consequently, I was a moron. The scales fell from my eyes and I realized that I had made a serious blunder. Bo's mother had been right all along.

It was really by attending the trade shows where different alcohols were advertised every year and much bally-hoo was made over each of them that the point was driven home to me.

I was actually at a trade show on 9/11, and the show drove the point home forcefully that this was really a pointless exercise in marketing. By about noon or so the entire trade show broke up and I was able to drive home but many of the other vendors were stuck there because none of the airlines were allowed to fly for several days.

I was once contacted by a firm making alcohol-infused Jell-O shots with a proposal to make them on a contract basis. I turned it down because I already had my hands full and I thought the idea of getting people drunk on Jell-O shots was disingenuous; but, a competitor took up the contract and made good money producing them for the brand owners. I don't know what's happened to the brand in recent years.

I've been in the alcohol business long enough now to see that it never stays the same and that people's tastes change rapidly. Keeping up with these changes requires constant innovation and the ability to guess correctly what the market is wanting. Looking at alcohol and also the beverage market in general, look at what happened to wine coolers, Tang, Fresca, Tab, Jolt, Nantucket Nectars, gold schlagger, or a hundred other brands that have come and gone. This is all well and good for the market. However, it just became a rabbit I was no longer willing to chase.

My goal was to make a product. I wanted to work hard and make a supply and then be able to have it sold through retail outlets so that I would not have to mediate each sale. I've run my business like a cannery. We work hard for four months to make a year's supply of whiskey and then go back to our regular jobs for the rest of the year. It has worked well enough.

There was some element of wanting to do something novel as a product, but I never wanted to become the Colonel Sanders of moonshine. My distillery started in a transmission shop in an industrial part of town. It was never meant to be a tourist destination.

The business model for small distilleries has changed to be destinations where hats and T-shirts are sold as a way to augment the income of the business. That never had any appeal to me.

Again, I was deluding myself. One needs hats and T-shirts to build a brand and one needs to market that brand day and night. It is a big job.

As a sole proprietor, simply making the product exhausted the time I had to devote to the project.

The successful small distillery firms that I've seen prosper are mostly family concerns where father, mother and one or two adult children and their spouses participate.

The other model is for large firms to poach on the small distillery market by having a front person or persons pretend to be the makers but the real operations are conducted at large bottling facilities.

A year after I started the distillery I actually became toxic to alcohol. Not from drinking it, but from exposure to vapors. I'd go home and want a drink but couldn't have one because I'd absorbed enough alcohol during the day that the idea of an alcoholic drink was repulsive. It was like people who work in chocolate factories get.

At one point I thought I'd never be able to drink gin again. I went through a year where any clear liquor was anathema. Fortunately that passed and I can again enjoy a gin and tonic or, on occasion, the only American contribution to world culture, a martini.

I eventually learned how to minimize my exposure to alcohol vapors and absorption through the skin so that I did not go home alcohol poisoned even though I had not had anything to drink.

It was a great adventure. Through it I learned how to not steam myself like a lobster or burn the place down or blow it up or fry myself with electricity. I learned how to build equipment, to weld, solder, and how to take data. I became a journeyman at my trade. I earned Bo's respect and while I will never be able to rebuild a transmission, I've acquired my own unique skill set that I am capable of exercising.

In 2008 I decided to write this work. It became apparent that the more marketable idea was to make a DVD of the operation, showing the steps throughout an entire season. This would be much better than a tour of the facility since on a tour one would only see one phase of the operation at any time. So, my friend Robert Williams and I shot a video of the entire season and I edited it down from 13 hours of tape to 2.5 hours that would fit on a DVD. I've sold that DVD to people all over the world and through it I have taught some folks a few things.

Eventually I fell for the technical side of how the operations were conducted and began to program them into worksheets.

Returning to the book in 2010 I realized that I needed to create spreadsheets (worksheets) of each blending procedure in order to explain them clearly. Without the table data I would just be publishing static snapshots and each person would then have to work the values for themselves. That seemed silly. I concluded that I needed to convert the TTB tables to numerical values in an array so that I could build working spreadsheets that would be useful to others and not require them to do the math each time. That project took a full year of part-time work but resulted in the ABS Software program which has been a success and taught me a great deal about being a distiller. I've sold copies of the program to dozens of distilleries, some of them very large operations, and I'm pretty sure that from 30 to 50 million dollars a year of alcohol excise tax flows to the government by virtue of calculations made using my program.

Yet again, I turned my attention to the book and I realized that I really didn't have the data I needed for the energy input side of the book and for many other operations other than fermentation and distillation. Going back to data already collected during the 2008–2009 distilling season, I had ample information from which to build the first drafts of my worksheets.

After gathering all that data and re-writing ABS Software in 2014 to apply to calibration temperatures other than 60° F, I was able to return to the book and finally in 2016 I was able to gather all my notes and data together and complete this book and the accompanying Excel workbook.

13.4 Respect for the Old Timers

Courtesy of Dr. David Fogarty, who owns the still shown here.

I am able to make whiskey in my shop with all the modern conveniences of lights, power, unlimited amounts of city water, and even a forklift to move things around, and it is still hard work.

I still have to move sacks of corn around, lift and stack hundreds of cases of bottles, stir intractable corn mash with a paddle and it is generally a good workout every day at the distillery. Even labeling bottle after bottle is fatiguing after two or three hours of doing it.

The effort involved made me appreciate just how much harder it was for old timers who had to do many similar tasks in the woods just to make a few bucks to help feed their families.

When I first started selling my products, many older folks would talk to me about how important moonshine making was to their family's livelihood. Little old ladies would tell me how their father made whiskey during the Depression and that they had oranges at Christmas and new shoes for Easter because of their dad's bootlegging. This happened frequently enough that I could tell that just ordinary people were partially dependent on this source of revenue. Good upstanding citizens who weren't trying to get rich, just trying to make ends meet.

Several of the historical books I've read describe just how far up the hollow people would have to go to find a place away from the prying eyes of the law to make a little corn whiskey. Implicit in these descriptions is that all the corn or sugar had to be carried to these remote places along with the barrels and whatever was being used as a still.

One man told me that when he was a boy his father stored his copper coil in the farm pond. When it was time to make a run of whiskey the son would have to wade out into the pond and fish around under the water to recover it.

When you see pictures of the generally rough and ready setups that people constructed it looks sloppy and un-organized but it represents a lot of hard work just to get to that level of organization. Generally the people look tired, because it was hard work.

So, when I was thinking about myself as slaving away at my job I would remind myself that it was nothing compared to what others had to do.

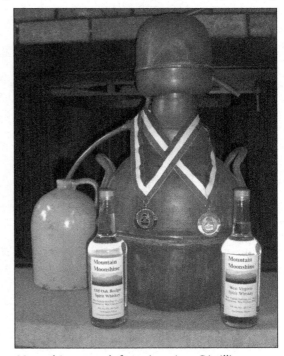

Moonshine awards from American Distilling Institute: 2009 Best Moonshine.

Thank you, patient reader.

APPENDIX

A. Regulatory Structure ─────────────────────────────

While this book describes the vicissitudes of being in the distillery business and provides a candid look at the practical operations of a distilled spirits plant, I want to take a moment and comment on the regulatory structure in which distilleries operate.

Distilleries are a highly regulated industry and there is absolutely no wiggle room in the regulations for faults, flaws or mistakes. You must perform to the highest standards of business practice and the ongoing documentation one needs to maintain and the oversight one will be subject to is extensive.

Make no mistake about it—you will have regulatory problems and issues throughout your business life as a distiller. You will be frustrated and not permitted to do things you feel are perfectly reasonable. You will spend a great deal of time reporting to the regulatory authorities and maintaining your good standing on an ongoing basis.

However, I have always found the regulatory oversight by TTB and the West Virginia ABC Commission to be evenhanded and responsible. The West Virginia ABCA is staffed by professionals who are devoting their careers to regulating a difficult business that is in essence licensing and regulating the most powerful drug which adults can legally obtain and imbibe in our society.

My experience with the regulators leads me to the conclusion that everyone is trying to do their best. It is an open and evenhanded process. No one is trying to keep you from doing something out of malice or ill will. There are no conspiracies or overarching agendas combining to keep someone from entering the business, or operating once they are. But the regulations are written narrowly and interpreted strictly and you must stay on the path.

The regulatory edifice and labyrinth that has been created is gothic and archaic but it seems to work and it is a level playing field.

So, when your third request for a label approval comes back with more corrections and objections, and you will miss the deadline for submission of your new product because you lack the approval, remember that it happens to everyone in some shape or form and you must simply slog on through like the rest of us.

Read the regulations. My only qualification for a license was that I had read the regulations several times and on those occasions when I did speak to someone I was able to at least converse about my responsibilities as a prospective distillery owner with some fluency.

B. Laws and Regulations ─────────────────────────────

There is no getting around it. In order to be a distiller you have to be familiar with the laws and regulations that govern the industry. The Code of Federal Regulations is not easy reading. There are many specific definitions to be assimilated and the language and structure of the regulations is sometimes difficult to follow but you have to be familiar with most of the information so you know what is required and what one can and cannot do while holding a basic permit for a distilled spirits plant.

- The Federal Alcohol Administration Act (FAA Act) is codified as 27 USC 201 *et seq*. The regulations under which it is implemented are contained in 27 CFR Part 5 titled Labeling and Advertising of Distilled Spirits.

- The Alcoholic Beverage Labeling Act of 1988 (ABLA) is codified as 27 USC 213 *et seq*. The regulations that implement it are contained in 27 CFR Part 16 titled Alcoholic Beverage Health Warning Statement.

- Finally the Internal Revenue Code (IRC) 26 USC Chapter 51governs the following topics:

    27 CFR Part 19 Distilled Spirits Plants

    27 CFR Part 250 Liquors and Articles from Puerto Rico and the Virgin Islands

    27 CFR Part 251 Importation of Distilled Spirits, Wine, and Beer

    27 CFR Part 252 Exportation of Liquors

C. Gauging Manual Sections

The *Gauging Manual* is essential reading for any distiller. The full text (available at my business websites) may be easier to read that way than section by section.

Main Laws and Regulations Link: http://www.ttb.gov/spirits/spirits-regs.shtml

Here are links to the several sections of the gauging manual.

Subpart A—Scope of Regulations

§ 30.1 Gauging of distilled spirits. Old Style § 186.1, http://www.ttb.gov/foia/gauging_manual_toc.shtml#27
:1.0.1.1.25.1.504.1

Subpart B—Definitions

§ 30.11 Meaning of terms. § 186.11, http://www.ttb.gov/foia/gauging_manual_toc.shtml#27:1.0.1.1.25.2.504.1

Subpart C—Gauging Instruments

§ 30.21 Requirements, http://www.ttb.gov/foia/gauging_manual_toc.shtml#27:1.0.1.1.25.3.504.1

§ 30.22 Hydrometers and thermometers, http://www.ttb.gov/foia/gauging_manual_toc.shtml#27:1.0.1.1.25.3.504.2

§ 30.23 Use of precision hydrometers and thermometers. §186.23, http://www.ttb.gov/foia
/gauging_manual_toc.shtml#27:1.0.1.1.25.3.504.3

§ 30.24 Specific gravity hydrometers, http://www.ttb.gov/foia/gauging_manual_toc.shtml#27:1.0.1.1.25
.3.504.4

§ 30.25 Use of precision specific gravity hydrometers, http://www.ttb.gov/foia/gauging_manual_toc.shtml#27
:1.0.1.1.25.3.504.2

Subpart D—Gauging Procedures

§ 30.31 Determination of proof, http://www.ttb.gov/foia/gauging_manual_toc.shtml#27:1.0.1.1.25.4.504.1

§ 30.32 Determination of proof obscuration, http://www.ttb.gov/foia/gauging_manual_toc.shtml#27:1.0.1.1.25
.4.504.2

Determination of Quantity

§30.36 General requirements, http://www.ttb.gov/foia/gauging_manual_toc.shtml#27:1.0.1.1.25.4.504.3

Determination of Quantity by Weight

§ 30.41 Bulk spirits. § 186.41, http://www.ttb.gov/foia/gauging_manual_toc.shtml#27:1.0.1.1.25.4.505.4

§ 30.42 Denatured spirits. §186.42, http://www.ttb.gov/foia/gauging_manual_toc.shtml#27:1.0.1.1.25.4.505.5

§ 30.43 Packaged spirits, http://www.ttb.gov/foia/gauging_manual_toc.shtml#27:1.0.1.1.25.4.505.6

§ 30.44 Weighing containers, http://www.ttb.gov/foia/gauging_manual_toc.shtml#27:1.0.1.1.25.4.505.7

§ 30.45 Withdrawal gauge for packages, http://www.ttb.gov/foia/gauging_manual_toc.shtml#27:1.0.1.1.25.4.505.8

Determination of Quantity by Volume

§ 30.51 Procedures for measurement of bulk spirits. §186.51, http://www.ttb.gov/foia/gauging_manual_toc.shtml#27:1.0.1.1.25.4.506.9

§ 30.52 Procedure for measurement of cased spirits, http://www.ttb.gov/foia/gauging_manual_toc.shtml#27:1.0.1.1.25.4.506.10. [New section not in Gauging Manual, per website, accessed September 15, 2015.]

Subpart E—Prescribed Tables

§ 30.61 Table 1, showing the true percent of proof spirit for any indication of the hydrometer at temperatures between zero and 100 degrees Fahrenheit, http://www.ttb.gov/foia/gauging_manual_toc.shtml#27:1.0.1.1.25.5.507.1

§ 30.62 Table 2, showing Wine Gallons and Proof Gallons by weight. § 186.62, http://www.ttb.gov/foia/gauging_manual_toc.shtml#27:1.0.1.1.25.5.507.2

§ 30.63 Table 3, for determining the number of Proof Gallons from the weight and proof of spirituous liquor. § 186.63, http://www.ttb.gov/foia/gauging_manual_toc.shtml#27:1.0.1.1.25.5.507.3

§ 30.64 Table 4, showing the fractional part of a gallon per pound at each percent and each tenth percent of proof of spirituous liquor. § 186.64, http://www.ttb.gov/foia/gauging_manual_toc.shtml#27:1.0.1.1.25.5.507.4

§ 30.65 Table 5, showing the weight per Wine Gallon (at 60 degrees Fahrenheit) and Proof Gallon at each percent of proof of spirituous liquor. § 186.65, http://www.ttb.gov/foia/gauging_manual_toc.shtml#27:1.0.1.1.25.5.507.5

§ 30.66 Table 6, showing respective volumes of alcohol and water and the specific gravity in both air and vacuum of spirituous liquor. § 186.66, http://www.ttb.gov/foia/gauging_manual_toc.shtml#27:1.0.1.1.25.5.507.6

§ 30.67 Table 7, for correction of volume of spirituous liquors to 60 degrees Fahrenheit, http://www.ttb.gov/foia/gauging_manual_toc.shtml#27:1.0.1.1.25.5.507.7

Subpart F—Optional Gauging Procedures §186.67

§ 30.71 Optional method for determination of proof for spirits containing solids of 400 milligrams or less per 100 milliliters, http://www.ttb.gov/foia/gauging_manual_toc.shtml#27:1.0.1.1.25.6.507.1

§ 30.72 Recording obscuration by proprietors using the optional method for determination of proof, http://www.ttb.gov/foia/gauging_manual_toc.shtml#27:1.0.1.1.25.6.507.2

D. DISCUS

The Distilled Spirits Council of the United States, DISCUS, http://www.discus.org/, is an industry organization that publishes a code of responsible practices that the overwhelming majority of distillers adhere to. The organization also provides a venue for the public and competing companies to file protests against advertisers who violate the rules, regardless of whether the offender is a member or not. A copy of the DISCUS code of practices is included in the resources section. The organization issues semi-annual reports that describe the cases they have considered and the enforcement actions they have taken.

Of course the tax and trade bureau also has extensive rules and regulations regarding the marketing of alcohol. Those rules and regulations are contained in the code of federal regulations. Cite.

27 CFR Part 5 titled Labeling and Advertising of Distilled Spirits, and The Alcoholic Beverage Labeling Act of 1988 (ABLA) is codified as 27 USC 213 *et seq.* The regulations that implement it are contained in 27 CFR Part 16 titled Alcoholic Beverage Health Warning Statement.

In general, the distilling industry does not allow one to denigrate their competitors, does not allow competitors to say one product is "better" than another, does not allow the use of excessive nudity or under-age representatives, etc. The rules are endless. This makes the competition among market participants more civilized. That aspect of the distilling industry appealed to me. It seemed like a better way to do business. However, usually any contested advertising campaign is over by the time DISCUS finishes discussing it so any proscriptive effect is prospective.

E. Bibliography & Resources

The resources folder has an extensive collection of public domain books, articles, forms, reports and instructions.

The Alcohol Textbook, 4th Edition. Edited by KA Jacques and TP Lyons and DR Kelsall. Published by Nottingham University Press, 2003, ISBN 1-897676-13-1.

Pocket Ref, compiled and written by Thomas J. Glover, 2nd Ed. 1999 ISBN 1-885071-00-0, LOC # 94-067826.

Making Pure Corn Whiskey, Second Edition, by Ian Smiley, Bsc, published by Amphora Society, 2003 ISBN 0-9686292-1-0.

The Art of Blending and Compounding Liquors, by Joseph Fleishman, 1885. A copy of this book is contained in the public resources section.

The Distilled Spirits Council of the United States, DISCUS, **http://www.discus.org/**.

Alcohol Fuel by Richard Freudenberger, 2009, New Society Publishers Paperback ISBN 978-0-86571-626-1.

Fermented Beverage Production: 2nd ed. 2003 Kluwer Academic / Plenum Publishers, NY Paperback ISBN 0-306-47706-8.

Making Gin & Vodka, by John Stone, see **http://www.gin-vodka.com/** This is a privately published book; it does not have an ISBN associated with it and no publisher is referred to.

There are also a very few books about traditional moonshine making that are worth referring to:

Moonshine Kellner, Esther, Moonshine. New York, The Bobbs-Merril Co. Inc, subsidiary of Howard W.Sams & Co. 1971. Library of Congress # 70-98289. This book contains good survey of alcohol production on the American frontier and an extensive description of the Whiskey Rebellion of 1794.

Wilkinson Alec, *Moonshine*. NY Alfred A. Knopf, distributed by Random House 1985. ISBN 0-394-54587-7.

Maurer David W. *Kentucky Moonshine*. University Press of Kentucky, 1974 ISBN 0-8131-0203-0. This work contains a discussion of historical moonshining in England as well as America.

Acknowledgements

I want to thank the following people who helped me to start my business. Without their friendship, knowledge, patience it never would have happened: Bo McDaniel, Dan Nagowski, Jerry Deal, Steve Sutton, Chuck Miller, and John Stone. Also, Roger A. Hanney, Joe Dangler and Tim Brown of the A. Smith Bowman Distillery.

About the Author

Payton Fireman is an attorney by trade and has practiced law in West Virginia for thirty years.

In 1998 he founded The West Virginia Distilling Company, LLC, which is West Virginia's first legal distillery licensed since Prohibition. Payton started this business for two reasons: First, because he always wanted to make a product or conduct a business apart from practicing law; and second, because it made more sense than working on race cars all week just to crash them or blow the engines up on weekends. Believing that there was a market for a legal version of moonshine as a heritage spirit he obtained his license and has made Mountain Moonshine as a product since 1999. Payton and his distillery have been featured in such notable publications as the *New York Times* and the *Daily Telegraph*. His company websites are **mountainmoonshine .com** and **alcoholblending.com**.

To improve upon the government regimen for alcohol blending and accounting he developed Alcohol Blending Software (ABS), a computer program which can be used to manage virtually every part of a distiller's business. In addition, he published a DVD, "Making Moonshine," which documents an entire production cycle for his distilling operations. Excerpts of this DVD appear on You-Tube video. His manual of distilling operations extends his work on ABS Software to the physical and biological processes of operating a distillery.

In addition to writing for legal publications, he has published work in club magazines relating to family history as well as written technically about Daimler automobiles for the Daimler & Lanchester motor club.

Payton was born in Boston in 1958 and raised in New York City as well as Lake Placid, New York. He attended high school in Clearwater, Florida. Moving to West Virginia in 1976 he completed his undergraduate and graduate studies at West Virginia University in 1983. In addition to his membership in the West Virginia Bar Association, in 1985 he was admitted to the Florida Bar Association. He was director of the Criminal Justice Program at Salem College from 1985 until 1989 and then served as a Trust Officer for Huntington Bank for ten years until establishing his private practice in 1997. In 1998 he began building his distillery.

If By Whiskey

This is one of my favorite speeches on the subject of whiskey:[61]

"If when you say whiskey you mean the devil's brew, the poison scourge, the bloody monster, that defiles innocence, dethrones reason, destroys the home, creates misery and poverty, yea, literally takes the bread from the mouths of little children; if you mean the evil drink that topples the Christian man and woman from the pinnacle of righteous, gracious living into the bottomless pit of degradation, and despair, and shame and helplessness, and hopelessness, then certainly I am against it.

But;

If when you say whiskey you mean the oil of conversation, the philosophic wine, the ale that is consumed when good fellows get together, that puts a song in their hearts and laughter on their lips, and the warm glow of contentment in their eyes; if you mean Christmas cheer; if you mean the stimulating drink that puts the spring in the old gentleman's step on a frosty, crispy morning; if you mean the drink which enables a man to magnify his joy, and his happiness, and to forget, if only for a little while, life's great tragedies, and heartaches, and sorrows; if you mean that drink, the sale of which pours into our treasuries untold millions of dollars, which are used to provide tender care for our little crippled children, our blind, our deaf, our dumb, our pitiful aged and infirm; to build highways and hospitals and schools, then certainly I am for it."

---

61   The label "if-by-whiskey" refers to a 1952 speech by Noah S. "Soggy" Sweat, Jr., a young lawmaker from Mississippi, on the subject of whether Mississippi should prohibit or legalize alcoholic beverages: Columnist William Safire popularized the term in his column in the *New York Times*, but wrongly attributed it to Florida Governor Fuller Warren. As to the logic of the speech and what it elucidates, in political discourse *if-by-whiskey* is a relativist fallacy where the response to a question is contingent on the questioner's opinions and use of dysphemisms and euphemisms (e.g. "terrorist" as dysphemism and "freedom fighter" as euphemism). An if-by-whiskey argument affirms both sides of an issue, and agrees with whichever side the questioner supports.

Made in the USA
Las Vegas, NV
21 November 2020